D1112214

Physical Electronics

Physical Electronics

Curtis L. Hemenway
Professor of Physics, Union College
Schenectady, New York

Richard W. Henry
Assistant Professor of Physics, Union College

Martin Caulton
Member of the Technical Staff, RCA Laboratories
Princeton, New Jersey

John Wiley and Sons, Inc.
New York London

Library of Congress Catalog Card Number: 62–15177
Printed in the United States of America

Preface

Electrical engineering and physics students have a recognized need to understand the basic physical principles governing the many new and exciting electronic devices which are playing an important role in modern engineering and scientific instrumentation. An understanding in depth of the physics of electronics is essential if scientific measurements and engineering techniques are to be exploited to their full capabilities.

It is obviously impractical to consider every device in detail. Such a treatment not only would be voluminous but also is likely to become outdated rapidly. Economy of thought can be achieved by the thorough learning of a relatively small number of basic principles. Our philosophy has been to develop these principles by studying simple models and to avoid whenever possible the use of the phrase "it can be shown." The text is deliberately "unbalanced" since some physical concepts are likely to have been studied adequately in previous courses and since some topics require much greater depth than others to achieve a useful operational understanding.

This textbook has been developed for a one-semester junior or senior level course in physical electronics for both electrical engineering and physics students. Such a course would normally be a prerequisite for a course or courses in electronic circuit theory and practice. The background assumed is introductory general physics and mathematics through integral calculus and the elements of differential equations. An elementary modern physics course, although not necessary, would be desirable as a prerequisite. The sections and portions of sections in reduced type provide supplemental material or examples which may be omitted without loss of essential continuity. MKS units are used. Answers to approximately half of the numerical problems are given at the end of the book, following Appendix D.

The first three chapters are concerned with the elements of quantum mechanics and statistical mechanics. Chapters 1 and 2 are devoted to a presentation of the wave nature of free and bound electrons. The quantization of the energy of a bound electron is illustrated by solving the Schroedinger equation for one- and three- dimensional potential energy boxes and by considering the solutions for the hydrogen atom. In Chapter 3 Maxwell-Boltzmann, Bose-Einstein, and Fermi-Dirac statistics are introduced by first treating a system of only three particles in order that the student will understand the basic assumptions underlying each type of statistics without floundering in the mathematics. With this understanding in hand the student should be able to follow the rigorous derivation and subsequent interpretation of the Fermi factor. The immediate purpose of these introductory chapters is to develop the "box" model of a metal for use in the study of electron emission in Chapter 4. The Fermi factor and density of states concepts used in this model are also used in later discussions of the band theory of solids and the electrical characteristics of semiconductors.

The motions of individual charged particles in various electric and magnetic field configurations are studied in Chapter 5. The linear magnetron is discussed in some detail as an example of the motion of electrons in crossed electric and magnetic fields and also as our first example of the general concept of amplification as an energy transfer process.

Chapter 6 treats various "classical" vacuum-tube devices, emphasizing the space-charge-limited diode, the triode, and amplification by triodes. The circuit aspects of vacuum tubes are explored further in Chapter 7, where the induced current concept is used to describe how signal energy is amplified by an energy conversion mechanism. Here also the standard vacuum-tube a-c equivalent networks are introduced in order to provide a jumping-off point for a subsequent circuits course.

In Chapter 8 we develop some of the techniques for treating the average behavior of groups of particles which may continually suffer collisions with surrounding atoms or molecules. The Einstein and Boltzmann relations, usually presented without proof at this level, are derived using a simple physical model.

Chapters 9 and 10 treat gaseous processes and devices. A derivation of the Bohr stopping power theory is given to make the detection of charged particles by ionization chambers and proportional counters more meaningful. In Chapter 11 a liquid state model and a discussion of electrolytic conduction provide a background for our introduction of the Debye length concept of plasma physics. The properties of plasmas are illustrated by a brief discussion of instabilities.

In order to understand the properties of semiconductors a thoughtful student requires convincing reasons why energy levels in a crystal are grouped into bands. In Chapter 12 graphical solutions of the Schroedinger equation for the Kronig-Penney model of a crystal are used to demonstrate the grouping of energy eigenvalues. The difficult and often slighted concepts of "holes" and effective masses are given a thorough discussion in terms of the group velocities of wavepackets. The use of the Hall effect to distinguish between hole and electron conduction and determine the density of the charge carriers is explained.

Chapter 13 uses the energy band, density of states, and Fermi factor concepts to treat electrical conduction in intrinsic and impurity semiconductors. In Chapter 14 the electrical characteristics of *p-n* junctions are explored in more detail than in the usual Boltzmann relation derivation of the current-voltage characteristic. After this detailed treatment of the *p-n* junction the student is prepared for brief discussions of the tunnel diode, the transistor, an equivalent network for transistors, and other solid-state devices.

In Chapter 15 we consider electron oscillations of the Langmuir-Tonks type in a plasma. The generation and propagation of fast and slow space-charge waves in an electron beam or moving plasma are studied through a detailed discussion of bunching in a klystron. These treatments are believed to be unique at the undergraduate level. The space-charge-wave concept is extended in Chapter 16, using the viewpoint of the coupling of modes, to include interactions between space-charge waves and electromagnetic waves. Amplification is interpreted in terms of energy conversion and a number of "modern" microwave amplifiers are studied, among them the traveling-wave tube, the parametric amplifier, and the maser.

We gratefully acknowledge the suggestions and constructive criticism made by many members of the RCA Laboratories staff. Dr. L. S. Nergaard, Dr. B. Hershenov, and Dr. F. E. Paschke were paintakingly thorough in their review of several chapters. Special mention should also be made of Dr. R. Braunstein, Dr. M. Glicksman, Dr. M. H. Lewin, Dr. B. Vural, Mr. F. H. Norman, and Mr. D. d'Agostini who critically read individual chapters and sections. It should also be noted that some approaches to vacuum-tube amplification were suggested in reading the notes "Principles of Electron Tubes," prepared by H. A. Watson for the Bell Telephone Laboratories' Communications Development Training Program.

We express our appreciation to Professor H. E. Way for his encouragement and support, to Professors K. L. Schick and D. M. McCall for many constructive comments and suggestions based on their teaching experience with this text, to Professor C. D. Swartz and others for their generously given and competent advice, to Mrs. M. Gill, Mrs. H. Quinn, and Mrs. L. Miles for devoted secretarial assistance, to our patient and understanding wives, and to our enormously capable students whose comments and questions have contributed greatly to the development of this book.

March 1962

C. L. Hemenway
R. W. Henry
M. Caulton

Contents

1. particles and waves

Man's view of his universe through his senses is a relatively restricted one. His everyday experience is generally confined to phenomena involving objects of a relatively narrow range of sizes. Classical physics provides adequate and powerful tools for the study of the physics of objects common to his ordinary environment. As he explores the realm of the very fast, however, relativistic effects become important. As he ventures into the submicroscopic world, the world of the atom, he also finds phenomena rather foreign to his everyday experience. It is our mission in Chapter 1 to consider briefly the wave nature of particles, a key concept for the understanding of the behavior of nature on the atomic scale. The material presented in this chapter and Chapters 2 and 3 is basic to much of our understanding of physical electronics.

In Chapter 1 the dual nature of particles and waves, wavepackets, and the uncertainty principle are considered. The Schroedinger equation is introduced and used to describe the penetration and reflection of beams of particles at potential energy barriers.

1.1 Particle-wave duality

Wave phenomena such as diffraction and polarization are familiar characteristics of electromagnetic radiation (such as light waves). In 1901, Planck, in his theoretical work on black-body radiation, showed that the energy of light waves is transported in discrete amounts which we call photons or quanta. The energy E of a photon

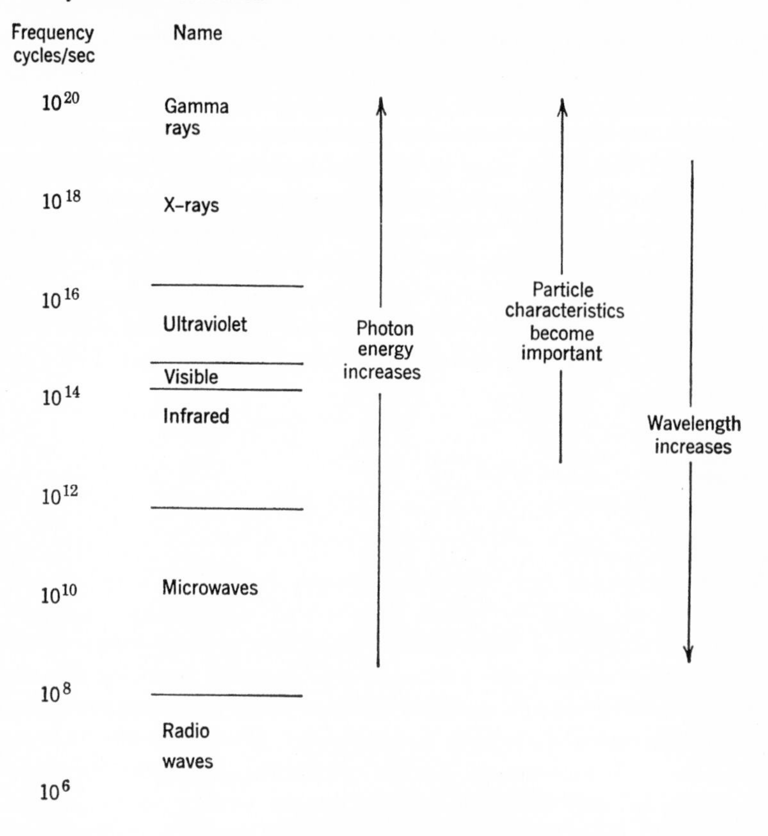

Fig. 1.1. Electromagnetic spectrum.

is given by

$$E = h\nu = \hbar\omega \tag{1.1}$$

where h is Planck's constant, ν is the frequency of the light wave, $\hbar$ is Planck's constant divided by 2π, and ω is 2π times the frequency. In 1905 Einstein reinforced the photon concept by showing that a satisfactory explanation of the photoelectric effect requires light waves to have a bulletlike concentration of energy. In 1923, Compton obtained direct evidence of the particle nature of electromagnetic waves by showing that collisions of x-rays with free electrons can be described in much the same way as collisions between billiard balls. In short, there are a number of bits of evidence which require electromagnetic waves to have both particle and wave characteristics.

Figure 1.1 lists the various types of electromagnetic waves in order of increasing photon energy. This figure suggests that wave characteristics are dominant at low photon energies and that the particle characteristics of electromagnetic waves become important at high energies.

In 1924 de Broglie suggested that particles should exhibit wave properties. His ideas were soon given experimental confirmation by Davisson and Germer and G. P. Thomson who demonstrated the diffraction of electrons by regular arrays of atoms within a plane metal surface. Since that time, electron diffraction and electron microscopy have become important analytical tools. The waves associated with high velocity electrons have much shorter wavelengths than visible light waves. It is well known that the limit of resolution of an optical

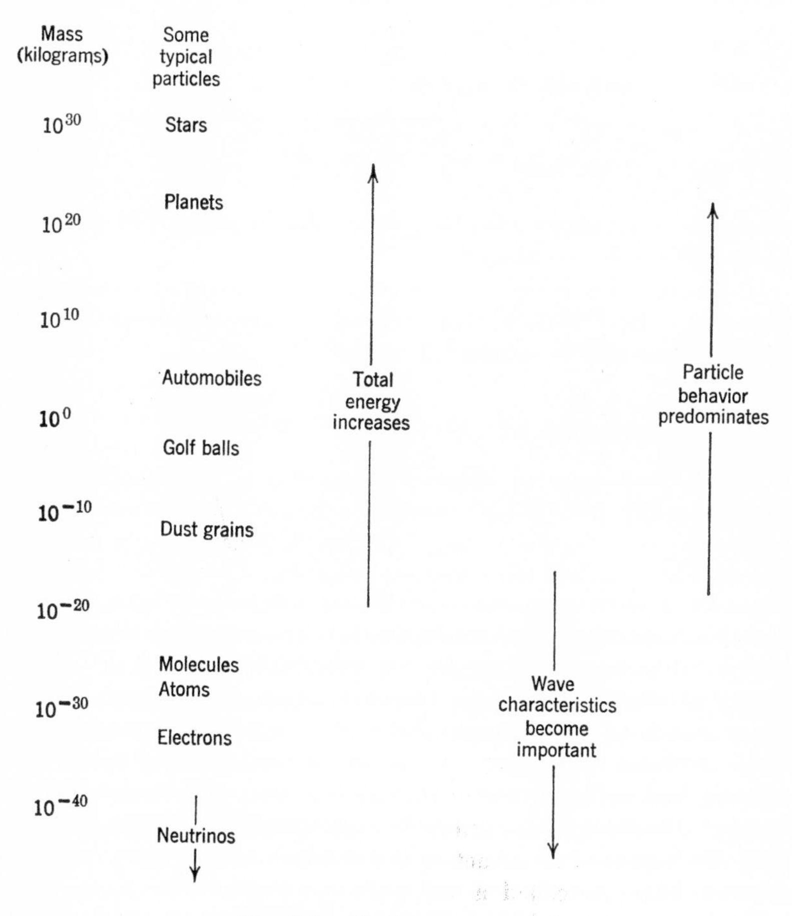

Fig. 1.2. Particle spectrum.

system depends on wavelength. Consequently, electron microscopes have much greater resolving powers than optical microscopes and may use much higher magnifications. Experiments with beams of neutrons have revealed that neutrons also may be diffracted and polarized.

The conclusion seems inescapable that particles have wave properties. Figure 1.2 lists particles as a function of mass, a particle spectrum. The wave characteristics of particles are most important for particles of small mass. In fact, experiments with beams of atomic-sized particles incident upon atomic gratings (crystals) indicate that the average wavelength λ of a particle is given by

$$\lambda = \frac{h}{p} \tag{1.2}$$

where h is Planck's constant and p is the momentum of the particle. Equation 1.2 may also be written

$$p = \frac{h}{\lambda} = \hbar \frac{2\pi}{\lambda} = \hbar k \tag{1.3}$$

where k is a quantity called the propagation constant and is equal to 2π divided by the wavelength.

In summary, particles have wave characteristics and electromagnetic waves have particle characteristics. The particle-wave duality is explored further in section 1.2.

1.2 Wavepackets

It may be helpful to consider geometrically how an object may simultaneously possess both particle and wave properties. For this purpose we consider how waves of different wavelengths add to produce a constructive interference pattern which has "particle" properties. Figure 1.3*a* is an instantaneous view of a portion of an interference pattern, such as might arise from the interference of two waves having slightly different wavelengths. If three different waves are used (Fig. 1.3*b*), the maxima of the interference pattern generally are further apart and have larger amplitudes. Note that the interference patterns of the waves of parts (*a*) and (*b*) are repetitive in space. This repetition is characteristic of the superposition of a finite number of waves. However, if we utilize properly an infinite number of waves, only one region of constructive interference occurs. This superposition of waves is called a wavepacket. Figure 1.3c shows a one-dimensional wavepacket, a geometrical representation of an object

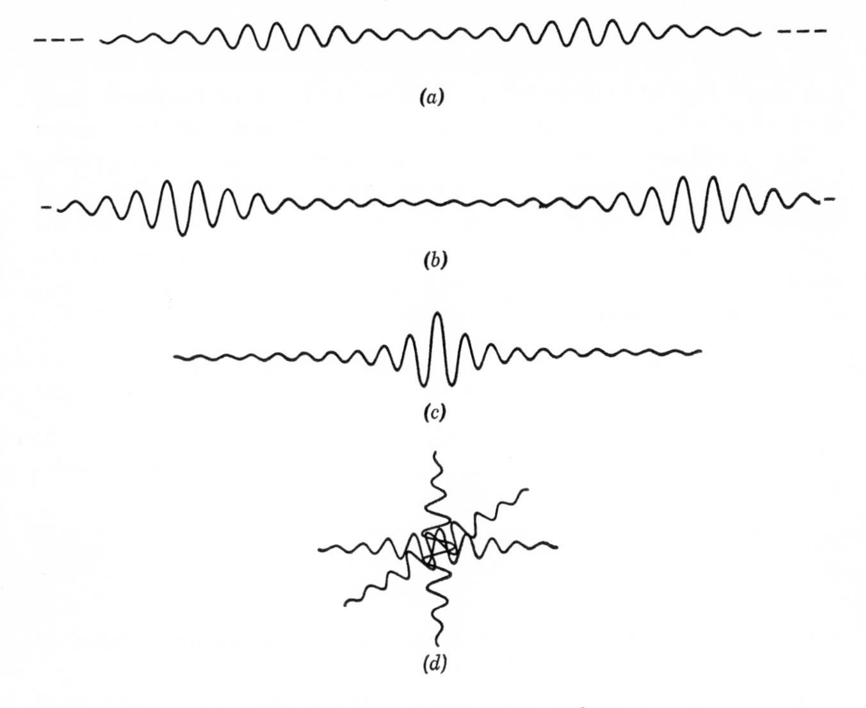

Fig. 1.3. Formation of wavepackets.

having both wave and particle properties. The particle property in this wavepacket is provided by the localization of the constructive interference. The bow-wave of a ship is an interesting example of a one-dimensional wavepacket moving on a two-dimensional surface. Figure 1.3*d* suggests how a particle can be constructed by the superposition of infinite numbers of waves traveling in the x, y, and z-directions.

1.3 Phase and group velocities

If two waves of slightly different wavelength such as those used in Fig. 1.3*a* in addition move with slightly different velocities, the interference pattern of the waves will move at a velocity different from that of either wave. The velocities of the individual wave components are called phase velocities. The velocity of the interference pattern or wavepacket is called the group velocity. Since particles are wavepackets, a particle travels at the group velocity. Phase and group velocities may be greatly different in magnitude. Generally,

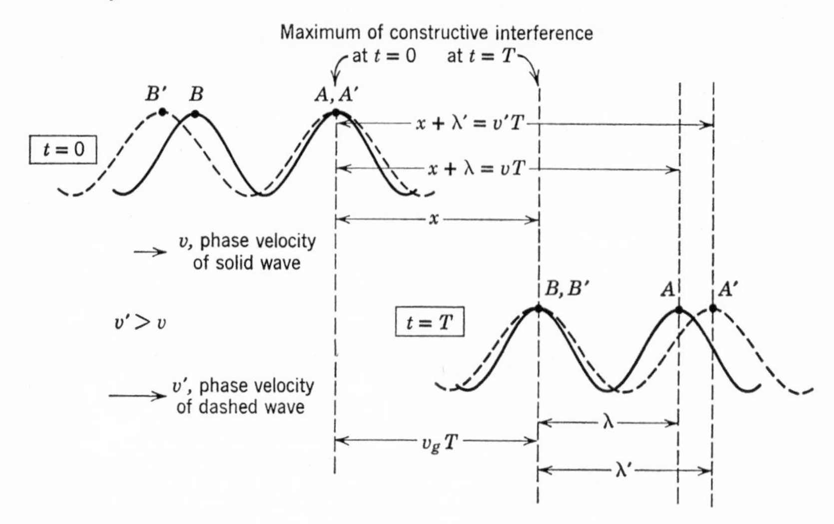

Fig. 1.4. The interference of two waves of different velocity and wavelength.

group velocities are also the velocities with which energy or information moves.

We now derive an expression for the group velocity of the interference pattern of two waves with wavelengths λ and λ' having phase velocities v and v' to the right. In Fig. 1.4 we consider the case for which $\lambda' > \lambda$ and $v' > v$; that is, the wave with the longer wavelength has the higher velocity. The two waves are drawn for two different times. At time $t = 0$, crests A and A' coincide giving a maximum for the interference pattern at AA'. During the time T, both waves move to the right and crest B' catches up with B. At time $t = T$, the coincidence of crests B and B' locates the maximum of the interference pattern. In the time T the maximum of the interference pattern has moved a distance x. The velocity at which the maximum travels is the group velocity v_g.

$$v_g = \frac{x}{T} \tag{1.4}$$

From the diagram

$$x = vT - \lambda = v'T - \lambda' \tag{1.5}$$

from which

$$T = \frac{\lambda' - \lambda}{v' - v} = \frac{\Delta\lambda}{\Delta v} \tag{1.6}$$

Using equations 1.5 and 1.6, we substitute into 1.4.

$$v_g = \frac{x}{T} = \frac{vT - \lambda}{T} = v - \frac{\lambda}{T} = v - \lambda \frac{\Delta v}{\Delta \lambda} \tag{1.7}$$

If the differences $\Delta\lambda$ and Δv are small, we may write

$$v_g = v - \lambda \frac{dv}{d\lambda} \tag{1.8}$$

Note that the group velocity v_g equals the phase velocity v only when the dispersion, $dv/d\lambda$, is zero, that is, when the two waves have the same velocity. The group velocity is less than the phase velocity when $dv/d\lambda > 0$ (normal dispersion), and greater than the phase velocity when $dv/d\lambda < 0$ (anomalous dispersion).

Equation 1.8 may be rewritten in terms of frequency and wavelength by substituting

$$v = \lambda\nu \tag{1.9}$$

Differentiation of 1.9 gives

$$\frac{dv}{d\lambda} = \nu + \lambda \frac{d\nu}{d\lambda} \tag{1.10}$$

Substitution of 1.9 and 1.10 into 1.8 yields

$$v_g = -\lambda^2 \frac{d\nu}{d\lambda} = -\lambda^2 \frac{d\nu}{dk}\frac{dk}{d\lambda} = \frac{2\pi d\nu}{dk} = \frac{d\omega}{dk} \tag{1.11}$$

Equation 1.11 is often considered to be the definition of group velocity and may be compared with a corresponding expression for phase velocity,

$$v = \frac{\nu}{1/\lambda} = \frac{\omega}{k} \tag{1.12}$$

1.4 Heisenberg uncertainty principle

The uncertainty principle was published by Heisenberg in 1927. This principle states that it is impossible to specify precisely and simultaneously the values of certain pairs of variables used to describe the behavior of physical systems. Pairs of variables subject to this restriction are linear position x and momentum p_x, angular position θ and angular momentum p_θ, and energy E and time t. The uncertainty principle states that the product of the uncertainties in the knowledge one may acquire of these pairs of variables must be at least

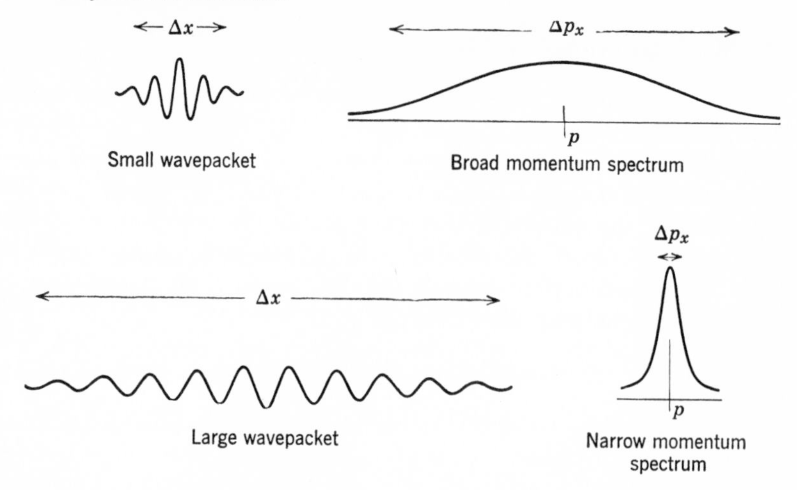

Fig. 1.5. Wavepacket sizes and corresponding momentum spectra.

as great as $\hbar$. In equation form the uncertainty principle becomes

$$\begin{aligned} \Delta x \, \Delta p_x &\geq \hbar \\ \Delta \theta \, \Delta p_\theta &\geq \hbar \\ \Delta E \, \Delta t &\geq \hbar \end{aligned} \tag{1.13}$$

Equation 1.13 states that the position of a particle cannot be specified precisely without our losing knowledge of the particle's momentum, or that we cannot measure the energy of a physical system accurately without having a sufficiently long time interval available for the measurement. Since Planck's constant is very small, the uncertainty principle is important only for very small particles, those of atomic sizes or smaller.

The uncertainty principle may be interpreted in terms of wavepackets. From a Fourier analysis of a pulse, we recognize that the narrower the pulse, the broader the frequency spectrum inherent in the pulse. Correspondingly, a broad pulse has a relatively narrow frequency or wavelength spectrum. Figure 1.5 shows sketches of two one-dimensional wavepackets, one short in spatial extent and the other long. With each wavepacket, the corresponding momentum spectrum is given. The narrow wavepacket has a broad momentum spectrum, whereas the broad wavepacket has a narrow momentum spectrum.

1.5 Wavefunctions

We have discussed the wave character of particles without saying what it is that is waving. The waves which represent particles are not electromagnetic waves or sound waves. In fact, the direct physical significance of the particle waves is not clear. However, the absolute value of the square of the wave amplitude does have a clearly understood physical significance. In a one-dimensional problem, where the wavefunction depends only on x and t, the probability of finding a particle in an interval dx is

$$|\psi(x,t)|^2\,dx = \psi(x,t)\psi^*(x,t)\,dx \tag{1.14}$$

where $\psi(x, t)$ is the wave displacement or wavefunction and $\psi^*(x, t)$ is its complex conjugate. In a three-dimensional problem, where the wavefunction may depend on x, y, z, and t, the probability of finding a particle in an element of volume $dx\,dy\,dz$ is

$$|\psi(x,y,z,t)|^2\,dx\,dy\,dz = \psi(x,y,z,t)\psi^*(x,y,z,t)\,dx\,dy\,dz \tag{1.15}$$

The answers to physical problems are obtained from wavefunctions. Wavefunctions must be well behaved in a mathematical sense. They and their first derivatives must be continuous and single-valued, and satisfy certain other requirements. Wavefunctions may be found by solving the Schroedinger equation into which one has inserted the proper environmental conditions for the particle or particles under consideration. The Schroedinger equation is discussed in the next section.

The mathematical representation of a wavepacket involves more mathematical complexities than we wish to go into. We can avoid these by considering an infinitely long beam of particles, each having the same momentum. Only if the beam is infinitely long so that the position of each particle is completely uncertain can we specify the momentum exactly. Such a beam may be represented by a plane wave which in its most useful form is

$$\psi = Ae^{j(kx-\omega t)} \tag{1.16}$$

where $j = \sqrt{-1}$, k is the propagation constant previously defined, and A is the amplitude of the wavefunction, often called the normalization constant. The value of the normalization constant must be so chosen that $|A|^2$ is numerically equal to the number of particles per unit volume. A plane wave may also be used to describe a single particle whose momentum is precisely known but whose position is completely indeterminant, that is, a wavepacket of infinite extent.

Equation 1.16 represents a beam traveling in the $+x$-direction. A beam, or plane wave, traveling in the $-x$-direction is represented by

$$\psi = Ae^{j(-kx-\omega t)} \tag{1.17}$$

1.6 The Schroedinger equation

In this section we present a plausibility argument leading to the Schroedinger equation, the differential equation whose solutions are the wavefunctions. We begin by writing an equation for which the plane waves 1.16 and 1.17 are solutions. Then we generalize to Schroedinger's equation.

An equation for which 1.16 and 1.17 are solutions is

$$\frac{d^2\psi}{dx^2} + k^2\psi = 0 \tag{1.18}$$

The kinetic energy K of a particle is

$$K = E - U(x) \tag{1.19}$$

where E is the total energy of the particle and $U(x)$ is its potential energy. From the relation between kinetic energy and momentum p,

$$E - U(x) = K = \tfrac{1}{2}mv^2 = \frac{p^2}{2m} = \frac{\hbar^2k^2}{2m} \tag{1.20}$$

where in the last step we have used equation 1.3. Solving for k^2 we have

$$k^2 = \frac{2m[E - U(x)]}{\hbar^2} \tag{1.21}$$

and equation 1.18 becomes

$$\frac{d^2\psi}{dx^2} + \frac{2m}{\hbar^2}[E - U(x)]\psi = 0 \tag{1.22}$$

This equation is known as the one-dimensional, time-independent Schroedinger equation. In three dimensions, Schroedinger's time-independent equation can be written

$$\nabla^2\psi + \frac{2m}{\hbar^2}[E - U(x,y,z)]\psi = 0 \tag{1.23}$$

where in Cartesian coordinates (see Appendix C)

$$\nabla^2 = \frac{\partial^2}{\partial x^2} + \frac{\partial^2}{\partial y^2} + \frac{\partial^2}{\partial z^2} \tag{1.24}$$

The time-independent Schroedinger equation applies when $|\psi|^2$ is constant in time at every point in space. It may be used to describe the behavior of a constant current of particles or of bound particles. If a beam current of particles is not constant or one wishes to consider transition probabilities, the time-dependent Schroedinger equation must be used. It may be shown that the time-dependent Schroedinger equation is

$$\nabla^2\psi - \frac{2m}{\hbar^2} U(x,y,z)\psi = \frac{2m}{j\hbar}\frac{\partial\psi}{\partial t} \tag{1.25}$$

It is left as an exercise for the student to show that equations 1.16 and 1.17 are solutions to the time-dependent Schroedinger equation, provided ω is equal to $E/\hbar$.

The Schroedinger equations are fundamental equations of physics whose significance does not lie in the foregoing suggestive demonstration, but rather in the fact that their solutions, that is, wavefunctions, predict correctly the results of an enormous number of experiments with atomic-sized particles.

1.7 Beams of particles and potential energy barriers

We consider briefly the effect of a potential energy barrier on a beam of particles. In Fig. 1.6 a beam of particles is shown impinging on a potential energy barrier $U_1 - U_0$. Each particle has an energy E which is greater than the barrier height U_1. The solution ψ_1 of the time-independent Schroedinger equation to the left of $x = 0$ is

$$\psi_1 = (A_i e^{jk_1 x} + A_r e^{-jk_1 x})e^{-j\omega t} \tag{1.26}$$

Equation 1.26 represents two waves, an incident wave of amplitude A_i (representing the incident beam) traveling to the right, and a reflected wave of amplitude A_r traveling to the left. In the region to the right of the barrier the solution ψ_2 of the Schroedinger equation is

$$\psi_2 = A_t e^{j(k_2 x - \omega t)} \tag{1.27}$$

Equation 1.27 represents a wave traveling to the right with an amplitude A_t.

The ratios A_r/A_i and A_t/A_i can be found from the condition that ψ and its first derivative $d\psi/dx$ are continuous at the boundary.

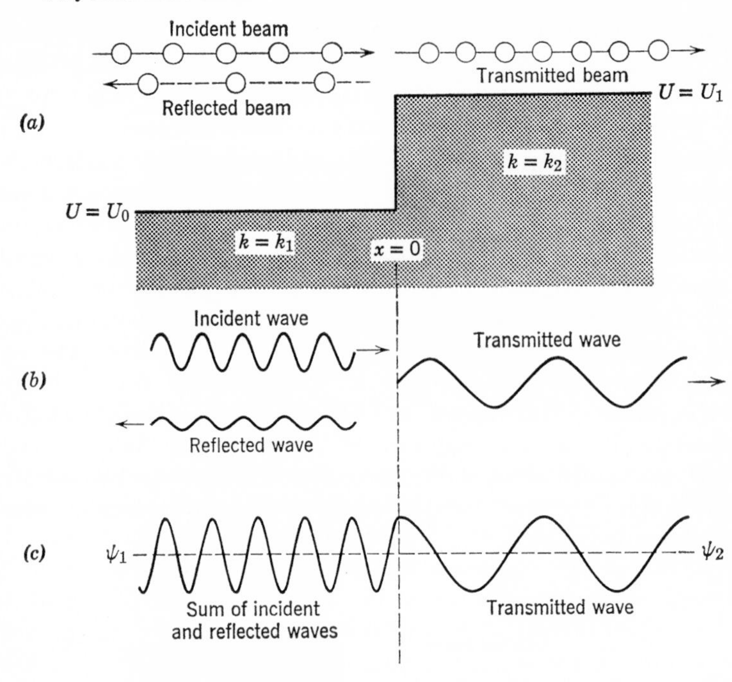

Fig. 1.6. Beam of particles each with energy greater than the barrier energy U_1.

This continuity is illustrated in Fig. 1.6*c*. In Fig. 1.6*b* the amplitude of the transmitted wave is larger than the amplitude of the incident wave, indicating that the density of particles in the transmitted beam is larger than that in the incident beam. This occurs because the particles in the transmitted beam are moving slower than those in the incident beam. Although A_t is greater than A_i, the rate of flow of particles in the transmitted beam must be less than that in the incident beam. Notice also, since k_2 is less than k_1 (see equation 1.21), that the wavelength of the transmitted wave is longer than that of the incident wave.

We next consider a beam of particles whose individual energies E lie between U_1 and U_0, shown in Fig. 1.7. The form of the solution to the Schroedinger equation in the region to the left of the barrier is the same as equation 1.26. However, to the right of the barrier the solution to the Schroedinger equation is

$$\psi_2 = A_t e^{-\alpha x - j\omega t} \tag{1.28}$$

The real attenuation coefficient α appears because the propagation constant k is imaginary in any region for which $E < U$ (see equation 1.21). Equation 1.28 represents a wave whose amplitude decays exponentially as x increases. Thus no particles can be found very far inside the barrier and the beam must be totally reflected.

If the barrier of Fig. 1.7 is of finite width, a small transmitted wave component can persist, as shown in Fig. 1.8. Hence, there is a small but finite probability that some of the particles will "leak" through the barrier even though they have insufficient energy to do so according to classical physics. This phenomenon is called the "tunnel" effect. In nuclear physics the theory of α-particle emission is based on the tunnel effect. In α-particle decay the wavepackets representing α-particles penetrate through nuclear potential energy barriers from the inside. We will see in Chapter 4 that high-field emission from surfaces is also an example of the tunnel effect. As an everyday example, the tunnel effect allows current to flow between two metals in contact despite the fact that the metal surfaces are normally coated with thin oxide layers.

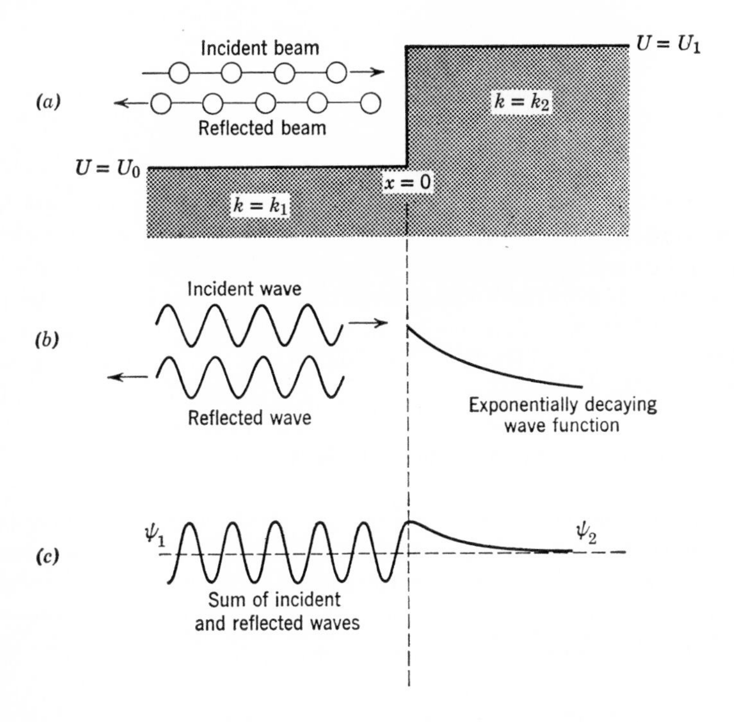

Fig. 1.7. Beam of particles each with energy less than the barrier energy U_1.

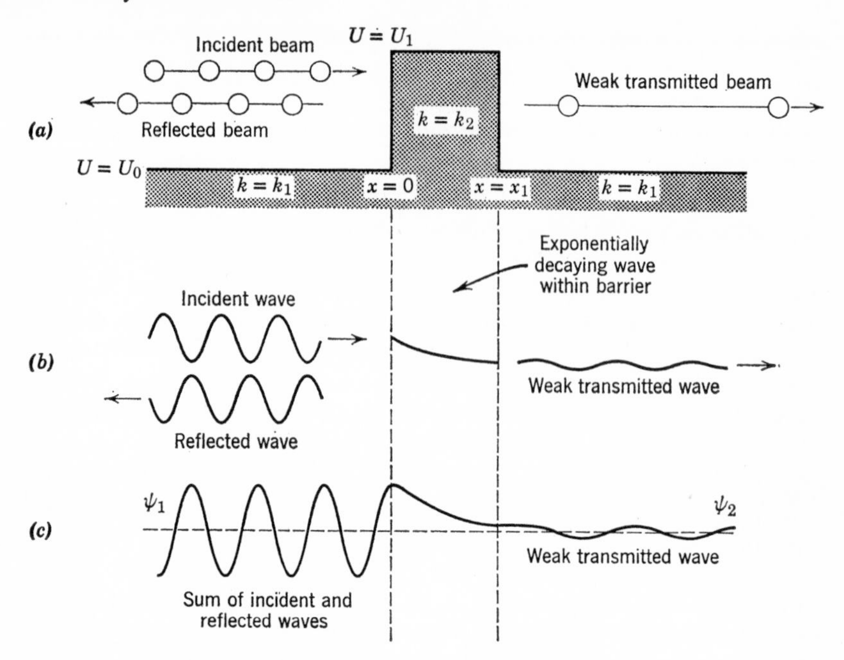

Fig. 1.8. Rectangular narrow-width barrier with particle energies less than the barrier energy U_1.

PROBLEMS

1.1. Compute the wavelength of a
(*a*) 1 Mev proton.
(*b*) "thermal" proton at 300° K (mean kinetic energy $\approx \frac{1}{40}$ ev).
(*c*) 10 ev electron.
(*d*) 150 lb man walking at 3 miles per hour.

1.2. (Alternative derivation of group velocity formula.) Consider two waves of equal amplitude but slightly different frequency and wavelength:

$$y_1 = a \sin (\omega t - kx)$$

$$y_2 = a \sin [(\omega + d\omega)t - (k + dk)x]$$

(*a*) Show that the resultant disturbance $y = y_1 + y_2$ is an amplitude modulated oscillation at nearly the original frequency f, and that the crests of the primary wave travel with velocity $v = \omega/k$, whereas the crests of the modulation (that is, the "group" crests) travel with velocity $v_g = d\omega/dk$.

(*b*) If $v = v_g$, show that the velocity of the waves must be independent of frequency.

1.3. Suppose that the wave nature of a stationary particle of rest mass m_0 is represented by the wavefunction $\psi = \sin \omega_0 t_0$, where $\hbar\omega_0 = m_0c^2$. This ψ

represents a stationary vibration associated with the particle. Use the transformation $t_0 = \dfrac{t - xv/c^2}{\sqrt{1 - v^2/c^2}}$ of special relativity to rewrite ψ in terms of a coordinate system in which the particle is moving with a velocity v in the x-direction.

(*a*) Determine the wavenumber k and angular frequency ω of the transformed wave.

(*b*) Show that the wavelength associated with the moving particle is given by $\lambda = \dfrac{h}{mv}$, where $m = \dfrac{m_0}{\sqrt{1 - v^2/c^2}}$

(*c*) Does the energy $\hbar\omega$ associated with the vibration depend on the velocity of the particle?

(*d*) Show that $v = v_g$ for this particle.

1.4. What does normalization of a single particle (or limited number of particles) wavefunction imply regarding ψ (and so $\partial\psi/\partial x$) at $\pm\infty$?

1.5. What is the inherent uncertainty in the velocity of an electron confined to a volume of

(*a*) 1 cm^3
(*b*) 10^{-12} cm^3
(*c*) 10^{-24} cm^3

1.6. Use the uncertainty principle to estimate the minimum depth in electron volts a potential well of 10 Å diameter must have to bind an electron.

1.7. Redraw Fig. 1.4 for the case in which the wave of longer wavelength has the smaller velocity.

1.8. Under what conditions will the interference pattern of two forward moving waves move in the backward direction?

1.9. Show that the fractional line width $d\lambda/\lambda$ for 5000 Å radiation from an excited state of lifetime 10^{-8} sec is approximately 2×10^{-8}.

1.10. Show that equations 1.16 and 1.17 are solutions to the time-dependent Schroedinger equation, provided the total energy E is equal to $\hbar\omega$.

1.11. Show for the situation illustrated in Fig. 1.6 that the amplitude ratios of the wavefunctions are given by

$$\frac{A_r}{A_i} = \frac{k_1 - k_2}{k_1 + k_2}$$

and

$$\frac{A_t}{A_i} = \frac{2k_1}{k_1 + k_2}$$

1.12. A beam of electrons having a kinetic energy of 1 ev is incident upon a barrier of height 0.1 ev. Calculate the amplitude ratios A_r/A_i and A_t/A_i and the ratios of the densities of electrons in the reflected and transmitted beams to the density in the incident beam.

1.13. (Tunnel effect) Solve in detail the problem of partial reflection and transmission at a rectangular potential barrier such as is shown in Fig. 1.8. Find the probability of transmission for 1 Mev protons through a 4 Mev, 10^{-12} cm thick rectangular potential energy barrier.

2. bound particles

In Chapter 1 we examined some of the properties of free particles. In Chapter 2 we consider some characteristics of bound particles, that is, those confined to a finite region of space. The problems of particles in one-dimensional and three-dimensional boxes are solved, and the hydrogen atom is briefly discussed. The Pauli exclusion principle is stated and applied to the problem of electrons confined to a metallic sample. Finally, the energy-band concept for solids is examined briefly.

2.1 Particle in a one-dimensional box

The one-dimensional particle in a box problem provides a simple, highly instructive example of the behavior of bound particles. Let us consider a particle of mass m constrained to move within a one-dimensional box of length L. The potential energy U of the particle is assumed to be

$$\begin{aligned} U &= 0 \qquad 0 < x < L \\ U &= \infty \qquad x \leq 0,\ x \geq L \end{aligned} \tag{2.1}$$

Figure 2.1 shows this variation of potential energy with distance x. We wish to determine the time average of the probability of finding the particle in a given interval dx within the box as a function of x and also to determine the energies that the particle may have.

The time-independent Schroedinger equation for the region $0 < x < L$ is

$$\frac{d^2\psi}{dx^2} + \frac{2mE}{\hbar^2}\psi = 0 \tag{2.2}$$

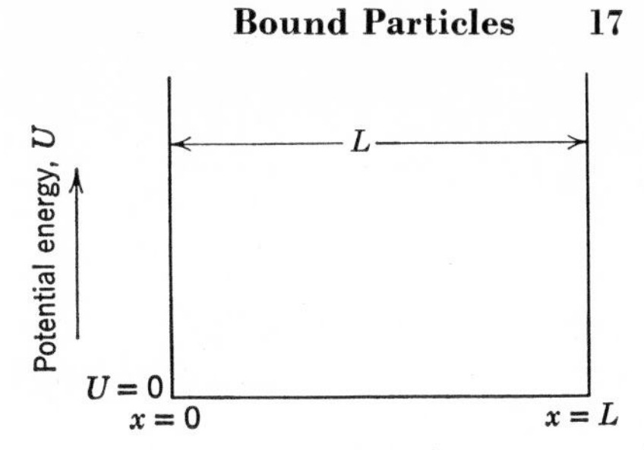

Fig. 2.1. The potential energy function of a one-dimensional box.

The wavefunctions or solutions to equation 2.2 may be sine or cosine functions of x. We adopt for our solution

$$\psi = A \sin (kx + \phi) \tag{2.3}$$

where A, k, and ϕ are constants to be evaluated. This time-independent solution, when multiplied by $e^{-j\omega t}$, represents a standing wave. A standing wave may be thought of as the sum of two waves such as described by equations 1.16 and 1.17, one traveling in the positive x-direction and the other traveling in the negative x-direction. The amplitudes of these oppositely traveling waves are equal, and their constructive interference may be represented by a sine or cosine function.

Since the barrier heights are infinite at the walls, there is no barrier penetration and the wavefunctions must be zero when x is equal to or greater than L, or x is equal to or less than zero. These boundary conditions imply

$$\begin{aligned} \phi &= 0 \\ k &= \frac{n\pi}{L} \end{aligned} \tag{2.4}$$

where n is restricted to positive integral values (1,2,3, . . .) and is called a quantum number.

Equation 2.3 now becomes

$$\psi = A \sin \frac{n\pi x}{L} \tag{2.5}$$

To evaluate A, the normalization constant, we recognize that the probability is unity that the particle is between $x = 0$ and $x = L$, the locations of the walls of the box. Since in our one-dimensional problem $|\psi|^2\,dx$ is the probability of finding a particle in an interval dx, the total probability of finding the particle in the box may be written

$$1 = \int_0^L |\psi|^2 \, dx = \int_0^L A^2 \sin^2 \left(\frac{n\pi x}{L}\right) dx \tag{2.6}$$

from which we obtain

$$A = \sqrt{2/L} \tag{2.7}$$

Equation 2.5 may now be written

$$\psi = \sqrt{2/L} \sin \frac{n\pi x}{L} \tag{2.8}$$

In Fig. 2.2, we plot equation 2.8 for the integer values $n = 1$, 2, and 3.

Note the resemblance between the solutions in Fig. 2.2 and the standing-wave patterns on a string. The integer n is the number of loops of the standing-wave pattern. Figure 2.2 graphically portrays the fact that only certain particle wavelengths meet the boundary conditions, namely, those for which

$$\lambda = \frac{2L}{n} \tag{2.9}$$

The probability per unit length of finding a particle is plotted versus x in Fig. 2.3 for the integer values $n = 1, 2, 3$. Note that the probability per unit length is a function of x. For example, when $n = 1$

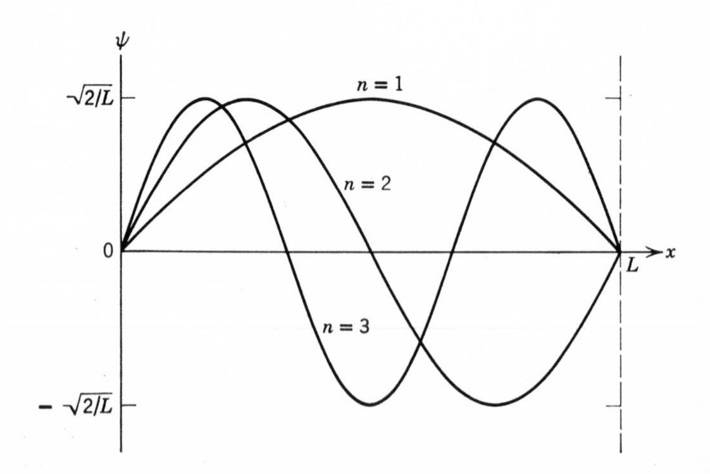

Fig. 2.2. Wavefunctions for a particle in a one-dimensional box.

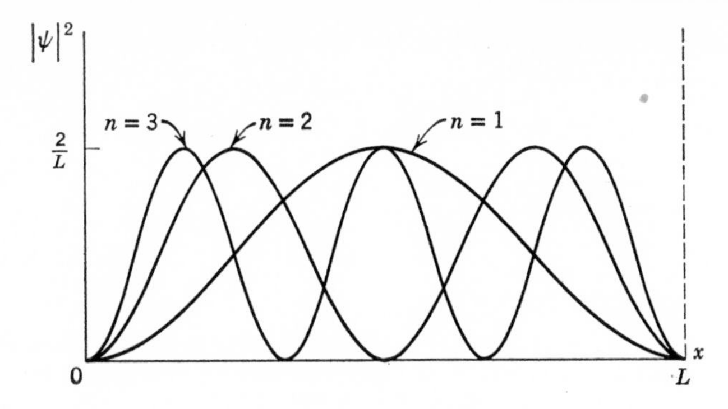

Fig. 2.3. Particle position probability.

the particle is most likely to be found at $x = L/2$. When n becomes large, the probability $|\psi|^2\,dx$ of finding the particle within any finite dx becomes constant in accord with classical concepts. This is because $|\psi|^2$ has many oscillations within dx when n is large and the probability $|\psi|^2\,dx$ becomes independent of x.

To determine the allowed energies of the particle we differentiate equation 2.8 twice to obtain

$$\frac{d^2\psi}{dx^2} = -\sqrt{\frac{2}{L}}\frac{n^2\pi^2}{L^2}\sin\frac{n\pi x}{L} \tag{2.10}$$

Substituting equations 2.8 and 2.10 into Schroedinger's equation 2.2, we obtain

$$E_n = \frac{n^2\pi^2\hbar^2}{2mL^2} = \frac{n^2h^2}{8mL^2} \tag{2.11}$$

Equation 2.11 states that the energy which the particle may have is not continuously variable but is restricted to discrete values, that is, quantized. In fact, whenever particles are bound, restrictions are placed on the wavelengths of the waves representing the particles. These restrictions lead as in the case of the present problem to the quantization of the energies that the bound particles may have. In the next section we will observe the quantization of the energy of the bound electron of the hydrogen atom. The particles in nuclei (nucleons) are bound and nuclei are restricted to discrete energies.

Figure 2.4 shows the possible particle energies given by equation 2.11. Diagrams such as that shown in Fig. 2.4 are called energy-level diagrams. They display graphically the quantized energies which bound

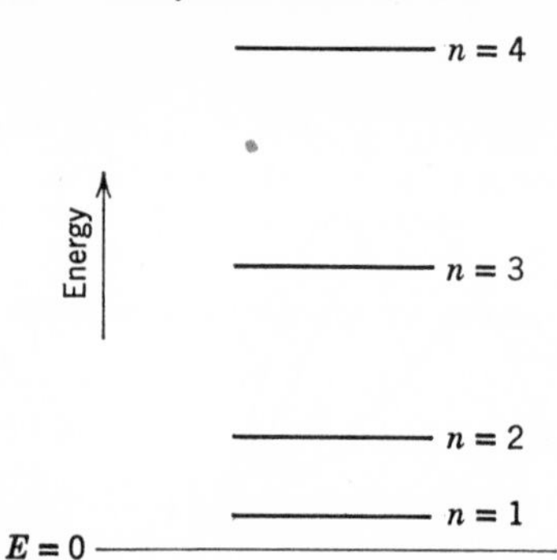

Fig. 2.4. An energy-level diagram for the one-dimensional particle-in-a-box problem.

particles may have. These discrete values of energy are often called eigenvalues.

2.2 Simplified solution for the hydrogen atom

In modern elementary physics courses the Bohr model of the atom is treated. In this atomic model the nucleus is considered to be a heavy, positively charged particle about which one or more negatively charged electrons of small mass revolve in satellitelike, quantized orbits. The Bohr atomic model can predict the energy levels for the hydrogen atom after several arbitrary assumptions have been invoked. Unfortunately, the Bohr theory is unable to predict the energy levels or spectral frequencies for atoms with more than one electron. The power of the quantum mechanical viewpoint lies in its ability not only to compute, at least in principle, the energy levels and spectral lines of all atoms and molecules with remarkable accuracy, but also to predict new and previously unknown phenomena. To aid in developing confidence in the wave-mechanical view of the microcosm, we present a simplified view of the hydrogen atom through the mathematics of quantum mechanics.

The time-independent Schroedinger equation is

$$\nabla^2\psi + \frac{2m}{\hbar^2}(E - U)\psi = 0 \tag{1.23}$$

For a hydrogenlike atom (an atom or ion with one electron), the potential energy U of an electron of charge $-e$ at a distance r from a nucleus of charge Ze is given by

$$U = -\frac{Ze^2}{4\pi\epsilon_0\kappa r} \tag{2.12}$$

where ϵ_0 is the permittivity of free space and κ is the dielectric constant of the medium. Substituting 2.12 into 1.23 gives

$$\nabla^2\psi + \frac{2m}{\hbar^2}\left(E + \frac{Ze^2}{4\pi\epsilon_0\kappa r}\right)\psi = 0 \tag{2.13}$$

From Appendix C, when the operand is a function of r, θ, and ϕ of spherical coordinates, the Laplacian operator may be written

$$\nabla^2 = \frac{1}{r^2}\frac{\partial}{\partial r}\left(r^2\frac{\partial}{\partial r}\right) + \frac{1}{r^2 \sin\theta}\frac{\partial}{\partial\theta}\left(\sin\theta\frac{\partial}{\partial\theta}\right) + \frac{1}{r^2\sin^2\theta}\frac{\partial^2}{\partial\phi^2} \tag{2.14}$$

When 2.14 is substituted into 2.13 the time-independent Schroedinger equation in spherical coordinates results. If we let

$$\psi = R(r)\Theta(\theta)\Phi(\phi) \tag{2.15}$$

we may separate the variables in Schroedinger's equation (a partial differential equation), and obtain three ordinary differential equations. These may be solved in turn for $\Phi(\phi)$, $\Theta(\theta)$, and $R(r)$ after invoking proper boundary conditions. The solutions to the $\Theta(\theta)$ wave equation depend upon the orbital angular momentum of the electron, and the orbital angular momentum quantum number l appears. The solutions to the $\Phi(\phi)$ equation describe the quantization of the z-component of the orbital angular momentum of the electron, and the m_l quantum number appears. We will consider only the simplest possible case, namely, that for which the total wavefunction is independent of θ and ϕ, that is, we seek only spherically symmetric solutions. It should be kept in mind that, in addition to these spherically symmetric solutions, there are solutions which depend on θ and ϕ.

For the spherically symmetric solutions the partial derivatives with respect to θ and ϕ are zero, and only the first term in the expression for the Laplacian in 2.14 is retained. The Schroedinger equation for the spherically symmetric radial wavefunctions of the hydrogenlike atom becomes

$$\frac{1}{r^2}\frac{\partial}{\partial r}\left(r^2\frac{\partial\psi}{\partial r}\right) + \frac{2m}{\hbar^2}\left(E + \frac{Ze^2}{4\pi\epsilon_0\kappa r}\right)\psi = 0 \tag{2.16}$$

which may be rewritten as

$$\frac{\partial^2\psi}{\partial r^2} + \frac{2}{r}\frac{\partial\psi}{\partial r} + \frac{2m}{\hbar^2}\left(E + \frac{Ze^2}{4\pi\epsilon_0\kappa r}\right)\psi = 0 \tag{2.17}$$

Since the above equation is a function of r only, we can substitute ordinary derivatives in place of the partial derivatives.

$$\frac{d^2\psi}{dr^2} + \frac{2}{r}\frac{d\psi}{dr} + \frac{2m}{\hbar^2}\left(E + \frac{Ze^2}{4\pi\epsilon_0\kappa r}\right)\psi = 0 \tag{2.18}$$

There are a whole family of solutions to this equation for the spherically symmetric wavefunctions. We shall henceforth refer to these as the *radial* wavefunctions. The simplest solution is of the form

$$\psi_1(r) = De^{-r/a_1} \tag{2.19}$$

where D is a normalization constant which is chosen to make the integral of the probability density $|\psi|^2$ over all space equal to 1. When the integral is carried out, it is found that $D = 1/\sqrt{\pi}\, a_1^{-3/2}$. To determine the value of a_1, we substitute this trial solution 2.19 and its derivatives back into equation

2.18. Differentiating 2.19 gives

$$\frac{d\psi_1}{dr} = -\frac{D}{a_1} e^{-r/a_1} \tag{2.20}$$

and

$$\frac{d^2\psi_1}{dr^2} = \frac{D}{a_1^2} e^{-r/a_1} \tag{2.21}$$

Substituting equations 2.19, 2.20, and 2.21 into equation 2.18 gives

$$\frac{D}{a_1^2} e^{-r/a_1} - \frac{2}{r}\frac{D}{a_1} e^{-r/a_1} + \frac{2m}{\hbar^2}\left(E + \frac{Ze^2}{4\pi\epsilon_0\kappa r}\right) De^{-r/a_1} = 0 \tag{2.22}$$

Canceling common factors,

$$\frac{1}{a_1^2} - \frac{2}{ra_1} + \frac{2m}{\hbar^2}\left(E + \frac{Ze^2}{4\pi\epsilon_0\kappa r}\right) = 0 \tag{2.23}$$

In order that the above equation be true for all values of r, the terms which depend on r and the constant terms must independently sum to zero. Hence

$$-\frac{2}{ra_1} + \frac{2m}{\hbar^2}\frac{Ze^2}{4\pi\epsilon_0\kappa r} = 0 \tag{2.24}$$

from which

$$a_1 = \frac{\hbar^2 4\pi\epsilon_0\kappa}{mZe^2} \tag{2.25}$$

If $Z = 1$ and $\kappa = 1$, a_1 is identical to the radius of the lowest energy orbit in the Bohr theory of the hydrogen atom and is often called the first Bohr radius. This value of a_1 is 5.3×10^{-11} meter or 0.53 Å.

From the constant terms of equation 2.23

$$\frac{1}{a_1^2} + \frac{2m}{\hbar^2} E = 0 \tag{2.26}$$

Solving for E which we now designate as E_1

$$E_1 = -\frac{\hbar^2}{2ma_1^2} \tag{2.27}$$

Substituting for a_1 from 2.25, the above equation becomes

$$E_1 = -\frac{mZ^2e^4}{32\pi^2\epsilon_0^2\hbar^2\kappa^2} \tag{2.28}$$

Other more complicated radial wavefunctions may be found and designated ψ_2, ψ_3, etc. Associated with each wavefunction there is a different value of energy or energy level. For the higher order wavefunctions the general formula which replaces equation 2.28 is

$$E_n = -\frac{1}{n^2}\frac{mZ^2e^4}{32\pi^2\epsilon_0^2\kappa^2\hbar^2} = \frac{E_1}{n^2} \tag{2.29}$$

where n is called the principal or radial quantum number. Equation 2.29 shows that E_1 is the lowest (most negative) of the sequence of energy levels.

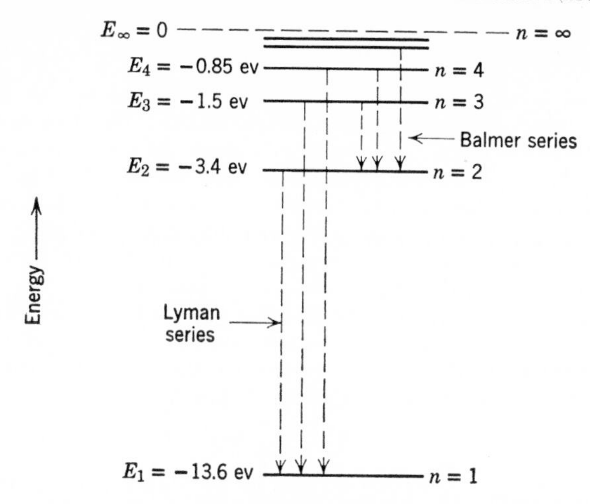

Fig. 2.5. Energy-level diagram of hydrogen atom.

This level is called the ground-state level. By substituting the values of the constants into equation 2.28 and letting $\kappa = 1$ and $Z = 1$, the value of E_1 is found to be -13.6 ev.

The energy of a level for which $n = \infty$ is zero. This corresponds to an electron at rest far away from the nucleus. The energy levels of the hydrogen atom are negative, so an electron in any of these levels is bound, that is, the electron may not escape from the atom without acquiring additional energy from an outside source. Figure 2.5 is an energy-level diagram for the hydrogen atom. It represents the set of allowed energy levels indicated by equation 2.29. The ionization energy is the minimum energy which must be added to an electron in the ground state to remove it from the atom. From Fig. 2.5 this is seen to be 13.6 ev, a value which agrees with experiment.

When an electron moves from one energy level to another, energy is emitted or absorbed in discrete amounts. If this energy is in the form of electromagnetic radiation, the frequency of the radiation may be computed with the aid of equation 1.1

$$E = h\nu \tag{1.1}$$

When an electron moves from a higher energy level to a lower energy level, a photon is emitted with an energy E equal to the difference in energy levels. Since atoms of different elements have different and characteristic sets of energy levels, each element may be identified uniquely by its spectral lines. The transitions responsible for the Lyman and Balmer spectral series of hydrogen are shown in Fig. 2.5.

It should be emphasized that particles which are bound may be represented by standing waves and that bound particles can store energy only in discrete amounts (energy levels). On the other hand, unbound particles can possess continuously variable amounts of energy.

2.3 The geometry of the hydrogen atom

In quantum mechanics the physical interpretation of the geometry of an atom is quite different from the classical Bohr model. One no longer attempts to speak of electron orbits. Instead, one speaks of wavefunctions or probability densities. We learned in Chapter 1 that the square of the magnitude of a wavefunction determines the probability per unit volume of finding a particle at a point in space. Figure 2.6 is an attempt to portray a one-dimensional instantaneous view of a hydrogen atom consisting of a small nuclear wavepacket immersed in a large electronic wavepacket.

We now calculate the probability dP_r that the electron in a hydrogen atom lies between r and $r + dr$ from the nucleus, that is, within a spherical shell of radius r and thickness dr. To do this we multiply the probability per unit volume $|\psi|^2$ by the element of volume $4\pi r^2\,dr$.

$$dP_r = |\psi|^2 4\pi r^2\,dr \tag{2.30}$$

For the ground state, the normalized radial wavefunction of the hydrogen electron is

$$\psi_1 = \frac{1}{\sqrt{\pi}}\,a_1{}^{-3/2}e^{-r/a_1} \tag{2.31}$$

Then

$$|\psi_1|^2 = \frac{1}{\pi}\,a_1{}^{-3}e^{-2r/a_1} \tag{2.32}$$

and

$$dP_{r1} = 4\pi r^2\,dr\,\frac{1}{\pi}\,a_1{}^{-3}e^{-2r/a_1} \tag{2.33}$$

or

$$\frac{dP_{r1}}{dr} = \frac{4r^2}{a_1{}^3}\,e^{-2r/a_1} \tag{2.34}$$

Figure 2.7, a plot of equation 2.34, shows how the probability per unit radius of finding an electron depends on r in the ground state ($n = 1$). It may be

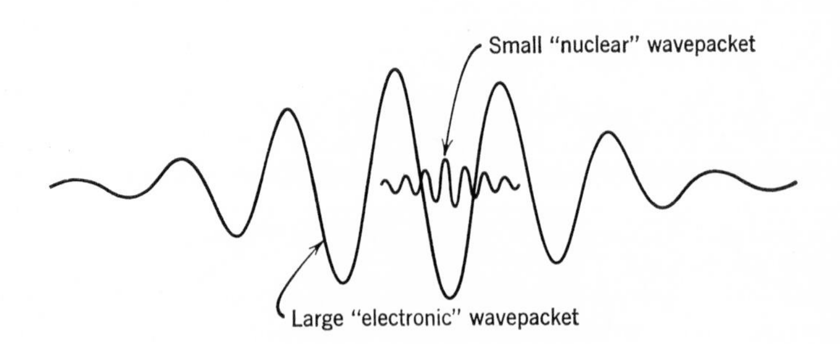

Fig. 2.6. Hydrogen atom wavepackets.

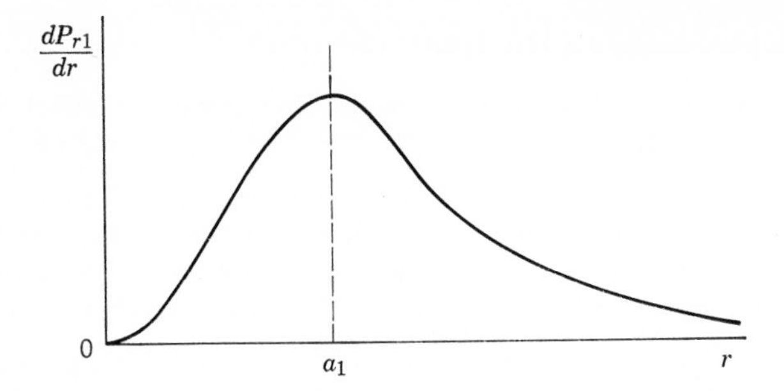

Fig. 2.7. Probability per unit radius versus radius for ground state of hydrogen.

shown by differentiation of 2.34 that the most probable value for r is a_1, the radius of the first Bohr orbit. Note from equation 2.32 that, although the probability per unit volume $|\psi|^2$ of finding the electron at any point in space is largest at the nucleus, where $r = 0$, the probability dP_r of finding the electron in any spherical shell of thickness dr is zero at $r = 0$. Figure 2.6 also suggests that the largest probability per unit volume occurs at the nucleus, but the volume of the nucleus is so small the electron is seldom there.

The spherically symmetric wavefunction for the state of next higher energy ($n = 2$) is given by

$$\psi_2 = \frac{1}{\sqrt{8\pi}} a_1^{-3/2} \left(1 - \frac{r}{2a_1}\right) e^{-r/2a_1} \tag{2.35}$$

If, as before, the probability per unit radius of finding an electron is determined and plotted as a function of r, Fig. 2.8 results. It will be noticed that an electron for which $n = 2$ is, on the average, further from the nucleus than an electron in the ground state ($n = 1$). Note that we cannot, as in the Bohr theory, speak of an electron being in a definite orbit. We can only speak of the probability of finding an electron in a given element of volume.

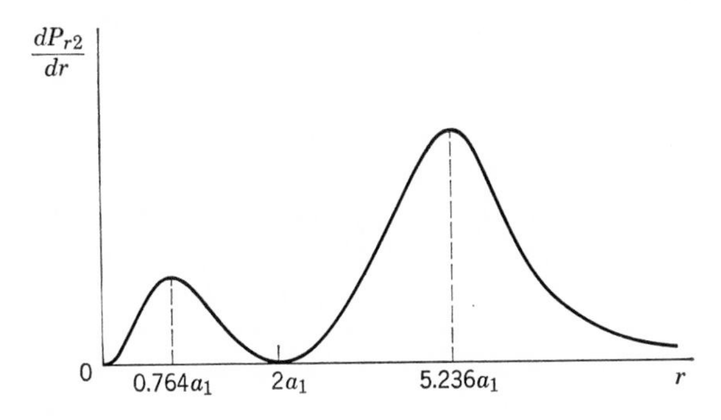

Fig. 2.8. Probability per unit radius versus radius for $n = 2$ state of hydrogen.

2.4 Pauli exclusion principle

In section 2.2 we implied that a general solution of the Schroedinger equation for the hydrogen atom must be characterized by the three quantum numbers: n, l, m_l. Experimentally it was found that an electron also has an intrinsic spin angular momentum. Actually an electron has two spin states which have different energies in the presence of a magnetic field. Classically these two states correspond to a spin angular momentum vector precessing about an axis either parallel or antiparallel to the direction of the magnetic field. These states or orientations can be identified by assigning the values $\pm\frac{1}{2}$ to an additional quantum number, the spin quantum number m_s. The four quantum numbers are listed in Table 2.1 along with the quantities they quantize and the restrictions on them which appear naturally in the mathematics.

Table 2.1. Quantum numbers appearing in the general solution of Schroedinger's equation

Quantum Number	Quantity Quantized	Permissible Values
n	Total energy	$1, 2, \ldots$
l	Orbital angular momentum	$0, 1, 2, \ldots, n-1$
m_l	Component of orbital angular momentum	$-l, -l+1, \ldots, 0 \ldots, l-1, l$
m_s	Component of spin angular momentum	$+\frac{1}{2}, -\frac{1}{2}$

When an atom containing more than one electron is treated quantum mechanically, a useful first approximation is that the electrons do not exert forces on one another. In this approximation the wavefunction describing each electron is a "hydrogen" wavefunction characterized by the quantum numbers n, l, m_l, and m_s. The Pauli exclusion principle states that in a multielectron system no two electrons can have identical sets of quantum numbers. In other words, no two electrons may have the same spatial distribution and spin orientation. It is appropriate to think of the exclusion principle as preventing two particles from being at the same "place" at the same time. An alternative statement of the exclusion principle is that no more than one electron may have the same wavefunction when spin is included in the wavefunction.

Example. Determine how many electrons may exist in the first two shells of an atom by counting the number of different sets of quantum numbers that can be constructed.

Using the rules given in Table 2.1, the possible sets for the shell with $n = 1$ are

n	l	m_l	m_s
1	0	0	½
1	0	0	−½

Hence at most 2 electrons may have $n = 1$ in a single atom. For $n = 2$ the possible sets are

n	l	m_l	m_s
2	1	−1	½
2	1	−1	−½
2	1	0	½
2	1	0	−½
2	1	1	½
2	1	1	−½
2	0	0	½
2	0	0	−½

Hence at most 8 electrons may be in the $n = 2$ shell. The Pauli principle correctly predicts the maximum number of electrons in the atomic shells of the periodic chart of the elements.

2.5 Particle in a three-dimensional box

In section 2.1, the quantum-mechanical problem of the particle in a one-dimensional box was treated. We now consider the problem of a particle in a three-dimensional box, since it is a useful first approximation to the problem of free electrons in a piece of metal.

In the one-dimensional problem we found that the normalized wavefunctions are

$$\psi = \sqrt{2/L}\,\sin\frac{n\pi x}{L}, \qquad n = 1, 2, 3, \ldots \tag{2.8}$$

and that the allowed values of energy are

$$E_n = \frac{n^2h^2}{8mL^2} \tag{2.11}$$

The energy may be expressed (see section 1.6) in terms of the magnitude of the momentum p of either of the two traveling waves that make up the standing wave. Thus, since $U = 0$,

$$E = \frac{p^2}{2m} \tag{2.36}$$

From equations 2.11 and 2.36 we see that the momentum may have

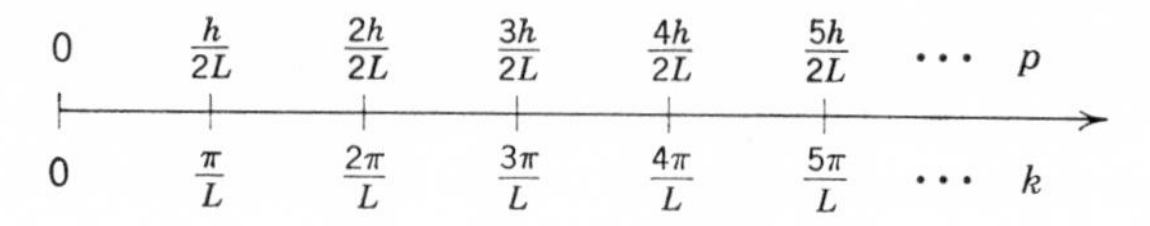

Fig. 2.9. The possible values of p and k for a particle in a one-dimensional box.

only the discrete values given by

$$p = \frac{nh}{2L} \tag{2.37}$$

In Fig. 2.9 we show possible values of momentum for the standing-wave solutions of the one-dimensional problem. The points in this one-dimensional momentum space are $h/2L$ apart. The values of the propagation constant k (see equation 1.3) corresponding to the possible values of momentum are also shown in Fig. 2.9.

The wavefunctions for a particle in a three-dimensional, rectangular box of sides L_x, L_y, and L_z are found by solving the Schroedinger equation in cartesian coordinates x, y, z. The reader may verify that these solutions are

$$\psi_{n_x n_y n_z} = \sqrt{2/L_x} \sin \frac{n_x \pi x}{L_x} \cdot \sqrt{2/L_y} \sin \frac{n_y \pi y}{L_y} \cdot \sqrt{2/L_z} \sin \frac{n_z \pi z}{L_z} \tag{2.38}$$

where n_x, n_y, and n_z are quantum numbers describing the wavefunction. Each may independently have any of the values 1, 2, 3, ... Note that each three-dimensional wavefunction is the product of three "one-dimensional" solutions.

The energy associated with a wavefunction can be evaluated as before by substituting the solution 2.38 back into Schroedinger's equation. The result is

$$E = \frac{1}{2m}\left[\left(\frac{n_x h}{2L_x}\right)^2 + \left(\frac{n_y h}{2L_y}\right)^2 + \left(\frac{n_z h}{2L_z}\right)^2\right] \tag{2.39}$$

By analogy with the one-dimensional case there is a quantized momentum associated with each direction.

$$p_x = \frac{n_x h}{2L_x}; \qquad p_y = \frac{n_y h}{2L_y}; \qquad p_z = \frac{n_z h}{2L_z} \tag{2.40}$$

Substituting 2.40 in 2.39 the energy may be expressed as

$$E = \frac{p_x^2 + p_y^2 + p_z^2}{2m} = \frac{p^2}{2m} \tag{2.41}$$

In Fig. 2.10 we represent a wavefunction as a point in the first octant of a three-dimensional momentum space. Figure 2.10 is the three-dimensional analogue of Fig. 2.9. The separations of the points in the three coordinate directions are $h/2L_x$, $h/2L_y$, $h/2L_z$. In Fig. 2.10 a cell of volume $h^3/8L_xL_yL_z$ is drawn around the point for which $n_x = 2$, $n_y = 3$, $n_z = 2$. The first octant of momentum space is completely filled with cells identical to that drawn. Each cell is associated with a set of three quantum numbers. Note that no particle may occupy a cell for which any of the quantum numbers equals zero, since the solution, equation 2.38, would be zero everywhere, and the particle would be nonexistent.

Our academic problem of a particle in a box is a useful approximation to the problem of electrons in a metal. The walls of the box correspond to the surface of the piece of metal. To a first approximation we assume that an electron sees a uniform potential field which is set up by the nuclei and the other electrons. The assumed uniform potential inside the metal corresponds to the uniform potential energy ($U = 0$) inside the box. The wavefunctions of electrons in a metal in this approximation are those of equation 2.38. However, besides the three momentum quantum numbers, a spin quantum number m_s is required to represent fully each electronic state. For this reason the Pauli exclusion principle, which permits only one electron to have a given wavefunction, allows two electrons to have the same set of momentum quantum numbers n_x, n_y, and n_z. Therefore in a momentum-space diagram such as Fig. 2.10 two electrons may exist in each cell of volume $h^3/8L_xL_yL_z$.

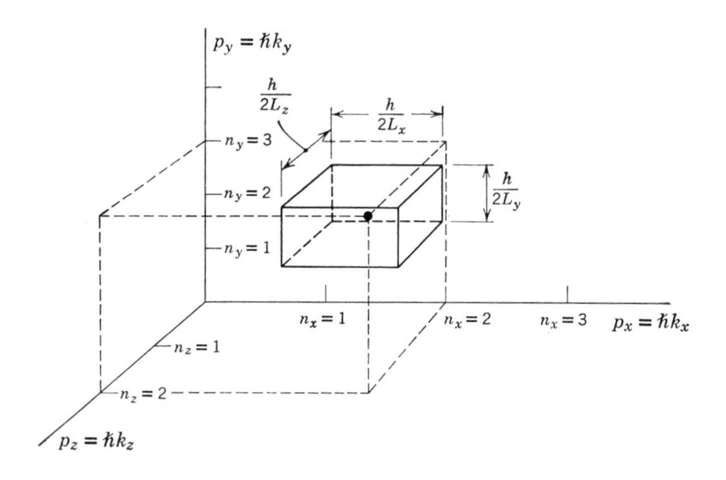

Fig. 2.10. Three-dimensional momentum space.

It should be pointed out that, since the quantum numbers n_x, n_y, n_z may not be zero, no electron in a metal may have zero momentum or zero kinetic energy, even at a temperature of absolute zero. The minimum total energy which a group of electrons can have is known as the zero-point energy.

It is important to note that the number of electronic states per unit volume of momentum space is constant and is given by

$$\frac{dS_\tau}{dp_x\,dp_y\,dp_z} = \frac{\dfrac{2\text{ (states)}}{h^3}}{8L_xL_yL_z} = \frac{16V}{h^3} \quad \begin{pmatrix}\text{points in first}\\ \text{octant only}\end{pmatrix} \tag{2.42}$$

where V is the ordinary volume of the piece of metal, and dS_τ is the number of electronic states within a "volume" element in momentum space $dp_xdp_ydp_z$. In Fig. 2.10, one point is plotted in the first octant for each possible wavefunction. It is worthwhile to emphasize that the total wavefunction consists of three standing waves, one oriented in each of the three coordinate directions. Each standing wave is the interference pattern of two traveling waves having equal and opposite momentum vectors. The momenta of the two traveling waves comprising the x-oriented standing wave are both denoted by the positive number p_x and similarly for the y- and z-oriented standing waves. Thus, in terms of traveling waves, each point in Fig. 2.10 represents six traveling waves, two in each of the three directions, which interfere to produce the total standing wave.

Later it will be convenient to represent a *total* wavefunction as a traveling wave rather than a standing wave. Traveling waves may be represented on a momentum-space diagram similar to that of Fig. 2.10, except that all eight octants are needed. The number of quantum states within an energy interval must be independent of the method of describing the states. Thus the density of points representing traveling waves which are plotted in all eight octants must be one-eighth the density of the points when plotted in a single octant. When points are plotted in all eight octants, the density of states in momentum space is still constant but equal to one-eighth the value in equation 2.42. Thus

$$\frac{dS_\tau}{dp_x\,dp_y\,dp_z} = \frac{2V}{h^3} \quad \begin{pmatrix}\text{points in all}\\ \text{8 octants}\end{pmatrix} \tag{2.43}$$

We next calculate how the allowed quantum states are distributed in energy. This distribution is characterized by the number of states per unit energy, or density of states factor which is given the symbol

dS/dE. To evaluate dS/dE as a function of energy we note from equation 2.41 and Fig. 2.10 that the momentum p represents the distance of a point from the origin in momentum space. Hence, using 2.41, all the electrons with energies between zero and E are represented by points in momentum space which lie within a sphere of radius

$$p = \sqrt{2mE} \tag{2.44}$$

The number S of such states is given by the volume of the sphere, $\frac{4}{3}\pi p^3$ times the number of states per unit volume $2V/h^3$ (equation 2.43). Using 2.44 we have

$$S = \frac{4}{3}\pi p^3 \frac{2V}{h^3} = \frac{16\pi V \sqrt{2}\, m^{3/2} E^{3/2}}{3h^3} \tag{2.45}$$

Differentiating 2.45 with respect to E yields

$$\frac{dS}{dE} = \frac{8\pi V \sqrt{2}\, m^{3/2} E^{1/2}}{h^3} \tag{2.46}$$

This expression for the density of states of a particle in a three-dimensional box will be needed in later chapters where the "box" model of a metal is employed.

Last, we check to see if we have gotten into trouble with the uncertainty principle by specifying the magnitude of the momentum of a particle exactly. Since we are dealing with bound particles, our wave-functions are standing waves, and if we think of a particle "bouncing" back and forth in the box we do not know at any instant which way a particle is moving. Thus the uncertainty in the x-component of momentum of a particle is given by

$$\Delta p_x = \pm \frac{n_x h}{2L_x} = \frac{n_x h}{L_x} \tag{2.47}$$

The uncertainty in position is

$$\Delta x = \pm \frac{L_x}{2} = L_x \tag{2.48}$$

so that

$$\Delta p_x \, \Delta x = \frac{n_x h}{L_x} L_x = n_x h > \hbar \tag{2.49}$$

The uncertainty principle is satisfied.

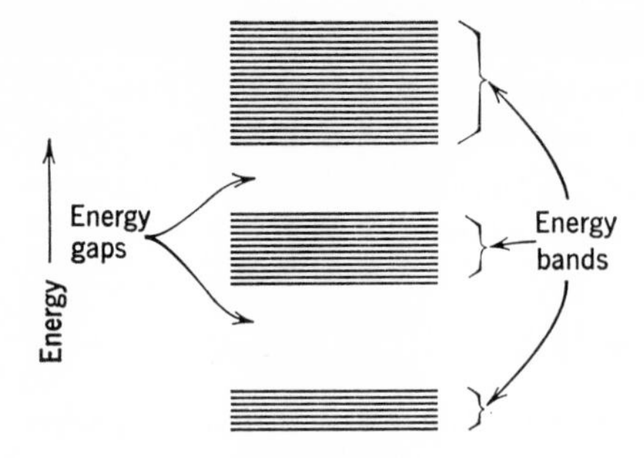

Fig. 2.11. Energy bands.

2.6 Energy bands

In the previous problems which we have considered in the light of the Schroedinger equation, the potential energy has been either constant or a continuously increasing function of radius. In each of these problems the possible particle energies are quantized. For problems in which the potential energy is periodic in space, the allowed particle energy levels are still quantized, and in addition they cluster together in groups called bands. These energy bands are separated by regions in which no energy levels can appear (see Fig. 2.11). We attempt here to convey a qualitative understanding of the formation of bands through a discussion of the influence of interatomic interactions.

When atoms are far apart, they possess individual characteristic sets of energy levels. In Fig. 2.12 we plot the potential energy of an electron as a function of the distance r from the center of a single idealized atom. In this figure, the three lowest energy levels of the atom are shown together with the principal quantum numbers. The population of these levels by electrons is subject to the restrictions of the exclusion principle.

Figure 2.13 shows two atoms in such close proximity that their potential energy curves overlap. Since potential energy is a scalar quantity, the total potential energy between the atoms is reduced.

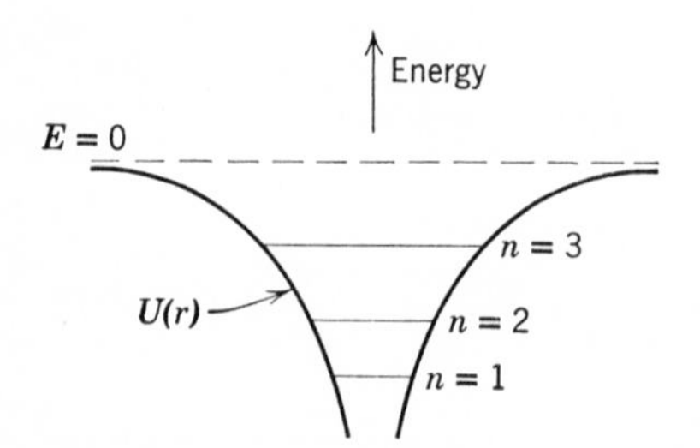

Fig. 2.12. Potential energy well of an atom.

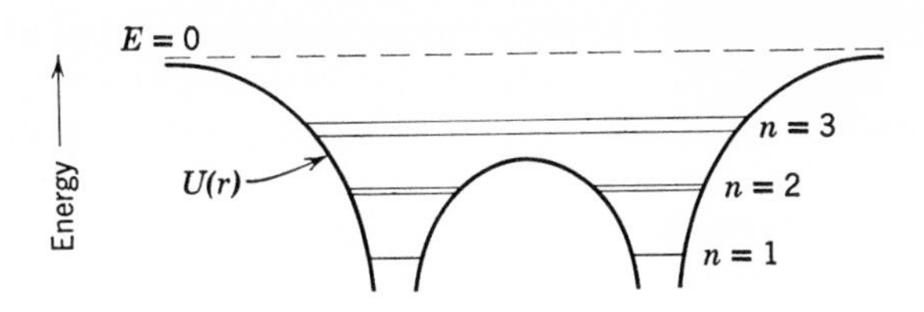

Fig. 2.13. Potential energy wells of two close atomic neighbors.

In fact, an electron in an $n = 3$ level of the atoms in Fig. 2.13 could wander and be found in the vicinity of either atom. Such an electron in classical physics would be called a free electron.

To describe the formation of energy bands we first note that the exclusion principle tells us that the wavefunctions of the electrons associated with these coupled atoms must all be different, because the two atoms together form a single atomic system. Since the individual wavefunctions must be different, it is not surprising that states which originally had the same energy now have slightly different energies. Two or more energy levels now appear in place of a single level. If N atoms are crammed together, the energy levels separate into bands of some multiple of N closely spaced levels.

Another way of viewing the formation of energy bands is to note that electrons bound to atoms are described by standing waves. When such bound systems are crammed close together so that there is some

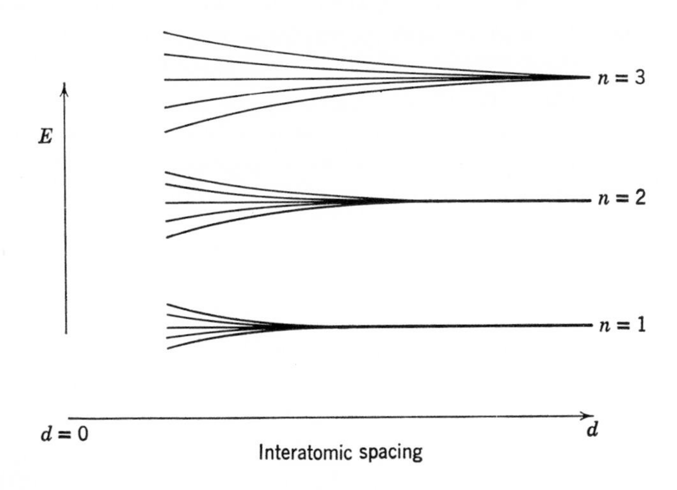

Fig. 2.14. Energy level splitting as a function of interatomic spacing d.

leakage of the electron waves from one neighboring system to another, each system modifies the frequency of oscillation of the others. This process is directly analogous to the frequency splitting of coupled mechanical or electrical oscillators.

From another viewpoint, when an electron responds not only to the charge distribution of its host atom but also feels forces from neighboring atoms, the potential energy functions used in Schroedinger's equation are modified. Consequently, the wavefunctions and their associated energies are also modified.

In Fig. 2.14, we plot the splitting of the three lowest energy levels of five atoms, each identical to that shown in Fig. 2.12, as a function of the interatomic separation. It will be noted that the higher energy levels split at larger separations. This is because the electrons in these levels are, on the average, further from their nuclei and consequently are more readily disturbed. It is found that the total width of each energy band depends on the interatomic spacing and not on the number of atoms grouped together. A more detailed treatment of the physics of energy bands is given in Chapter 12.

SUGGESTED REFERENCES

C. W. Sherwin, *Introduction to Quantum Mechanics*, Holt, Reinhart, and Winston, 1959. In this very successful attempt to present the fundamentals of quantum mechanics to the undergraduate student, Sherwin begins with five postulates and proceeds clearly and carefully through many simple but illuminating examples, including the hydrogen atom.

D. Bohm, *Quantum Theory*, Prentice-Hall, 1951. Although this book is aimed primarily at the graduate student, Chapters 1 through 8 present the underlying concepts of quantum mechanics in a philosophical and not too mathematical manner.

A. T. Goble and D. K. Baker, *Elements of Modern Physics*, The Ronald Press Company, 1962. Chapter 11 of this elementary modern physics text presents a "derivation" of the Schroedinger equation and uses it to perform some of the simpler calculations.

R. T. Weidner and R. L. Sells, *Elementary Modern Physics*, Allyn and Bacon, 1960. Chapters 3 and 4 introduce the elementary quantum effects, such as the Compton effect and electron diffraction, without the use of the Schroedinger equation.

PROBLEMS

2.1. Show that

$$\psi = A_1 \cos (k_1 x + \phi_1)$$

is also a solution to equation 2.2, the Schroedinger equation, for a particle in a one-dimensional box. Determine how the constants A_1, k_1, and ϕ_1 are related to the constants k, ϕ, and A of equations 2.4 and 2.7.

2.2. If an electron were confined to a one-dimensional box 10 Å long, what "spectral" frequencies might result from the transitions between the energy levels of Fig. 2.4?

2.3. Show that the first Bohr radius for the hydrogen atom is 0.53 Å by direct substitution into equation 2.25.

2.4. Show that the ionization energy of a hydrogen atom is 13.6 ev by direct substitution into 2.28.

2.5. Show that the area under the curve of Fig. 2.7 is one. (*Hint:* Look up the integral in a table of definite integrals.)

2.6. Show that the most probable radius for the electron in the ground state of hydrogen is a_1 by finding the value of r for which dP_{r1}/dr is a maximum.

2.7. Show, by substituting 2.35 into the Schroedinger equation, that the energy of an electron in the next to ground-state level is $E_1/4$.

2.8. Show that the maxima of the curve in Fig. 2.8 occur at $r = (3 \pm \sqrt{5})a_1$ and that the minimum occurs at $r = 2a_1$.

2.9. How many valence electrons (electrons not in a filled n-shell) are there for an atom with 32 electrons?

2.10. How many states have $n = 5$ in a hydrogen atom?

2.11. (*a*) What are the dimensions of a cell in a momentum space for an electron confined to a box of dimensions 1 Å × 2 Å × 3 Å? (*b*) How many electron states are there per unit volume of momentum space in this problem?

2.12. What are the energies in joules of the four lowest energy states of an electron in the box of Problem 2.11? What are the quantum numbers of these four states? Draw an energy-level diagram showing these four energies.

2.13. For a box 1 cm on a side, how many electron states exist with total momentum $p = \sqrt{p_x^2 + p_y^2 + p_z^2}$ less than 10^{-25} kg-meter/sec?

2.14. Solve in detail the one-dimensional potential box problem when the walls are not infinitely high. Take the top of the well as the zero of possible energy and consider states of negative total energy. Find a graphical method of solving for the energy eigenvalues. Find the two lowest states for an electron in a 10 ev well of width 10^{-7} cm. Draw the corresponding normalized wavefunctions. (See Pitkaner, *Am. J. Phys.*, **23,** 111 (1955), or Schiff, *Quantum Mechanics*.)

2.15. The "harmonic oscillator" potential energy may be written as $U(x) = \frac{1}{2}\beta x^2$ (for all x). Write down the Schroedinger equation for this potential energy and try solutions of the type $\psi(x) = e^{-\alpha x^2}f(x)$, where $f(x)$ is a simple (positive) power series in x. Start with $f(x) =$ constant, and then try the linear and quadratic forms. Evaluate the constant α and find the energy eigenvalues.

3. statistics

In Chapter 2 we discussed situations in which particles are in bound states. In doing so we restricted ourselves to quantum-mechanical systems containing only one particle, or if more than one we imagined the particles to be noninteracting. When there is a large number of particles in a system, the problem of describing the system becomes in one respect more complex, and in another respect more simple. It would obviously be hopeless to try to follow the behavior of one molecule of a gas as it interacts with the other molecules in an ordinary sized container. Likewise it is hopeless to try to find the total wavefunction for the electrons in an ordinary sized crystal. However, if we abandon the requirement that we know what each particle is doing, it is usually possible to predict the *average* behavior of a large group of particles. This type of investigation lies in the field of statistical mechanics and, for certain systems, in the field of quantum statistical mechanics. In this chapter we develop the more elementary concepts of statistical mechanics and quantum statistical mechanics by finding how the particles of a system are distributed among discrete energy states. The statistical behavior of electrons is an important concept in thermionic emission from metals and in most other processes involving metals or semiconductors.

3.1 How different assumptions lead to different kinds of statistics

For simplicity, we consider a system containing regularly spaced energy levels. If we choose the zero point of total energy to coincide with the lowest allowed level, then a particle may have an energy of

0 units, 1 unit, 2 units, and so on. We consider a fixed number N of particles sharing a fixed amount of energy, and ask how the particles will be distributed among the various energy levels. A convenient parameter for describing the distribution of the particles among the levels is the time average of the number of particles in a level. Our task is to find how the time average depends on the energy of the level in question. The time average for a level of energy E_i is denoted by P_i and is defined in a manner similar to that for any average.

$$P_i \equiv \frac{1t_1 + 2t_2 + \cdots + Nt_N}{t_0 + t_1 + t_2 + \cdots + t_N} = \frac{t_1}{T} + 2\frac{t_2}{T} + \cdots + N\frac{t_N}{T} \tag{3.1}$$

where t_0 is the time that no particles occupy the ith level, t_1 is the time that one particle occupies the ith level, and so on. The total time is denoted by T. For example, if during a period of 10 sec a level contained no particles for 3 sec, 1 particle for 2 sec and 2 particles for 5 sec, the average number of particles in the level would be

$$P = 2/10 + 2 \times 5/10 = 1.2 \tag{3.2}$$

Since the particles of a system may interact in a complex manner, any distribution of particles among the energy levels that conserves energy is possible. In fact, a fundamental assumption of statistical mechanics is that each "different distribution" that conserves energy is equally probable, that is, occurs the same fraction of the time. There are three ways of defining the phrase "different distribution" that lead to values of P as a function of E that agree with experiments. The first treats the particles as distinguishable and counts each permutation of particles among levels as a different distribution. The average distribution (P versus E) derived from this method of counting is named after Maxwell and Boltzmann and applies, for example, to a low density gas. The second way treats the particles as indistinguishable and counts only the number of different *combinations* of particles in levels. The type of statistics arising from this assumption is called Bose-Einstein statistics, which, for example, apply to a photon gas. The third method of counting arises when the particles obey the Pauli exclusion principle (for example, electrons). The combination of indistinguishability (Bose-Einstein statistics) and the Pauli exclusion principle (at most one electron in each state) leads to a third type of statistics named after Fermi and Dirac.[1]

We now show how the three different assumptions lead to different

[1] In our examples, we consider that the energy of a state somehow depends on the spin of an electron so that only one and not two electrons may occupy each level.

Energy of level ⟶

0	1	2	3	4	5	6	7	8
ab								*c*
bc								*a*
ca								*b*
a	*b*						*c*	
a	*c*						*b*	
b	*c*						*a*	
b	*a*						*c*	
c	*a*						*b*	
c	*b*						*a*	
a		*b*				*c*		
a		*c*				*b*		
b		*c*				*a*		
b		*a*				*c*		
c		*a*				*b*		
c		*b*				*a*		
a			*b*		*c*			
a			*c*		*b*			
b			*c*		*a*			
b			*a*		*c*			
c			*a*		*b*			
c			*b*		*a*			
a				*bc*				
b				*ca*				
c				*ab*				
	ab					*c*		
	bc					*a*		
	ca					*b*		
	a	*b*			*c*			
	a	*c*			*b*			
	b	*c*			*a*			
	b	*a*			*c*			
	c	*a*			*b*			
	c	*b*			*a*			
	a		*b*	*c*				
	a		*c*	*b*				
	b		*c*	*a*				
	b		*a*	*c*				
	c		*a*	*b*				
	c		*b*	*a*				
		ab		*c*				
		bc		*a*				
		ca		*b*				
		a	*bc*					
		b	*ca*					
		c	*ab*					

Maxwell-Boltzmann

Fig. 3.1. The 45 possible arrangements of three distinguishable particles sharing eight units of energy (Maxwell-Boltzmann statistics). Each horizontal line represents a different distribution and occurs $\frac{1}{45}$ of the time.

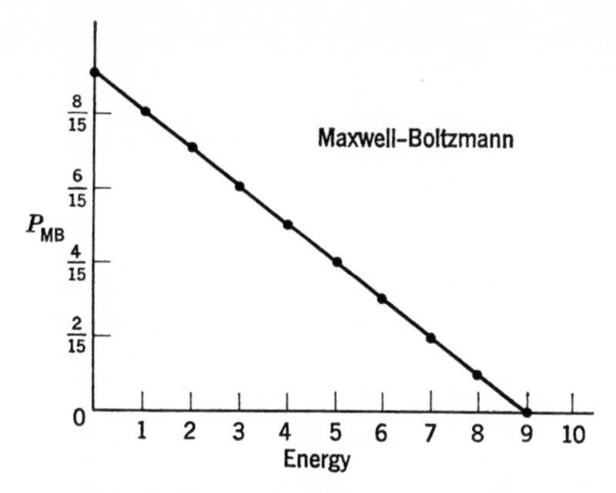

Fig. 3.2. The average distribution of particles among states (P_{MB} versus E) for three particles sharing eight units of energy and obeying Maxwell-Boltzmann statistics.

average distributions of particles among a set of levels by a simple counting process. The underlying physical principles governing the counting are that the *number of particles and their total energy must be conserved.* In our first example we suppose that three particles share a total of eight units of energy. For Maxwell-Boltzmann statistics, we label the particles a, b, c. Each different distribution occupies

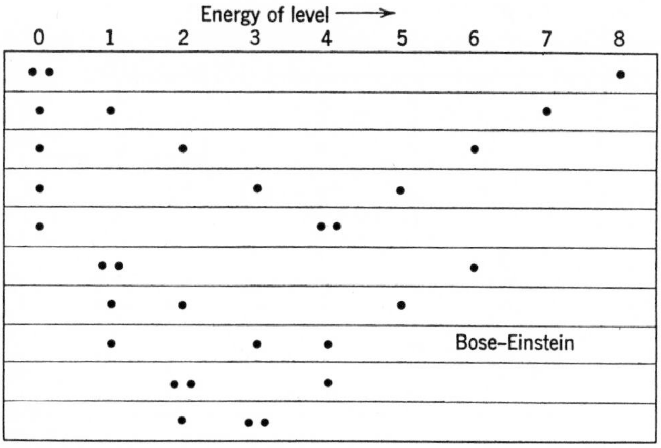

Energy of level ⟶

0	1	2	3	4	5	6	7	8
••								•
•	•						•	
•		•				•		
•			•		•			
•				••				
	••					•		
	•	•			•			
	•		•	•		Bose-Einstein		
		••		•				
		•	••					

Fig. 3.3. The ten possible arrangements of three indistinguishable particles sharing eight units of energy (Bose-Einstein statistics). Each horizontal line represents a different distribution and occurs $\frac{1}{10}$ of the time.

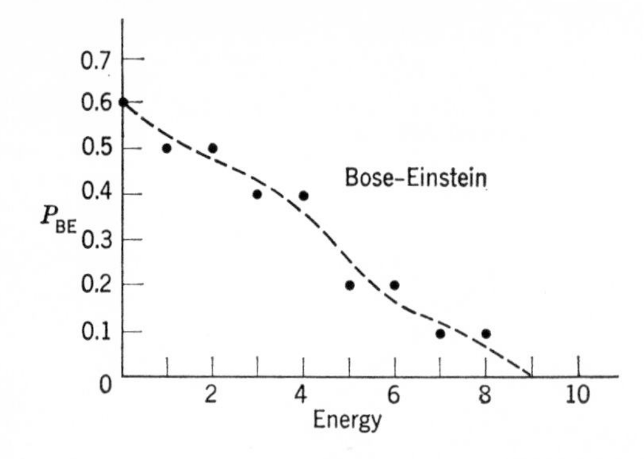

Fig. 3.4. The average distribution of particles among states (P_{BE} versus E) for three indistinguishable particles sharing eight units of energy.

a horizontal line in Fig. 3.1. For example, the first horizontal row represents a situation in which particles a and b are in states of zero energy and particle c is in a state with eight units of energy. We now compute the time average number of particles in each of the energy levels. Since each of the 45 different distributions is equally probable and occurs 1/45 of the time, the time average of the number of particles in level 0 is (using equation 3.1)

$$P_0 = \frac{t_1}{T} + 2\frac{t_2}{T} + 3\frac{t_3}{T} = \frac{21}{45} + 2 \cdot \frac{3}{45} + 3 \cdot \frac{0}{45} = 0.6 \qquad (3.3)$$

In a similar manner the time averages for levels one through eight may be calculated using 3.1. The results are summarized in a graph of time average P_{MB} versus energy of state E in Fig. 3.2.

For Bose-Einstein statistics, since the particles are indistinguishable, we represent each particle by a dot. The different possible dis-

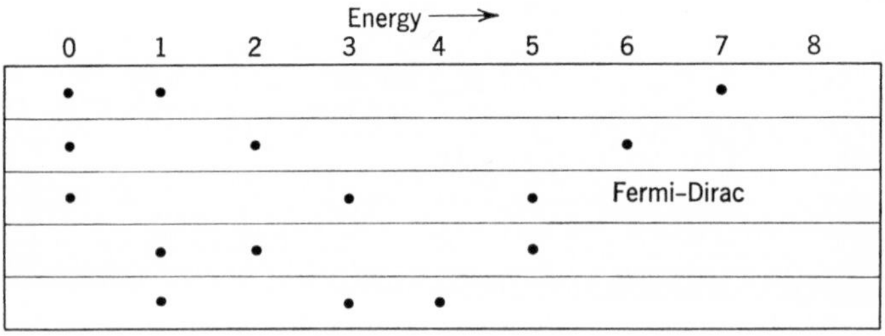

Energy →

0	1	2	3	4	5	6	7	8
•	•						•	
•		•				•		
•			•		•	Fermi-Dirac		
	•	•			•			
	•		•	•				

Fig. 3.5. The five possible arrangements of three indistinguishable particles sharing eight units of energy and obeying the Pauli exclusion principle (Fermi-Dirac statistics). Each horizontal line represents a different distribution and occurs ⅕ of the time.

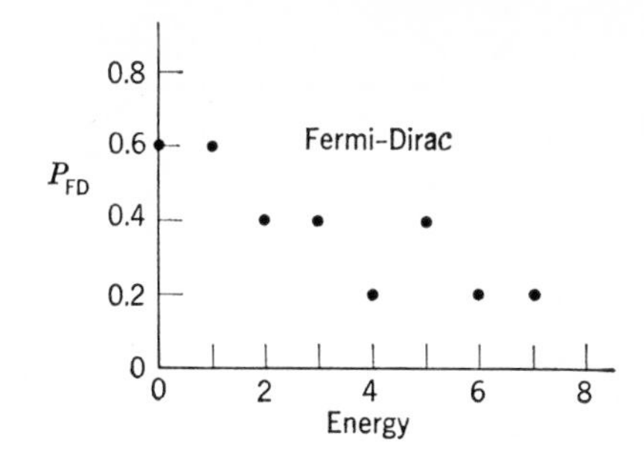

Fig. 3.6. The average distribution of particles among states (P_{ED} versus E) for three particles sharing eight units of energy and obeying Fermi-Dirac statistics.

tributions are tabulated in Fig. 3.3. This time there are only ten different distributions because permutations of particles among energy levels may not be counted. Note that these ten distributions correspond to the ten groups of distributions separated by horizontal lines in Fig. 3.1. The average distribution (P_{BE} versus E) may be found from Fig. 3.3 using equation 3.1. It is plotted in Fig. 3.4.

Figures 3.5 and 3.6 show the individual distributions and the average distribution for the particles when, in addition to being indistinguishable, they obey the Pauli exclusion principle. The number of different distributions is even smaller for this case (Fermi-Dirac statistics) than for the Bose-Einstein case because of the impossibility of having two particles in one level at the same time. (Figure 3.5 contains only those distributions in Fig. 3.3 which have at most one particle in an energy level.) It should be noted that for Fermi-Dirac statistics the time average of the number of particles in a level is identical to the probability that a level is occupied by a particle at a particular instant of time. (This is the reason we denoted the time average by the sym-

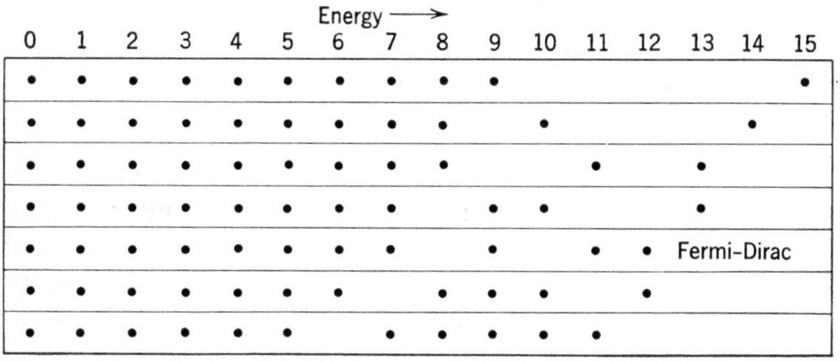

Energy ⟶

0	1	2	3	4	5	6	7	8	9	10	11	12	13	14	15
•	•	•	•	•	•	•	•	•	•						•
•	•	•	•	•	•	•	•	•		•				•	
•	•	•	•	•	•	•	•	•			•		•		
•	•	•	•	•	•	•	•		•	•			•		
•	•	•	•	•	•	•	•		•		•	•	Fermi-Dirac		
•	•	•	•	•	•	•		•	•	•		•			
•	•	•	•	•	•		•	•	•	•	•				

Fig. 3.7. The seven possible arrangements of eleven particles sharing sixty units of energy under Fermi-Dirac statistics.

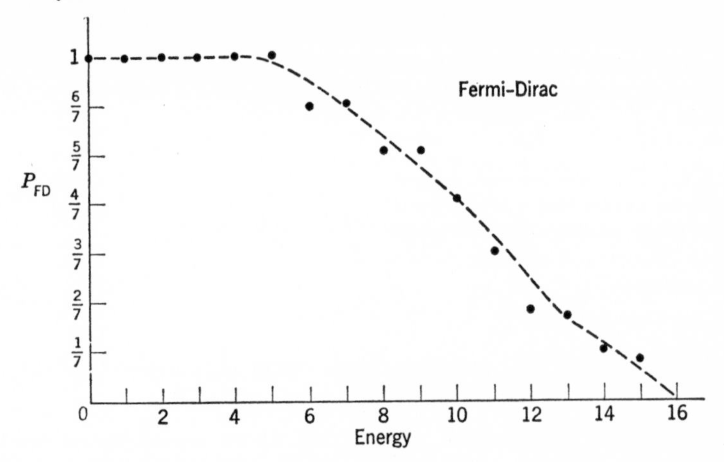

Fig. 3.8. The average distribution of particles (P_{FD} versus E) for eleven particles sharing sixty units of energy and obeying Fermi-Dirac statistics.

bol P, although for the Einstein-Bose and Maxwell-Boltzmann cases the interpretation of the time average as a kind of probability is more difficult).

It is apparent from a glance at Figs. 3.4 and 3.6 that there were not enough different distributions to obtain a smooth plot of P versus E. Since in physical electronics we are most concerned with Fermi-Dirac statistics, it is worthwhile to consider another numerical example for the Fermi-Dirac case which hints at what the average distribution would look like if a large number of particles were sharing a large amount of energy. Specifically, we consider eleven particles sharing sixty units of energy. The different distributions are tabulated in Fig. 3.7 and the average distribution (P_{FD} versus E) plotted in Fig. 3.8.

3.2 Information contained in the average distribution curves

The average distribution curves still contain, unambiguously, the information used to construct them. That is, the number of particles and the energy shared by them can be inferred directly from a graph of the average distribution. Since, on the average, the number of particles in a level i is P_i, the total number of particles in the system is given by

$$N = \sum_i P_i \tag{3.4}$$

where the summation extends over all levels including zero. Furthermore, on the average, the energy associated with the particles in a level i is E_iP_i so that the total energy of all the particles is

$$E_T = \sum_i E_iP_i \tag{3.5}$$

The average energy $\bar{E}$ of the particles is defined by

$$\bar{E} \equiv \frac{E_T}{N} \tag{3.6}$$

Example. Find N, E_T, and the average energy per particle $\bar{E}$ for the average distribution plotted in Fig. 3.8.

Using 3.4, 3.5, and 3.6,

$$N = 1 + 1 + 1 + 1 + 1 + 1 + 6/7 + 6/7 + \cdots + 1/7 + 1/7 = 11$$

$$E_T = 0 \cdot 1 + 1 \cdot 1 + 2 \cdot 1 + 3 \cdot 1 + \cdots + 14 \cdot 1/7 + 15 \cdot 1/7 = 60 \text{ units}$$

$$\bar{E} = E_T/N = 60/11 = 5.45 \text{ units}$$

In many physical problems the number of particles under consideration may be of the order of 10^{10} or larger. In such cases the intervals between energy levels lose all significance and the levels form essentially a continuum. In such a case a useful parameter for the description of the distribution of particles among energy levels is the number of particles per unit of energy dN/dE. dN/dE expressed as a function of energy is called the energy distribution function. A continuous curve of dN/dE versus E can be used to infer the total number of particles N and their total energy much as the discontinuous curve of P_{FD} versus E was used in the previous example. The total number of particles is equal to the area under a curve of dN/dE versus E, since

$$N = \int_{\text{all } N} dN = \int_{\text{all } E} \frac{dN}{dE}\, dE = \text{area under curve of } dN/dE \text{ versus } E \tag{3.7}$$

Furthermore, since the total energy of all the particles in a range dE is given by $E\, dN$, where E is the average energy within the range, the total energy of all the particles is

$$E_T = \int_{\text{all } N} E\, dN = \int_{\text{all } E} E \frac{dN}{dE}\, dE \tag{3.8}$$

By using the definition of the average energy $\bar{E}$ given by 3.6, $\bar{E}$ for a continuous distribution may be found by dividing 3.8 by 3.7.

$$\bar{E} = \frac{\int_{\text{all } N} E\, dN}{\int_{\text{all } N} dN} = \frac{\int_{\text{all } E} E \frac{dN}{dE}\, dE}{\int_{\text{all } E} \frac{dN}{dE}\, dE} \tag{3.9}$$

In fact, the average of any function f over a continuous distribution may be written

$$\bar{f} = \frac{\int_{\text{all } N} f\, dN}{\int_{\text{all } N} dN} \tag{3.10}$$

Equations 3.7 and 3.8 may be written in such a way as to show an explicit dependence on P, the average number of particles per level. (At this point we may relax our earlier assumption that each energy level could contain at most one electron by redefining P as the number of particles per quantum state rather than per energy level. A quantum state is specified by a spatial wavefunction and a spin quantum number. Whereas the Pauli principle forbids more than one electron in a given state it places no restriction on the number of electrons that may have the same energy.) The number of particles dN within a range of energy dE may be expressed as the number of quantum states dS, with energies in the range dE, times the average number P of particles in each quantum state. Thus

$$dN = P\, dS \tag{3.11}$$

and equations 3.7 and 3.8 become

$$N = \int_{\text{all } E} P \frac{dS}{dE}\, dE \tag{3.12}$$

$$E_T = \int_{\text{all } E} PE \frac{dS}{dE}\, dE \tag{3.13}$$

In equations 3.12 and 3.13 both P and dS/dE are, in general, functions of E. The factor dS/dE, the density of states, must be calculated by the techniques of quantum mechanics, as was done in section 2.5 for the case of particles in a box. On the other hand, P is calculated by the techniques of statistical mechanics as is done in the next section. Those who wish to avoid the mathematical details of this somewhat lengthy derivation may turn directly to section 3.4 where the interpretation of the basic result (equation 3.30) is begun.

3.3 Derivation of the form of P_{FD}

The following derivation is an analytic approach to what we did graphically in section 3.1. We begin the derivation of the dependence of P_{FD} on energy by dividing the range of energies which particles may have into a large number n of intervals. These energy intervals are chosen so that each contains a large number of quantum states. For the ith interval the number of quantum states is denoted by S_i and the average energy of the states included in the interval by E_i. The number of electrons occupying states in the ith interval is denoted by N_i. These quantities are illustrated in Fig. 3.9. As time goes on the numbers of electrons N_i in the various intervals change, but are always subject to the two conditions that the total number of electrons and their total energy remain constant. In equation form these two conditions may be written

$$\text{Total number of electrons} = N_1 + N_2 + \cdots + N_n = \text{constant} \tag{3.14}$$

$$\text{Total energy} = N_1E_1 + N_2E_2 + \cdots + N_nE_n = \text{constant} \tag{3.15}$$

Although each different distribution (according to the Fermi-Dirac definition) occurs with equal probability, each set of the N_i does not. In fact, one particular set of N_i will occur far more often than any other set and will adequately represent the *average* values of the N_i. We shall calculate how the ratio N_i/S_i depends on energy E_i for this most probable set. This ratio is, by analogy with equation 3.11, the probability P_i that a state is occupied (that is, the time average of the number of particles in the state). Our method of attack is to write the total number of ways W in which a given set of the N_i can occur, and find the particular values of the N_i that maximize W, subject to the two conditions 3.14 and 3.15.

The number of ways in which N_i (indistinguishable) electrons can be

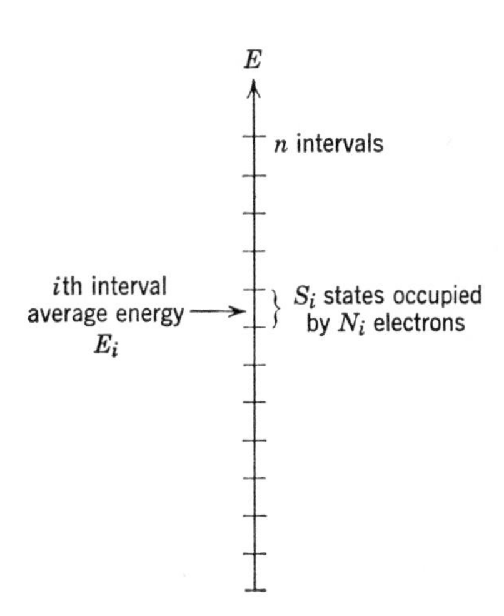

Fig. 3.9. Illustration of quantities used in derivation of P_{FD} versus E.

divided among S_i states is

$$W_i = \frac{S_i!}{N_i!(S_i - N_i)!} \tag{3.16}$$

which the reader may verify by counting for a case in which S_i and N_i are small. A *set of* N_i is defined by assigning a particular value of N to each energy interval. The total number of ways W a *set of* N_i can occur is the product of the W_i for all of the n groups of states.

$$W = W_1 \cdot W_2 \cdot W_3 \cdots W_n$$

or

$$W = \frac{S_1!}{N_1!(S_1 - N_1)!} \times \frac{S_2!}{N_2!(S_2 - N_2)!} \times \cdots \times \frac{S_n!}{N_n!(S_n - N_n)!} \tag{3.17}$$

It is more convenient to work with ln W than W, and since ln W is a monotonically increasing function of W, the set of N_i that maximizes ln W is the set that maximizes W. Thus, taking the natural logarithm of 3.17

$$\ln W = \sum_i [\ln S_i! - \ln N_i! - \ln (S_i - N_i)!] \tag{3.18}$$

This expression may be simplified by using a form of Stirling's approximation for the natural logarithm of $n!$, which is

$$\ln n! \approx n \ln n - n, \qquad \text{(for large } n\text{)} \tag{3.19}$$

Using 3.19, equation 3.18 may be simplified to give

$$\ln W = \sum_i [S_i \ln S_i - N_i \ln N_i - (S_i - N_i) \ln (S_i - N_i)] \tag{3.20}$$

This expression for ln W is to be treated as a function of the n variables N_i and maximized subject to conditions 3.14 and 3.15. The most convenient method for maximizing a function of many variables subject to auxiliary conditions is Lagrange's method of undetermined multipliers.

The condition for ln W to be a maximum is that its total differential must be zero. By taking the differential of ln W (realizing that the S_i are constants) and simplifying slightly

$$d\,(\ln W) = \sum_i [-\ln N_i + \ln (S_i - N_i)]\, dN_i = \sum_i \ln \left(\frac{S_i - N_i}{N_i}\right) dN_i \tag{3.21}$$

The differentials dN_i are not completely independent because of the auxiliary conditions 3.14 and 3.15. For example, if we choose a value for dN_1, and set $dN_4 = dN_5 = \cdots = dN_n = 0$, then the auxiliary conditions suffice to determine dN_2 and dN_3 such that d (ln W) = 0.

Now according to Lagrange's method we take the differentials of the two auxiliary condition equations, multiply each resulting equation by a constant, and add to $d(\ln W) = 0$. Then

$$d\,(\ln W) + \alpha \sum_i dN_i + \beta \sum_i E_i\, dN_i = 0 \tag{3.22}$$

and using 3.21

$$\sum_i \left[\ln\left(\frac{S_i - N_i}{N_i}\right) + \alpha + \beta E_i \right] dN_i = 0 \tag{3.23}$$

Let us imagine that the constants α and β are chosen such that both

$$\ln\left(\frac{S_1 - N_1}{N_1}\right) + \alpha + \beta E_1 = 0$$

and

$$\ln\left(\frac{S_2 - N_2}{N_2}\right) + \alpha + \beta E_2 = 0 \tag{3.24}$$

Then in the special case in which all the dN_i are zero except the first three, equation 3.23 becomes

$$0 \cdot dN_1 + 0 \cdot dN_2 + \left[\ln\left(\frac{S_3 - N_3}{N_3}\right) + \alpha + \beta E_3 \right] dN_3 = 0 \tag{3.25}$$

or

$$\ln\left(\frac{S_3 - N_3}{N_3}\right) + \alpha + \beta E_3 = 0 \tag{3.26}$$

We can equally well take dN_1, dN_2, dN_4 to be the only three nonzero differentials, which leads by a similar process to

$$\ln\left(\frac{S_4 - N_4}{N_4}\right) + \alpha + \beta E_4 = 0 \tag{3.27}$$

Continuing this procedure, we can write n equations of the form

$$\ln\left(\frac{S_i - N_i}{N_i}\right) + \alpha + \beta E_i = 0 \tag{3.28}$$

which, together with the auxiliary conditions, provide $n + 2$ equations for the $n + 2$ quantities α, β, N_i. Although in principle it is possible to evaluate α, β, and the N_i in terms of the total number of particles and total energy, we shall take a different tack. We will solve for the N_i in the form of N_i/S_i (which is equal to P_i) in terms of α and β and determine α and β by another means. Solving 3.28 for N_i/S_i we find

$$P_i = \frac{N_i}{S_i} = \frac{1}{1 + e^{\alpha + \beta E_i}} \tag{3.29}$$

Denoting P_i by P_{FD} (since equation 3.16 employed the Fermi-Dirac assumptions) and dropping the subscript i, we write

$$P_{\text{FD}} = \frac{1}{1 + e^{\alpha + \beta E}} \qquad \text{Fermi-Dirac statistics} \tag{3.30}$$

This is the basic result of Fermi-Dirac statistics. The constants α and β are evaluated and interpreted in the next two sections.

By using the technique of this section but with different expressions for W_i to replace equation 3.16 it can be shown that the expressions corresponding to 3.30 for Bose-Einstein and Maxwell-Boltzmann statistics are

$$P_{\text{BE}} = \frac{1}{e^{\alpha_1+\beta_1 E} - 1} \qquad \text{Bose-Einstein statistics} \tag{3.31}$$

$$P_{\text{MB}} = \frac{1}{e^{\alpha_2+\beta_2 E}} \qquad \text{Maxwell-Boltzmann statistics} \tag{3.32}$$

where α_1, α_2, β_1, and β_2 are constants.

3.4 The Fermi energy, E_F

In section 3.3 we derived the probability P_{FD} that an energy state is occupied by a particle under the assumptions of Fermi-Dirac statistics. This is the type of statistics which electrons must obey. In fact, all particles with spin ½ obey Fermi-Dirac statistics and as a class are known as fermions.

The basic result of Fermi-Dirac statistics is

$$P_{\text{FD}} = \frac{1}{1 + e^{\alpha+\beta E}} \tag{3.30}$$

where α and β are constants that are related to the total number of particles and their total energy. Equation 3.30 may be written in terms of a constant E_F, which has a simple physical significance by defining

$$E_F \equiv -\frac{\alpha}{\beta} \tag{3.33}$$

Then 3.30 becomes

$$P_{\text{FD}} = \frac{1}{1 + e^{\beta(E-E_F)}} \tag{3.34}$$

From the form of 3.34, E_F must have the units of energy. It is called the Fermi energy. The significance of the Fermi energy, or Fermi level as it is sometimes called, is that it is the energy at which a state has a probability of being occupied of one-half. Thus, when $E = E_F$,

$$P_{\text{FD}}(E_F) = \frac{1}{1 + e^0} = \frac{1}{2} \tag{3.35}$$

3.5 Temperature considerations

One of the ways in which energy can be added to a system of particles is to place it in contact with another system at a higher temperature. In fact, the idea that heat, or energy, flows from an object at a higher temperature to one at a lower temperature is the basis of the thermodynamic temperature scale. From elementary kinetic theory it is evident that temperature is somehow associated with the average energy of the particles in a system. That is, when the temperature is very low, we expect that the lowest energy states of a system are heavily populated, but that when the temperature is high, the higher energy states become populated at the expense of the lower energy states. We now show how the constants β and E_F in equation 3.34 depend on temperature.

As the temperature T of a system of fermions approaches absolute zero we expect that the fermions will settle into the lowest available energy states. Because of the Pauli principle, at $T = 0$, N fermions must occupy the N states of lowest energy and all higher states must be unoccupied. For $T = 0$, 3.34 can represent the distribution of fermions among states only if E_F is equal to the energy of the highest occupied state[1] and if $\beta \rightarrow \infty$. Then, from 3.34

$$\begin{aligned} \lim_{\substack{T\to 0 \\ \beta\to\infty}} P_{\mathrm{FD}} &= 1 \qquad \text{for } E < E_F \\ \lim_{\substack{T\to 0 \\ \beta\to\infty}} P_{\mathrm{FD}} &= 0 \qquad \text{for } E > E_F \end{aligned} \tag{3.36}$$

At very high temperatures P_{FD} must become very small for any E. This can only happen if $e^{\beta(E-E_F)} \gg 1$ (see 3.34). Hence, we may write

$$\lim_{T\to \text{large}} P_{\mathrm{FD}} = e^{-\beta(E-E_F)} = e^{\beta E_F} e^{-\beta E} \tag{3.37}$$

If we choose $E = 0$ for the lowest energy state, this expression can only be small for all energies if βE_F is negative. Since the probability of a state being occupied must decrease with increasing energy (as was demonstrated by counting in section 3.1), β must be positive and therefore E_F must be negative for very high temperatures. Graphs of the low- and high-temperature limits of P_{FD} are shown in Fig. 3.10. A graph of P_{FD} for an intermediate temperature is included for comparison with Fig. 3.8. It should be emphasized that we have chosen the zero of energy to be the energy of the lowest quantum state purely for convenience. As always, only differences in total energy have physical significance and it is only the difference between E and E_F that determines the value of P_{FD}.

At this point we conclude that since $\beta \rightarrow \infty$ as $T \rightarrow 0$, β must be some inverse function of T. Furthermore, we know that as T becomes

[1] This is not strictly true when the highest occupied state lies exactly at the top of a band of states. We discuss that case in Chapter 13.

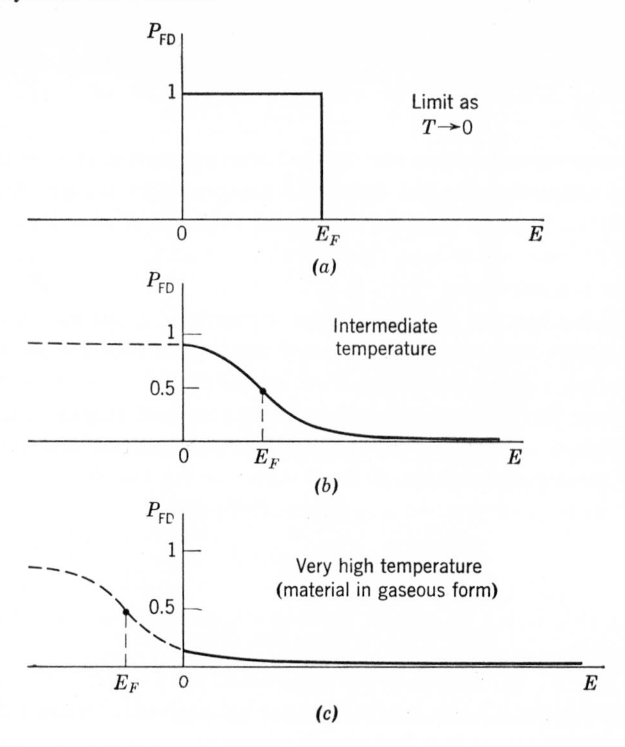

Fig. 3.10. The Fermi-Dirac probability factor versus energy at three temperatures.

large E_F must become negative, and the Fermi factor approaches a simple exponential function of energy. To evaluate β in terms of the temperature, a macroscopic concept, we must use our theory to calculate an observable quantity, and compare the results of the theory with experiment. The observable quantity which we will use is the pressure. In kinetic theory a low-density gas may be analyzed using the assumption that the gas particles do not interact except during collisions. A gas under such conditions is called an ideal gas. The pressure p of such a gas follows the experimental "ideal gas law"

$$p = nkT \tag{3.38}$$

where n is the number of gas particles per unit volume, T is the absolute temperature, and k is a constant. All real gases at sufficiently low pressure follow this law with the same experimental value for the constant k. This constant is called Boltzmann's constant (or the gas constant per molecule) and has the value

$$k = 1.380 \times 10^{-23} \text{ joule/°K} = 8.63 \times 10^{-5} \text{ ev/°K} \quad (3.39)$$

If in equation 3.34 E is set equal to $\frac{1}{2}m(v_x^2 + v_y^2 + v_z^2)$, and this expression used in a kinetic theory derivation to calculate the pressure of a gas of fermions in a box at very high temperature, the result is

$$p = \frac{n}{\beta} \quad (3.40)$$

The derivation of 3.40, which is left as a problem, is directly analogous to that carried out in most elementary textbooks in terms of the average rate of change of momentum of monoenergetic particles striking the walls, except that a velocity distribution of particles obtained from 3.34 and 2.43 is utilized. Comparing 3.40 with 3.38 we see that in the Fermi-Dirac probability factor

$$\beta = \frac{1}{kT} \quad (3.41)$$

Note that this value of β is in agreement with our earlier statement that, when $T \to 0$, $\beta \to \infty$.

Using 3.41 we put the general expression 3.34 for the Fermi-Dirac probability factor, often called more simply the "Fermi factor," into its most familiar and important form.

$$P_{\text{FD}} = \frac{1}{1 + e^{(E-E_F)/kT}}, \quad \text{the Fermi factor} \quad (3.42)$$

The corresponding expressions for Bose-Einstein and Maxwell-Boltzmann statistics are

$$P_{\text{BE}} = \frac{1}{A_1 e^{E/kT} - 1} \quad (3.43)$$

and

$$P_{\text{MB}} = A_2 e^{-E/kT} \quad (3.44)$$

The constants E_F, A_1, and A_2 in the three statistical laws are normalization constants which depend essentially on the number of particles in the system.

3.6 The energy distribution of Fermi particles in a box

The problem of finding the distribution dS/dE of the allowed values of energy of the particles of a physical system must be solved by quantum mechanics. An elementary example, that of an electron confined

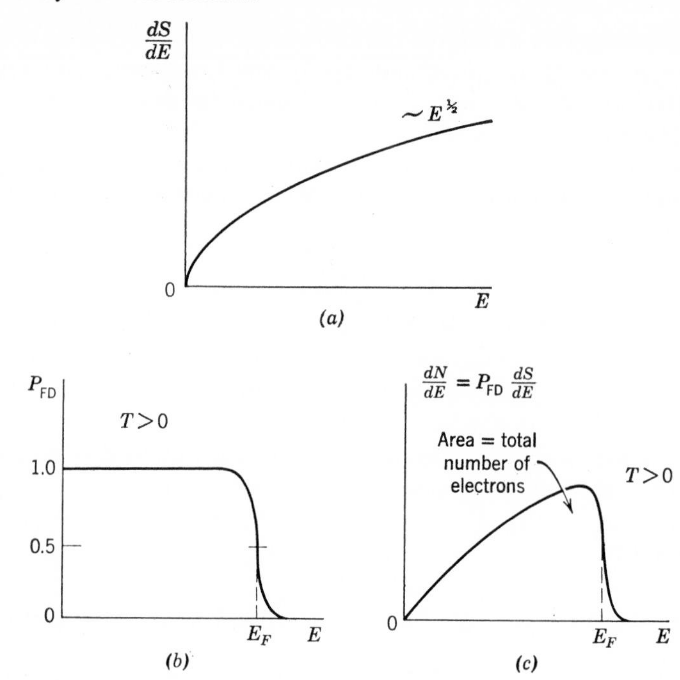

Fig. 3.11. (*a*) The density of states. (*b*) The Fermi factor. (*c*) The energy distribution function (product of *a* and *b*).

to a region of constant potential, was worked out in Chapter 2. The result obtained there for the number of states per unit energy, that is, the density of states, was

$$\frac{dS}{dE} = \frac{8\pi V\sqrt{2}\, m^{3/2}E^{1/2}}{h^3} \tag{2.46}$$

where m is the mass of the fermion (the restriction to electrons was not necessary) and V is the volume of the box to which it is confined.

When many particles occupy the box, the distribution in energy of the allowed states does not change, provided the particles are noninteracting. (The assumption of noninteraction or weak interaction is adhered to in all quantum-mechanical treatments in this text.) Then the energy distribution function dN/dE is found by using 2.46 and 3.42 in 3.11

$$\frac{dN}{dE} = P_{FD}\frac{dS}{dE} = \frac{8\pi V\sqrt{2}\, m^{3/2}E^{1/2}}{h^3(1 + e^{(E-E_F)/kT})} \tag{3.45}$$

Graphs of the factors P_{FD} and dS/dE as functions of E are drawn in

Fig. 3.11 along with a graph of the energy distribution function dN/dE. The graphs are drawn for a moderately low temperature to conform approximately to the situation in a real metal for any temperature for which the metal remains a solid.

An estimate of the Fermi energy can be made by calculating E_F for a temperature of absolute zero. Thus, using the form of the Fermi factor for $T = 0$ (equation 3.36),

$$\begin{aligned} \frac{dN}{dE} &= \frac{8\pi V m^{3/2} \sqrt{2}\, E^{1/2}}{h^3} \qquad \text{for } E < E_F \\ \frac{dN}{dE} &= 0 \qquad \text{for } E > E_F \end{aligned} \tag{3.46}$$

This is called the degenerate distribution function and is plotted in Fig. 3.12. The way in which E_F at $T = 0$ depends on the number of electrons may be found by integrating dN/dE over all energies (see equation 3.7)

$$\begin{aligned} N &= \int_0^\infty \frac{dN}{dE}\, dE = \int_0^{E_F} \frac{8\pi V m^{3/2} \sqrt{2}\, E^{1/2}}{h^3}\, dE \\ N &= \frac{16\pi V m^{3/2} \sqrt{2}}{3h^3} E_F^{3/2} \end{aligned} \tag{3.47}$$

Note that E_F is proportional to the $2/3$ power of the density of electrons N/V. Equation 3.47 is true only at absolute zero. At higher temperatures E_F must shift slightly downward in order for the area under the dN/dE curve (equal to the number of electrons) to remain constant. It requires either approximations or a numerical integration to find the magnitude of the shift; fortunately, it turns out to be negligible for ordinary temperatures. For problems associated with semiconductors, however, the dependence of E_F on temperature may not be negligible.

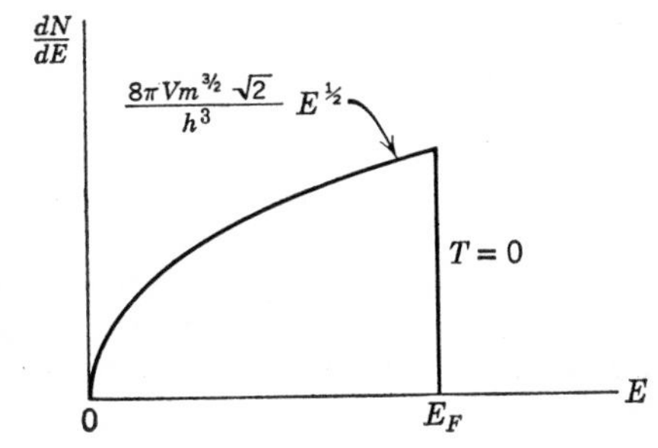

Fig. 3.12. dN/dE versus E at absolute zero for electrons in a box, the degenerate distribution function.

Before ending this chapter we again point out that the problem of electrons in a box is a useful approximation to the problem of electrons in a metal. The energy zero in the box problem corresponds to the "average" potential energy inside a metal; the walls of the box where the potential energy becomes infinite correspond to the surfaces of the metal where the potential energy increases enough to prevent the escape of electrons at ordinary temperatures. The energy E_F, roughly the maximum energy of any electron in the box, corresponds to the maximum kinetic energy of the electrons inside the metal. In Chapter 4, this "box" or "electron gas" model of a metal is used to derive an expression for the way in which the rate of emission of electrons from a hot metal surface depends on temperature.

Suggested References

R. W. Gurney, *Introduction to Statistical Mechanics*, McGraw-Hill Book Company, 1949. Chapter 1 is an excellent discussion of the distribution of particles among energy levels for Maxwell-Boltzmann statistics. Brief treatments of Fermi-Dirac and Bose-Einstein statistics are given in Chapter 12.

R. T. Weidner and R. L. Sells, *Elementary Modern Physics*, Allyn and Bacon, 1960. A summary of assumptions and results for the three types of statistics appears in Chapter 11 along with a useful discussion of the "box" model of a metal.

A. T. Goble and D. K. Baker, *Elements of Modern Physics*, The Ronald Press Company, 1962. A very readable discussion of distribution functions is given in Chapter 5. Chapter 14 contains an introduction to Fermi-Dirac statistics as used in solid-state physics.

R. B. Leighton, *Principles of Modern Physics*, McGraw-Hill Book Company, 1959. Although many parts of this text are at the graduate level, Chapter 10 contains an excellent parallel derivation of the three statistical laws at about the level of section 3.3. Especially noteworthy are the derivations of our equation 3.16 for Fermi-Dirac statistics and the corresponding equations for Maxwell-Boltzmann and Bose-Einstein statistics.

PROBLEMS

3.1. A group of seven indistinguishable particles has a total energy of $5E$; any individual particle is allowed to have energy $0, E, \ldots, 5E$. List the possible distributions of the particles among the energy levels; find the average number of particles at each level and plot this average versus energy. What would happen if the number of particles were greatly increased while the total energy remained fixed?

3.2. At 300° K at what value of E does the probability of a state being occupied by an electron become less than 10^{-2}? ($E_F = 8$ ev).

3.3. Use the quantized momenta for a rectangular box together with the deBroglie relation to show that the density of states for a photon gas is $8\pi VE^2\,dE/c^3h^3$. (Remember that a photon can have two independent directions of polarization corresponding to two orientations of spin.)

3.4. Find the relative numbers of hydrogen atoms that are in the ground state and in the first, second, and third energy levels ($n = 2, 3, 4$) in the solar chromosphere. Take $T = 5000°$ K and include the *statistical* weight of each level (the number of states with a given value of n).

3.5. In a photon gas, which obeys Bose-Einstein statistics, the number of photons is not constant. What must be the value of the constant α in 3.31 for a photon gas? (*Hint:* Examine the derivation of P_{FD} in section 3.3.)

3.6. The method of Lagrangian multipliers is generally useful for maximizing or minimizing functions of more than one variable, subject to auxiliary conditions. For example, calculate the point on the plane $x - 3y + 4z = 13$ which is nearest the origin. (*Hint:* Minimize $r^2 = x^2 + y^2 + z^2$ subject to the condition that (x, y, z) lies in the plane.)

3.7. (*a*) What is the order of magnitude of the maximum pressure of an ideal gas of fermions of mass 14 amu at room temperature for which the Maxwell-Boltzmann approximation to the Fermi factor (neglect of the 1 in the denominator of P_{FD}) is applicable? (*Hints:* Use dS/dE for particles in a box. Choose E_F so that $e^{(E-E_F)/kT} \geq 100$ for all energy levels. Integrate dN/dE over all energy levels to find N/V.)

(*b*) Assuming the fermions to be 2 Å diameter hard spheres, how does the density at the pressure of part (*a*) compare with that when the spheres are in their closest packed arrangement?

3.8. At absolute zero, compute the total energy possessed by the 10^{23} electrons in a piece of metal of volume 1 cm^3.

3.9. Calculate the values of the Fermi energy E_F for Na, Cu, and Al, assuming that these metals have one, two, and three free electrons per atom, respectively.

3.10. Show that the Fermi-Dirac distribution for particles in a box may be written as

$$\frac{dN}{dE} = \frac{3NE_F^{-3/2}E^{1/2}}{2(1 + e^{(E-E_F)/kT})}$$

3.11. Calculate the energy difference between the first excited state E_2 of hydrogen and the ground state E_1. If a flame at 2700° K contains 10^{20} atoms of hydrogen, how many are in each of the two states, assuming no other states are possible? If the excited state has a mean lifetime of 10^{-8} sec., how many photons are emitted per unit time? How many watts of light?

3.12. (Planck radiation law) Show, using the results of Problems 3.3 and 3.5, that the total photon energy per unit volume and energy inside a cavity is

$$\frac{E_T}{V}\frac{dN}{dE} = \frac{8\pi E^3}{c^3h^3(e^{E/kT} - 1)}$$

3.13. (*a*) Determine the speed distribution formula dN/dv as a function of v for fermions in a box at absolute zero.

(*b*) Show that the average speed of a fermion at absolute zero is three-fourths the maximum speed.

3.14. Show that the number of electrons in states with energies $\geq E_F$, is $kT \ln 2 \; dS/dE|_{E_F}$ if dS/dE can be considered constant in the range $\geq E_F$. (*Hint:* Use the substitution $u = 1 + e^{(E-E_F)/kT}$.)

4. electron emission

The first three chapters have provided a background for the study of physical electronics which we are now ready to begin. Chapter 4 treats the four processes by which electrons are emitted from metal surfaces and is the first of four chapters dealing mainly with the production and behavior of electrons in vacuum tubes.

4.1 Photoemission

In order for an electron inside a crystal to escape from the surface it must have at least a certain critical amount of energy. The maximum energy which electrons have inside a metal crystal at a temperature of absolute zero is the Fermi energy E_F. Even at temperatures much higher than room temperature relatively few electrons have energies that are enough greater than the Fermi energy to escape. The amount by which the energy of an electron must exceed the Fermi energy in order for the electron to just barely escape from the crystal is called the work function and given the symbol W. The work functions of metal crystals are of the order of 1 to 5 ev, depending on the crystal and the condition of its surface. In view of the definition of the work function, a necessary condition on the energy E of an electron in order for it to escape from the surface of a crystal is

$$E > E_F + W \tag{4.1}$$

Nearly all the electrons of a crystal have energies of E_F or less. In order to escape, any of these electrons must acquire an additional energy of at least W.

One mechanism for the acquisition of additional energy by an inter-

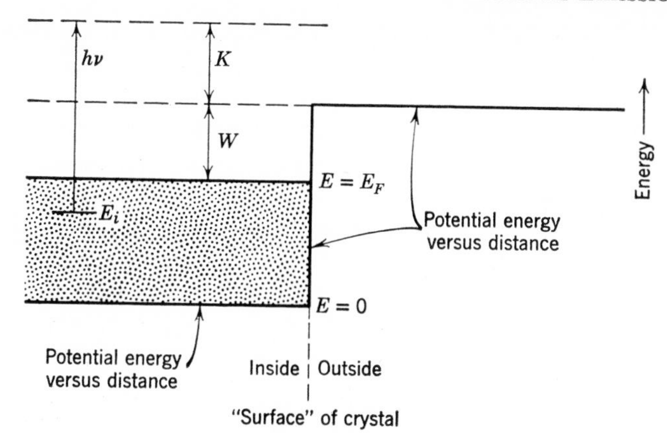

Fig. 4.1. Box model of a metal crystal indicating photoelectric emission.

nal electron is the absorption of a photon. If a single electron can receive the energy of, at most, one photon, as is found to be the case, then the energy $h\nu$ of the photon must be greater than the work function in order to enable an electron to escape from the surface. If an electron, originally with an energy E_i inside the crystal, absorbs a photon and escapes, its kinetic energy K outside the crystal is

$$K = (E_i + h\nu) - (E_F + W) \tag{4.2}$$

In Fig. 4.1 the box model of a metal is used to illustrate the relationships between the quantities appearing in equation 4.2. For photons of a given frequency, the kinetic energy K is largest when the internal energy E_i is largest. Since the largest value of E_i for all but a small fraction of the total number of electrons is E_F, the maximum kinetic energy K_m of an emitted electron is

$$K_m = h\nu - W \tag{4.3}$$

Equation 4.3 is the famous Einstein photoelectric equation. Note that the foregoing theory agrees with the experimental fact that only a negligible number of electrons can be ejected from a crystal by photons of a given frequency unless $h\nu > W$.

4.2 Thermionic emission

It is well known that electrons are emitted from the surfaces of metals at temperatures of the order of 1000° K and higher. Certain coatings on metals can make them more efficient emitters of electrons (more emitted electrons per watt of heating power). The physics of coated cathodes is not completely understood; indeed, an exact treatment of thermionic emission from pure metals is prohibitively complicated. Using simplifying assumptions about the structure of a metal, we now derive a formula for the rate of emission of electrons from a metal surface as a function of the temperature.

When an electron approaches the surface of a crystal from the inside, it experiences a force directed back into the surface because of the attraction of unbalanced nuclear charges at or near the emission surface. If a coordinate system is chosen so that the x-axis is perpendicular to the surface, the force is directed into the crystal along the x-axis and cannot affect the y- or z-components of velocity of the electron. The x-directed force decreases the x-component of velocity, and unless the x-component of velocity exceeds a critical value, the electron will be "reflected" back into the crystal.

It will simplify the mathematics if we use the box model of a metal with finite walls as in Fig. 4.1. For convenience we choose the zero of potential energy to be the potential energy inside the crystal. Then, in view of the discussion of the previous section, the potential energy of an electron outside the crystal is $E_F + W$, where E_F is the Fermi energy and W is the work function. If we let U denote the potential energy,

$$\begin{aligned} U_{\text{inside}} &= 0 \\ U_{\text{outside}} &= E_F + W \end{aligned} \tag{4.4}$$

From conservation of energy the decrease in an electron's kinetic energy as it crosses the surface of the crystal is equal to the increase in its potential energy. In our case the decrease in kinetic energy is due entirely to the decrease in its x-component of velocity v_x. The minimum value of v_x inside the crystal for which an electron can escape is given by

$$\begin{aligned} \tfrac{1}{2}mv_{x(\text{min})}^2 &= E_F + W \\ v_{x(\text{min})} &= \sqrt{2(E_F + W)/m} \end{aligned} \tag{4.5}$$

The outline of the derivation is as follows:

1. We calculate the rate at which electrons in the velocity range v_x to $v_x + dv_x$, v_y to $v_y + dv_y$, v_z to $v_z + dv_z$ reach the surface.
2. We integrate this expression over all y- and z-velocities and x-velocities greater than $v_{x(\text{min})}$ to find the total number of electrons per unit time reaching the surface with enough x-directed velocity to escape.

3. We assume that a negligible fraction of the electrons having enough x-velocity to escape is reflected at the potential energy discontinuity at the surface (see section 1.7).

The number of electrons with velocities in the differential range v_x to $v_x + dv_x$, v_y to $v_y + dv_y$, v_z to $v_z + dv_z$ reaching an area A of the surface in time dt is simply the number having velocities in that range within a distance $v_x\,dt$ of the surface, or the number within a volume $v_xA\,dt$. The number of allowed *electronic states* corresponding to velocities within a differential range may be found from equation 2.43

$$dS_\tau = \frac{2V}{h^3}\,dp_x\,dp_y\,dp_z \tag{2.43}$$

by making the substitutions

$$\begin{aligned} p_x &= mv_x, & dp_x &= m\,dv_x \\ p_y &= mv_y, & dp_y &= m\,dv_y \\ p_z &= mv_z, & dp_z &= m\,dv_z \end{aligned} \tag{4.6}$$

Thus

$$dS_\tau = \frac{2Vm^3}{h^3}\,dv_x\,dv_y\,dv_z \tag{4.7}$$

If we multiply equation 4.7 by the Fermi factor (the probability a given state is occupied) and substitute $v_xA\,dt$ for the volume V, we obtain an expression for the number dN_τ of electrons within the differential velocity range that reach area A in time dt.

$$dN_\tau = \frac{2v_xA\,dt\,m^3}{h^3}\cdot\frac{1}{1+e^{(E-E_F)/kT}}\,dv_x\,dv_y\,dv_z \tag{4.8}$$

Since the potential energy inside the crystal is taken to be zero, the energy E appearing in the Fermi factor is just the kinetic energy

$$E = K = \tfrac{1}{2}m(v_x^2 + v_y^2 + v_z^2) \tag{4.9}$$

The total number of particles per unit time and area (the total emitted flux density of electrons) crossing the surface is then seen to be

$$\iiint\limits_{\substack{\text{all velocities}\\ \text{satisfying}\\ \text{escape criterion}}} \frac{dN_\tau}{A\,dt} = \int_{v_{x(\min)}}^{\infty}\int_{-\infty}^{\infty}\int_{-\infty}^{\infty}\frac{2m^3}{h^3}\cdot\frac{v_x}{1+e^{-E_F/kT}\cdot e^{m(v_x^2+v_y^2+v_z^2)/2kT}}\,dv_x\,dv_y\,dv_z \tag{4.10}$$

This integral can be evaluated to a good approximation by realizing that for any electron with $v_x \geq v_{x(\min)}$, the 1 in the denominator may be neglected. In other words, only electrons in the "tail" of the Fermi distribution (those with E more than a few kT greater than E_F) have a chance of escaping. Therefore,

$$\iiint \frac{dN_\tau}{A\,dt} \approx \frac{2m^3 e^{E_F/kT}}{h^3} \int_{v_{x(\min)}}^{\infty} \int_{-\infty}^{\infty} \int_{-\infty}^{\infty} v_x e^{-mv_x^2/2kT} e^{-mv_y^2/2kT} e^{-mv_z^2/2kT}\, dv_x\, dv_y\, dv_z \tag{4.11}$$

The v_y and v_z integrals may be found in a table of definite integrals (see, for example, Dwight #861.3)

$$\int_{-\infty}^{\infty} e^{-mv_y^2/2kT}\, dv_y = \sqrt{2\pi kT/m} \tag{4.12}$$

The v_x integral may readily be evaluated by making a substitution

$$u = \frac{mv_x^2}{2kT}, \qquad du = \frac{mv_x\, dv_x}{kT} \tag{4.13}$$

The result of the integrations is

$$\iiint \frac{dN_\tau}{A\,dt} = \frac{4m\pi k^2T^2}{h^3} e^{E_F/kT} e^{-mv_{x(\min)}^2/2kT} = \frac{4m\pi k^2T^2}{h^3} e^{-W/kT} \tag{4.14}$$

where in the last step we have used 4.5 to substitute for v_x.

The current per unit area or current density for emitted electrons is designated by J_{th} and is found by multiplying equation 4.14 by the charge on an electron.

$$J_{th} = \frac{4me\pi k^2T^2}{h^3} e^{-W/kT} = AT^2 e^{-W/kT} \tag{4.15}$$

Equation 4.15 is known as the Richardson-Dushman equation. It agrees fairly well with experimental evidence. The major discrepancy is that for many metals the theoretical factor $4me\pi k^2/h^3$ is larger than the value of A experimentally determined by a factor of the order of two. Several explanations for this discrepancy have been advanced. One is that partial reflections of the electronic wavefunctions occur at the crystal surface even for those electrons with enough x-directed velocity to escape. Thus, for such an electron there is a finite probability that it will *not* escape when it reaches the surface. Another explanation of the discrepancy is that the surface of a metal is com-

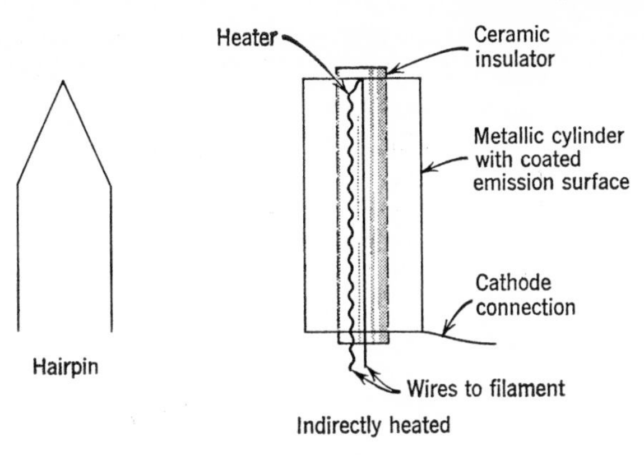

Fig. 4.2. Cathode geometries.

posed of different crystal faces with significantly different work functions. Because of the strong dependence of emission upon work function, the faces with the lowest work function contribute most of the electrons. Thus the remainder of the surface is a relatively ineffective emitter.

Experimentally the constants A and W in equation 4.15 can be determined by measuring J_{th} versus T for a given cathode material. A plot of ln J_{th}/T^2 versus $1/T$, known as a Richardson plot, should be a straight line. The ordinate intercept determines A and the slope determines the work function W. However, the value of J_{th} that must be used is for zero electric field applied to the cathode. This cannot be measured directly and is found by extrapolating equation (4.20) from the Schottky effect (section 4.4).

Cathodes for thermionic emission utilize several different geometries and emission surfaces. The most common geometries are the hair pin and the indirectly heated cylindrical forms shown in Fig. 4.2. Hairpin filaments usually use direct-current heating. Indirectly heated cathodes permit the use of a-c heating power and isolate the heating and emission functions of a cathode. It should be noted that most of the heating power required for thermionic emission is lost in thermal radiation (Stefan-Boltzmann law), and conduction to supports and the metal or glass envelope of a tube and only a small fraction of the heating power goes into emitting electrons.

Some properties of cathode surfaces are listed in Table 4.1. Emission surfaces having lower work functions generally operate at lower temperatures and have higher emission efficiencies.

Table 4.1. Properties of four types of commercial cathodes

Type of Cathode	Construction	Operating Temperature	Work Function	Emission Current Density	Uses
Tungsten	Pure metal	2500° K	4.5 ev	½ amp/cm^2	Whenever ion bombardment is a problem
Thoriated tungsten	Single layer of thorium atoms on tungsten	2000° K	~2.6 ev	4 amp/cm^2	High current density requirements
Oxide coated	Metal base covered by a mixture of alkaline earth oxides such as those of barium and strontium	1000° K	~1.1 ev	½ amp/cm^2	Its high efficiency and long life make it useful for almost all receiving type tubes (low voltage applications)
Phillips or "L"	Porous tungsten, filled with barium and strontium oxides	1400° K	1.6 ev	5 amp/cm^2	High current density requirements

Example. Calculate the average value of the normally directed kinetic energy of thermionically emitted electrons.

We seek the average value of $\frac{1}{2}mv_x^2$ of emitted electrons. From the definition of an average (equation 3.10) we have

$$\overline{\tfrac{1}{2}mv_x^2} \equiv \frac{\iiint \tfrac{1}{2}mv_x^2 \, dN_\tau}{\iiint dN_\tau} \tag{4.16}$$

where dN_τ is the number of electrons within a differential velocity range v_x to $v_x + dv_x$, etc. The range of integration in 4.16 is the same as that in 4.10. When dN_τ is expressed in terms of the velocity components and the integrals in 4.16 are performed we obtain

$$\overline{\tfrac{1}{2}mv_x^2} = E_F + W + kT \tag{4.17}$$

However, this expression is for the average x-directed kinetic energy *inside the crystal* of those electrons which *can* escape. In crossing the surface, each electron gains $E_F + W$ of potential energy and loses the same amount of x-directed kinetic energy. Therefore the average x-directed kinetic energy of *emitted* electrons is

$$\overline{\tfrac{1}{2}mv_x^2} \text{ (emitted)} = kT \tag{4.18}$$

4.3 Secondary emission

When a material, either a metal or a dielectric, is subjected to bombardment by ions or electrons, secondary electrons may be emitted. In secondary emission the energy for emission is derived from the kinetic energy of the incident particle. Electrons beneath the surface may be emitted when they are given enough energy to overcome the forces tending to keep them within the surface.

Figure 4.3 indicates a possible experimental setup to demonstrate secondary emission. Primary electrons from a cathode strike electrode B. The current I_B collected by electrode B is different from the current I_K emitted by the cathode, since secondary electrons are emitted from B and strike the collector. I_B may even be negative if there are more secondaries than primaries. The current from the cathode is equal to the algebraic sum of I_B and the secondary electron emission current I_C. We define the secondary emission ratio s as

$$s \equiv \frac{I_C}{I_K} \tag{4.19}$$

For primary electrons of a given incident energy I_C is found experimentally to be directly proportional to I_K, so that s is a constant.

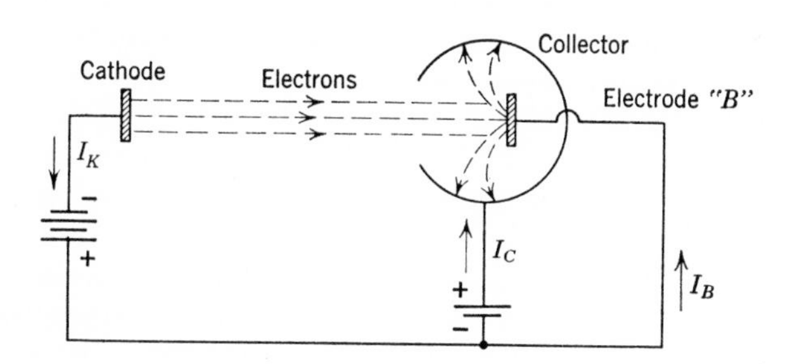

Fig. 4.3. System to demonstrate secondary electron emission. Currents shown are "conventional" currents.

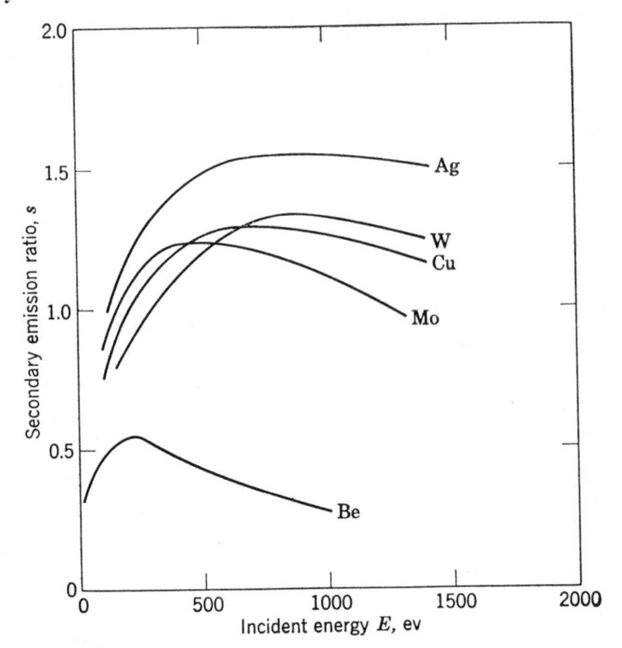

Fig. 4.4. Secondary emission ratio of different metals as a function of the energy of incident electrons.

Some other important experimental properties of secondary emission are described below.

1. Figure 4.4 plots the secondary emission ratio for several metals as a function of primary electron energy. The same general shape holds for a number of metals. The maximum secondary emission ratio generally lies in the range between 0.5 and 1.5 for pure metals, and occurs for incident electron energies between 200 and 1000 ev.

2. The approximate energy distribution of the secondary electrons emitted from a pure metal is shown in Fig. 4.5. Ninety percent of the emitted electrons have energies less than 20 ev. Perhaps 7% have energies in the range from 20 ev to 98% of the primary energy. About 3% of the secondaries appear to be incident electrons that have undergone elastic reflections from surface atoms. These are emitted with very nearly the energy of the primaries and constitute the spike at the right.

3. The ratio of secondary electrons to primary electrons is least when the primary electrons strike the surface normally, and the ratio

increases with the angle of incidence. The intensity of secondary electrons is greatest for those emitted normally to the surface.

4. Metal surfaces can be treated to increase the emission of secondary electrons. One of the best known emitters is cesium oxide partly reduced on a base of silver. For primary electron energies in the range from 400 to 700 ev this surface has a secondary emission ratio of about 10.

5. Positive ion bombardment can also cause secondary emission, but it is much less efficient than electron bombardment. This is because in the collision process between a heavy ion and an electron only a small fraction of the ion's energy can be imparted to the electron even in a head-on collision. The analogy may be made that a locomotive would have to have an enormous amount of kinetic energy to have sufficient velocity to send a golf ball down a fairway, compared to the relatively insignificant kinetic energy of a swinging golf club. Hence, the energies of impinging ions must be much greater than those of electrons in order to yield a comparable secondary emission ratio. Nevertheless, secondary emission by ions does play a role in some situations.

6. Secondary electrons are also emitted from insulators. The

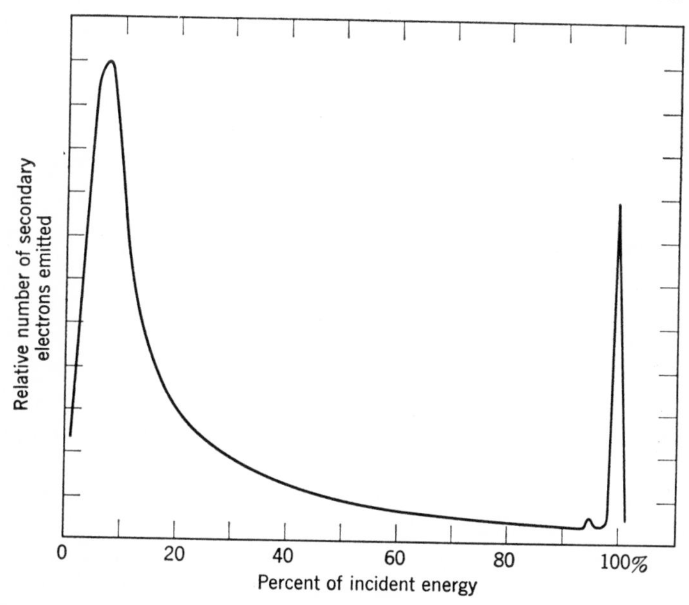

Fig. 4.5. Relative number of secondary electrons versus the energy of the secondary electrons, where the energy is expressed as a percent of the energy of the primary electrons.

dependence of secondary emission ratio on primary energy for insulators is similar in form to the curves of Fig. 4.4. Some insulators have secondary emission ratios in the range of 10 to 15. In experiments to measure this type of emission the surface of the insulator soon becomes charged, so that it is difficult to determine the kinetic energy of the incident electrons. The surface will acquire a positive charge if s is greater than one and a negative charge if s is less than one. The secondary emission properties of insulators are applied in such tubes as the image orthicon, discussed in Chapter 6.

It is appropriate to explain some of these experimental facts qualitatively. Primary electrons striking a surface normally can knock out electrons from the surface atoms, and those electrons with sufficient surface-directed velocities can escape. Each primary electron can strike several atoms. Momentum considerations indicate that a normally directed primary electron cannot give a free electron a component of velocity directed toward the surface, but the surface atom electrons can be given such a component. As the energy of the primary is increased it can strike more atoms near the surface and release more electrons. When the energy is increased past the maximum emission points of Fig. 4.4, the surface atoms experience the electron force for a shorter time, and the collision probability decreases. It is surmised that the majority of secondary electrons are released at a depth of several atoms in the metal at the maximum emission energies. With greater energies the deeper penetration brings about a smaller probability that the electrons released will reach the surface. There is evidence that some secondary electrons originate from as deep as 15 to 30 atomic layers below the surface.

Secondary emission can affect the design of electron tubes. For example, we will see in Chapter 6 that secondary emission limits the usefulness of tetrodes. On the other hand, photomultiplier tubes are designed to take advantage of secondary emission.

4.4 The influence of electric fields on electron emission

Electron emission is influenced by the application of electric fields to emission surfaces. The following treatment deals with situations where the electric field exerts an outward force on surface electrons. Such fields lead to an increased emission current. There are two basic mechanisms responsible for the increase in emission. (1) If the applied field is weak or moderate, it lowers the potential energy barrier seen by electrons and decreases the effective work function. This

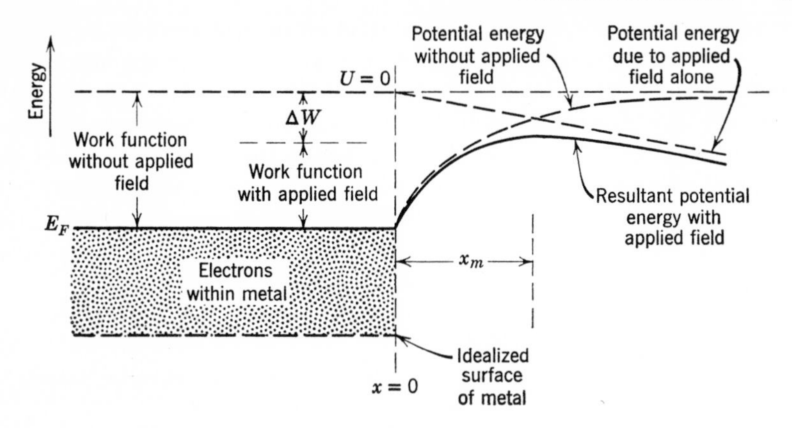

Fig. 4.6. Potential energy of the electrons near the surface of a metal with a moderate applied field.

second order phenomenon is known as the Schottky effect. (2) For very strong electric fields the thickness of the potential energy barrier becomes small enough for quantum-mechanical tunneling to occur (see section 1.7). This important phenomenon is known as high-field emission or cold-cathode emission. Let us first examine the Schottky effect.

In Fig. 4.6 the potential energy barrier at the surface of a metal is shown, both with and without a moderate electric field. The potential energy due to the uniform applied external field is a linear function of position. Since potential energy is a scalar, the total potential energy in the presence of an applied electric field is the sum of the potential energy due to the applied field and the potential energy in the field free case. Since the energy to escape is classically the energy to overcome the total potential energy, and since the barrier height is lowered by the application of an electric field, more electrons are able to escape and the total emission current is increased in the presence of an electric field. The current density J in the presence of a moderate electric field is given by the Schottky equation

$$J = J_{th}e^{0.440\sqrt{\mathcal{E}}/T} \tag{4.20}$$

where $\mathcal{E}$ is the field strength in volts per meter and T is the temperature in degrees Kelvin. A simplified classical derivation of the Schottky equation follows.

In Fig. 4.7 the lines of force from an electron in the vicinity of a plane metallic surface are shown. It will be noticed that the lines of force are normal to

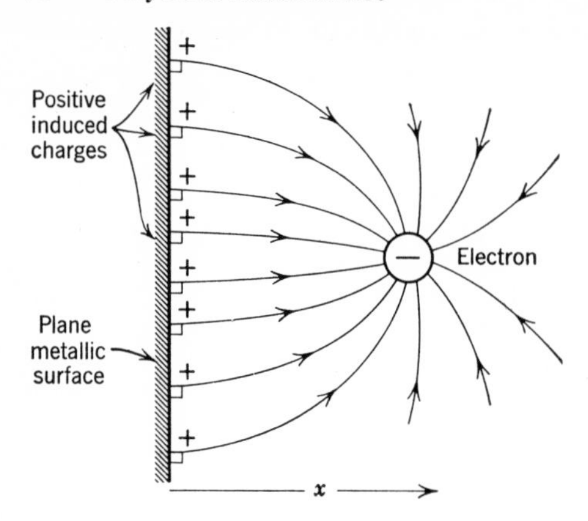

Fig. 4.7. Induced charge attracts an electron outside a metal surface.

the surface at the metallic surface, because a static tangential component of an electric field cannot exist at the surface of a conductor. In Fig. 4.8 it is suggested that the same field distribution in the vicinity of the electron can, in the absence of the metallic surface, be created by an image charge of equal magnitude but of opposite sign located an equal distance from the metallic surface location. It may be shown analytically that the field distributions given in Figs. 4.7 and 4.8 are identical in the region outside the metallic surface. The force on the electron in Figs. 4.7 and 4.8 is a Coulomb image force F_I given by

$$F_I = \frac{-e^2}{16\pi\epsilon_0 x^2} \tag{4.21}$$

This is the force associated with the potential energy in the absence of an applied field.

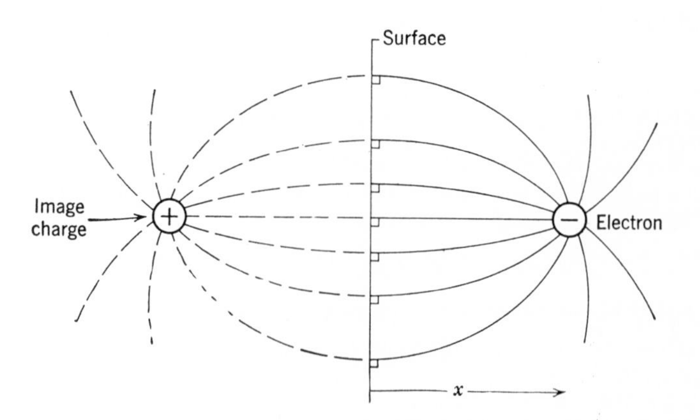

Fig. 4.8. An electron attracted by a positive "image" charge.

The outward directed force $F_\mathcal{E}$ outside the surface due to the applied electric field $\mathcal{E}$ is given by

$$F_\mathcal{E} = e\mathcal{E} \tag{4.22}$$

At the maximum height of the potential energy barrier (see Fig. 4.6), the total electric force is zero since there the potential energy gradient is zero. The position of the maximum is found by equating the total force to zero.

$$F_I + F_\mathcal{E} = \frac{-e^2}{16\pi\epsilon_0 x_m{}^2} + e\mathcal{E} = 0 \tag{4.23}$$

from which

$$x_m = \sqrt{e/16\pi\epsilon_0\mathcal{E}} \tag{4.24}$$

Any electron which can reach the maximum point of the total potential energy barrier has sufficient energy to escape from the surface.

We now calculate the magnitude of the reduction ΔW of the total potential energy barrier (the decrease in the effective work function). If for convenience we let the potential energy far from the surface in the absence of the applied field be zero, then the reduction in potential energy is numerically equal to the total potential energy at $x = x_m$. The total potential energy at $x = x_m$ is the sum of the potential energy $U_\mathcal{E}$ due to the applied field and the potential energy U_I due to the image force. We write

$$\Delta W = U_{\text{total}}(x_m) = U_I(x_m) + U_\mathcal{E}(x_m) = \int_{x_m}^{\infty} F_I\,dx + \int_{x_m}^{0} F_\mathcal{E}\,dx \tag{4.25}$$

Substituting 4.21 and 4.22,

$$\Delta W = \int_{x_m}^{\infty} \frac{-e^2}{16\pi\epsilon_0 x^2}\,dx + \int_{x_m}^{0} e\mathcal{E}\,dx = \frac{-e^2}{16\pi\epsilon_0 x_m} - e\mathcal{E}x_m \tag{4.26}$$

Substituting for x_m from equation 4.24,

$$\Delta W = -\sqrt{e^3\mathcal{E}/4\pi\epsilon_0} \tag{4.27}$$

In section 4.2 it was shown that the thermionic-emission equation is

$$J_{th} = AT^2e^{-W/kT} \tag{4.15}$$

Since the derivation of the thermionic-emission equation does not depend on the shape of the potential energy barrier, we assume that, in the presence of an electric field, the thermionic-emission equation may be used, except that W must be replaced by $W + \Delta W$. Thus the current density $J_\mathcal{E}$ in the presence of an applied field becomes

$$J_\mathcal{E} = AT^2e^{-(W+\Delta W)/kT} = J_{th}e^{-\Delta W/kT} \tag{4.28}$$

and using 4.27, we arrive at the Schottky equation

$$J_\mathcal{E} = J_{th}e^{\sqrt{e^3\mathcal{E}/4\pi\epsilon_0}/kT} \tag{4.29}$$

which, for MKS units, becomes

$$J_\mathcal{E} = J_{th}e^{0.440\sqrt{\mathcal{E}}/T} \tag{4.20}$$

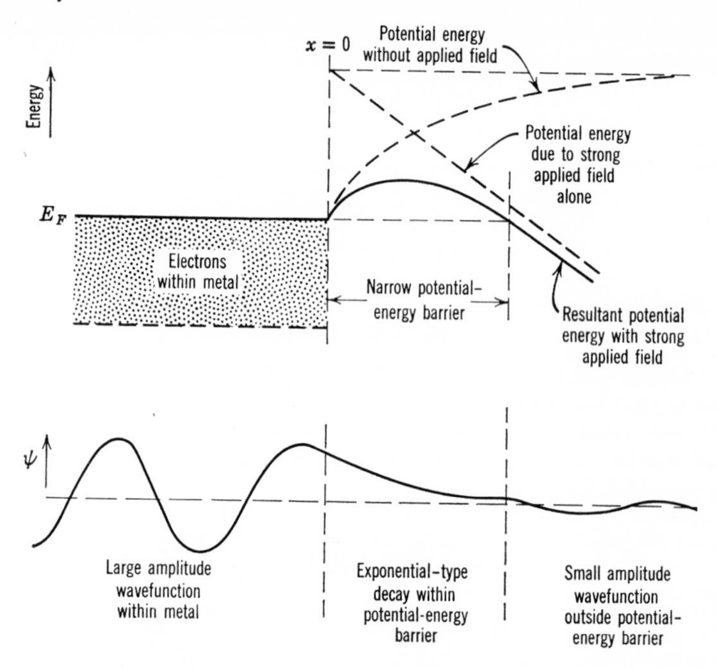

Fig. 4.9. Potential energy and wavefunction of an electron near the surface of a metal with strong applied field.

When larger fields are applied, as shown in Fig. 4.9, the effective work function is lowered still further and the contribution of the Schottky effect to the emission current increases. For very strong applied fields the emission currents become independent of temperature and much greater than the Schottky effect predicts. This excess current is known as high-field emission. By comparing Fig. 4.9 with Fig. 4.6 we see that the potential energy barrier becomes narrower when the applied field is increased. For high-field emission to occur, the barrier must become sufficiently thin so that a small but finite probability amplitude wave leaks through the barrier and appears outside. Since the probability of finding an electron near a given point is given by the square of the wavefunction, there is a finite probability that electrons will appear outside the barrier. Note that the electrons do not, in high-field emission, have to have enough energy to go over the barrier. Since any electron may participate in the tunneling involved in high-field emission, enormous numbers of electrons are available for this process and even a very small escape probability leads to very large emission current densities. Experimentally it is found and theoretically it may be shown that the high-field emission current density J_{hf} is given by

$$J_{hf} = C\mathcal{E}^2 e^{-D/\mathcal{E}} \tag{4.30}$$

where, for a tungsten emitter, the constants C and D are given by

$$C = 1.26 \times 10^5 \text{ amp/volt}^2$$

$$D = 2.76 \times 10^{10} \text{ volts/meter}$$

High-field emission represents another useful source of electrons. For example, it is used in the field emission electron microscope and has led to the highest resolution of atomic detail thus far achieved. In many cases, however, high-field emission phenomena are a nuisance which one attempts to avoid in high voltage experiments through the use of electrodes having large radii of curvature and coated by high work function materials.

Suggested Reference

K. R. Spangenberg, *Vacuum Tubes*, McGraw-Hill Book Company, 1948. Chapter 4 parallels our treatment of electron emission with numerous references to the literature. This book finds large use as a reference in the field of vacuum tubes.

PROBLEMS

4.1. The density of gold is 19.3 gm cm^{-3}, its atomic weight 197, and its work function approximately 4.5 volts. Assuming one free electron per atom, calculate the depth of the effective potential well in which the electrons move.

4.2. The box model may be applied, in a rough approximation, to neutrons and protons in nuclei. If the binding energy of the most loosely bound nucleon in a nucleus is $B_0 = 8$ Mev, and the nuclear Fermi well is a sphere of radius $R = r_0 A^{1/3}$, where $A = N + Z$ (number of neutrons plus protons in nucleus) and $r_0 = 1.2 \times 10^{-13}$ cm, calculate the depth U of the well and the average binding energy per particle. (Assume $N \approx Z \approx A/2$.)

4.3. Carry out in detail the steps leading from equation 4.11 to 4.14.

4.4. By how many electron volts must the work function of a surface change in order to reduce the emission from that surface at 2400° C by 10%?

4.5. In a certain metal the potential-energy well is 10 ev deep and $E_F = 4$ ev. What is $E - E_F$ for an electron which can just escape? How does this compare with kT at $T = 1700°$ K? Does this result justify the neglect of the 1 in going from equation 4.10 to 4.11?

4.6. Calculate the theoretical thermionic emission current density from tungsten at 2500° K and compare with the value given in Table 4.1.

4.7. Find the applied field strength required to reduce the effective work function of a metal surface by 0.1 ev.

4.8. A diode tube consists of plane parallel anode and cathode 0.01 meter apart with 1000 volts potential difference between them. Find (*a*) the field at the cathode, (*b*) the distance x_m defined in Fig. 4.6, (*c*) the amount of the Schottky effect lowering of the work function, (*d*) the percentage increase in emission current at 1700° K.

4.9. Calculate the approximate fraction of the electrons having energies greater then E_F by the amounts kT, $2kT$, $10kT$, $50kT$ for $T = 1250°$ K. Using the data and results of Problem 4.1, make a rough estimate of the thermionic emission current density that might be expected from gold at 1250° K.

4.10. Calculate the distance from a tungsten metal surface to which an electron must be brought in the absence of an external field in order that 99.99% of its minimum escape energy (work function) be expended.

4.11. What fraction of the electrons emitted from a metal have normally directed energies greater than the average normally directed energy?

4.12. Suppose the work function W is temperature dependent, in the form $W = W_0 + \alpha T$. Find the value of α such that the Richardson-Dushman value of thermonic emission current is reduced by 50%. (See Seely, *Phys. Rev.* **59,** 75, 1941).

4.13. Find the field strength at the surface of a tungsten filament at 2400° K that will decrease the effective work function by 3%. Find also the consequent percentage increase in thermionic current, and the maximum distance that an electron may reach from the cathode surface without escaping.

4.14. A potential difference of V volts is applied between a hot metal surface and a wire grid 0.5 cm away, so that thermionically emitted electrons may escape through the grid.

(*a*) Draw a potential energy diagram for the electrons if the field is retarding. Include some of the region outside the grid.

(*b*) What is the effective work function of the whole system if the work function of the surface is W ev?

(*c*) Calculate V for the emission through the grid to be 10% of the emission when $V = 0$, the emitter temperature being 2400° K.

4.15. Calculate the cold-cathode high-field emission current densities for tungsten for fields of 10^8 volts/meter, 10^9 volts/meter, 10^{10} volts/meter.

4.16. A photocell cathode has a work function of 3.5 ev. What is the maximum velocity of the emitted electrons when the cell is irradiated with light of frequency of 4×10^{15} cps ? How could the maximum velocity of emission be determined experimentally?

4.17. A photocell has electrodes of different metals. Monochromatic light of wavelength 2480 Å falling on electrode A requires a retarding potential of 2.5 volts just to stop the flow of current, whereas if it falls on B, a retarding potential of 1.5 volts is required. Find the work functions of the two metals. Illustrate the energy relations diagrammatically for the two situations.

4.18. The cathode of a photocell is illuminated by light of wavelength 6000 Å. An anode potential of -1 volt is found just to prevent electrons from reaching the anode.

(*a*) Calculate the work function of the cathode.

(*b*) If the anode is made positive, what is the maximum wavelength that will produce a current in the photocell?

5. charged particle dynamics

This chapter is a study of the motions of charged particles in electric and magnetic fields. The development and solution of the equations of motion of a charged particle in various field configurations is fundamental to an understanding of all electron tube devices.

5.1 Uniform electric fields

Using Newton's second law and the fact that a particle of charge q in an electric field $\boldsymbol{\mathcal{E}}$ experiences a force $q\boldsymbol{\mathcal{E}}$, we calculate the trajectory of an electron in a uniform electric field. In Fig. 5.1 a uniform electric field is directed upward along the y-axis, and an electron enters the field region at the origin with an initial velocity v_0 at an arbitrary angle θ with the x-axis. In this case there is no component of force on the electron in the x-direction and a constant downward force in the y-direction. This problem is analogous to that of a projectile fired

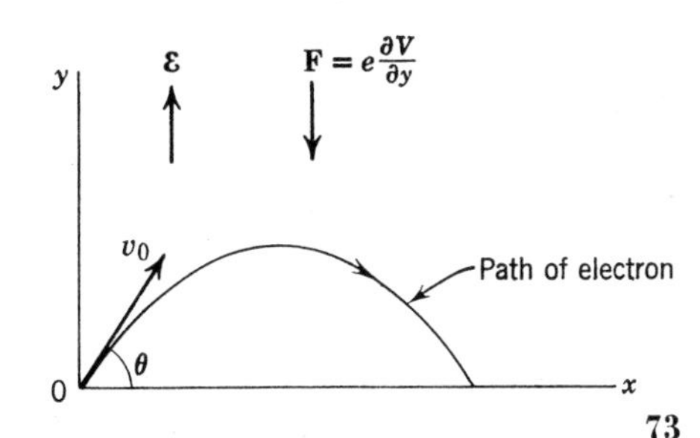

Fig. 5.1. Motion of an electron in a uniform electric field.

at an elevation angle θ and acted upon by a constant gravitational force. Using Newton's second law, and writing $-e$ for the charge on an electron,

$$F_y = q\mathcal{E}_y = -e\mathcal{E} = m\frac{d^2y}{dt^2} \tag{5.1}$$

or

$$\frac{d^2y}{dt^2} = -\frac{e\mathcal{E}}{m} = -\eta\mathcal{E} \tag{5.2}$$

where

$$\eta \equiv \frac{e}{m} \tag{5.3}$$

The absolute value of the charge to mass ratio for the electron is abbreviated η for convenience. For the x-component of Newton's second law,

$$F_x = 0 = m\frac{d^2x}{dt^2} \tag{5.4}$$

We abbreviate differentiations with respect to time by superscript dots, that is, one dot for the first derivative, two dots for the second derivative. The equations of motion are then written

$$\ddot{y} = -\eta\mathcal{E} \tag{5.5}$$

$$\ddot{x} = 0 \tag{5.6}$$

At time $t = 0$, the initial conditions are

$$\left.\begin{aligned} x &= 0 \\ y &= 0 \\ \dot{x} &= v_0 \cos\theta \\ \dot{y} &= v_0 \sin\theta \end{aligned}\right. \tag{5.7}$$

The integration of equation 5.6 yields

$$\dot{x} = \text{constant} = v_0 \cos\theta \tag{5.8}$$

and

$$x = v_0 t \cos\theta \tag{5.9}$$

Equation 5.5 integrates to

$$\dot{y} = \eta\mathcal{E}t + \text{constant} = -\eta\mathcal{E}t + v_0 \sin\theta \tag{5.10}$$

and

$$y = -\frac{\eta\mathcal{E}}{2}t^2 + v_0 t \sin\theta \tag{5.11}$$

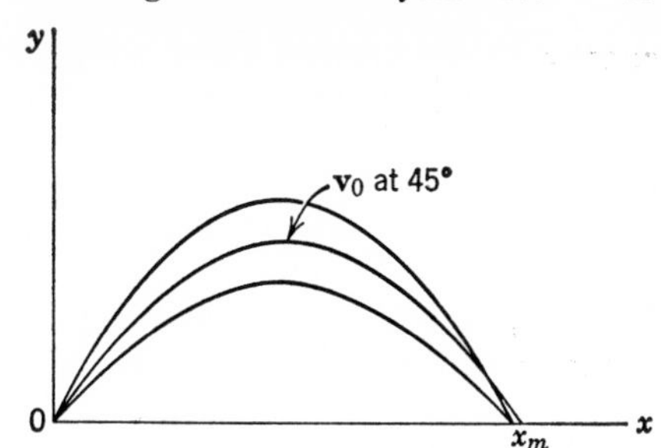

Fig. 5.2. Paths of electrons starting at angles near 45°.

In 5.8 through 5.11 all the constants of integration have been evaluated by using the initial conditions.

Using equation 5.9 we eliminate t from equation 5.11 to find the equation of the path.

$$y = -\frac{\eta\mathcal{E}}{2v_0^2 \cos^2 \theta} x^2 + x \tan \theta \tag{5.12}$$

This is the equation of a parabola, the same trajectory as that of an ideal projectile in a uniform gravitational field.

From Fig. 5.1, when $\dot{y} = 0$, y is a maximum. This maximum occurs at a time

$$t_m = \frac{v_0 \sin \theta}{\eta\mathcal{E}} \tag{5.13}$$

as found from equation 5.10. The maximum value of y is

$$y_m = \frac{v_0^2 \sin^2 \theta}{2\eta\mathcal{E}} \tag{5.14}$$

From equation 5.12 when y becomes zero again, x has the value x_m where

$$x_m = \frac{2v_0^2 \sin \theta \cos \theta}{\eta\mathcal{E}} = \frac{v_0^2 \sin 2\theta}{\eta\mathcal{E}} \tag{5.15}$$

If we set $dx_m/d\theta$ equal to zero, we find that x_m is a maximum for $\theta = 45°$. Even at slight variations from 45° the electron will still cross the x-axis near x_m because $dx_m/d\theta$ is still close to zero. Figure 5.2 shows that electrons starting at slightly different angles will be "focused" near x_m. This is analogous to the focusing of light rays by a lens.

An alternate way of examining the motion is from the energy viewpoint. Conservation of energy states that the sum of the kinetic energy K and the potential energy U must remain constant.

$$K + U = \text{a constant} \tag{5.16}$$

or

$$\tfrac{1}{2}mv_x^2 + \tfrac{1}{2}mv_y^2 + U = \text{a constant} \tag{5.17}$$

In this problem there is no component of force in the x-direction, so the x-component of velocity remains constant and we have

$$\tfrac{1}{2}mv_y^2 + U = \text{constant} \tag{5.18}$$

A proper potential energy function to use is

$$U = e\mathcal{E}y \tag{5.19}$$

since this yields the force when differentiated.

$$F_y = -\frac{\partial U}{\partial y} = -e\mathcal{E} \tag{5.20}$$

Therefore equation 5.18 becomes

$$\tfrac{1}{2}mv_y^2 + e\mathcal{E}y = \tfrac{1}{2}mv_0^2 \sin^2 \theta \tag{5.21}$$

where the constant is evaluated by setting $y = 0$.

Since at the highest point of the path $v_y = 0$, the maximum value of y is, from equation 5.21

$$y_m = \frac{mv_0^2 \sin^2 \theta}{2e\mathcal{E}} = \frac{v_0^2 \sin^2 \theta}{2\eta\mathcal{E}} \tag{5.22}$$

which is identical to equation 5.14.

The differential equation approach although cumbersome is a general one and can provide a complete solution to a problem. The energy approach is usually simpler but is limited to giving a relation between velocity and position, which in turn can provide information about the extremes of the motion. The energy method cannot easily detail the trajectory as can the differential equation method.

5.2 Electrostatic deflection in a cathode-ray tube

In this section we apply the results of section 5.1 to the deflection of an electron beam in a cathode-ray tube. The essential construction of the tube is indicated in Fig. 5.3.

Electrons, emitted thermionically from the cathode, are accelerated through a potential difference V_0 in an electron gun where they obtain a velocity v_0. (We neglect initial thermal velocities, which are small compared with v_0.)

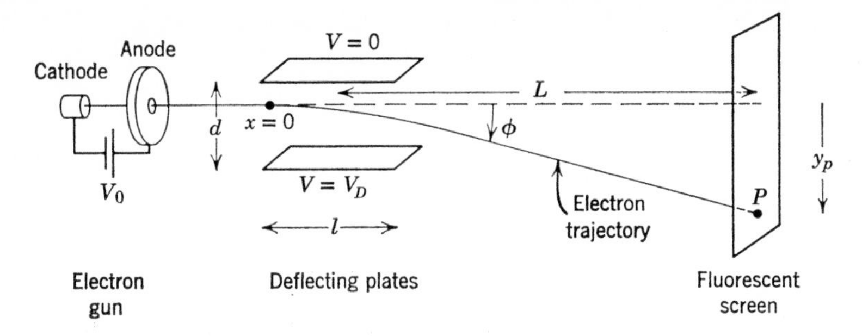

Fig. 5.3. A cathode-ray tube.

From conservation of energy

$$\tfrac{1}{2}mv_0^2 = eV_0 \tag{5.23}$$

or

$$v_0 = \sqrt{2\eta V_0} \tag{5.24}$$

The electrons from the gun pass between the deflecting plates and eventually strike the fluorescent screen where a visible spot of light is produced. The trajectory of an electron after leaving the gun is divided into three parts: (1) a linear path between the anode and the deflecting plates, (2) a parabolic path between the deflecting plates due to the transverse uniform electric field, and (3) another straight line path from the plates to the screen. We wish to compute the resultant deflection y_p of an electron as a function of the potential difference V_0 in the gun and the potential difference V_D between the deflecting plates.

In part (1) of the path the electron is not accelerated, so the velocity with which it enters the uniform field is given by equation 5.24. The equation of the path between the deflecting plates is given by equation 5.12 with θ set equal to zero. (We neglect the fringing fields near the edges of the deflecting plates.)

$$y = -\frac{\eta \mathcal{E}}{2v_0^2}x^2 = -\frac{\mathcal{E}}{4V_0}x^2 \tag{5.25}$$

If the separation of the deflecting plates is d, then

$$\mathcal{E} = \frac{V_D}{d} \tag{5.26}$$

so equation 5.25 becomes

$$y = -\frac{V_D x^2}{4dV_0} \tag{5.27}$$

The trajectory between the plates is illustrated in Fig. 5.4. The slope of the path between the plates and the screen is the slope of the parabola at the point of emergence from the plates. This slope can be found by differentiating equation 5.27 and setting $x = l$.

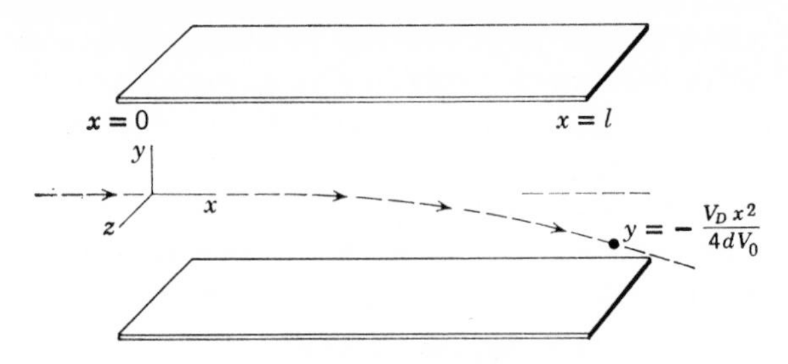

Fig. 5.4. The parabolic trajectory between the deflecting plates.

It is left as a problem to write the equation of the straight line path between the plates and the screen and to show that if this line is extended backwards it crosses the x-axis at $x = l/2$. (This assumes there are no fringing fields.) Since the electrons seem to originate from the point $x = l/2$, $y = 0$, this point is often called a virtual cathode. By using the slope of the path from the plates to the screen it can readily be shown that if L is the distance from the virtual cathode to the screen the total deflection of the electron is given by

$$y_p = \frac{V_D l L}{2dV_0} \tag{5.28}$$

or

$$\frac{y_p}{V_D} = \frac{lL}{2dV_0} \tag{5.29}$$

The ratio y_p/V_D is often called the electrostatic deflection sensitivity. Equation 5.28 indicates that the deflection is proportional to the deflecting voltage V_D and inversely proportional to the accelerating voltage V_0.

In an actual cathode ray tube the vertical deflection plates are followed or preceded by a pair of horizontal deflection plates so that the beam can be aimed at any point on the fluorescent screen.

It is appropriate to point out the nonrelativistic nature of these equations, and the approximation involved in the material discussed in this text. Relativistic effects become important when the electron velocity is greater than 0.1 the velocity of light. This corresponds to an accelerating voltage (for an electron accelerated from rest) of approximately 3 kv.

5.3 Uniform magnetic fields

We now examine the motion of an electron under the influence of a uniform magnetic field. In the following two situations the magnetic force is zero: (1) the particle is at rest, (2) the particle is moving parallel to the direction of the field.

If the electron has a component of velocity perpendicular to the magnetic field, a magnetic force is present. Any velocity component parallel to the magnetic field will not be changed by this magnetic force. We shall develop the equations of motion for the special case of no velocity component parallel to the field and show that the resulting trajectory is a circle.

Figure 5.5 portrays an electron moving with a velocity **v** perpendicular to a uniform magnetic field **B** which is into the page. The magnetic force $\mathbf{F}_m$ on a moving charge q is, from Appendix D,

$$\mathbf{F}_m = q\mathbf{v} \times \mathbf{B} \tag{D.4}$$

The components of the magnetic force are

$$F_x = qv_yB_z - qv_zB_y \tag{5.30}$$

$$F_y = qv_zB_x - qv_xB_z \tag{5.31}$$

$$F_z = qv_xB_y - qv_yB_x \tag{5.32}$$

Since B has only a z-component, $B_x = B_y = 0$ and $B_z = -B$. Substituting the resulting force components into Newton's second law, with $q = -e$ we have

$$F_x = ev_yB = m\ddot{x} \tag{5.33}$$

$$F_y = -ev_xB = m\ddot{y} \tag{5.34}$$

$$F_z = 0 = m\ddot{z} \tag{5.35}$$

To summarize, the equations of motion are

$$\ddot{x} = \eta B\dot{y} \tag{5.36}$$

$$\ddot{y} = -\eta B\dot{x} \tag{5.37}$$

$$\ddot{z} = 0 \tag{5.38}$$

Our problem is to find solutions of these differential equations sub-

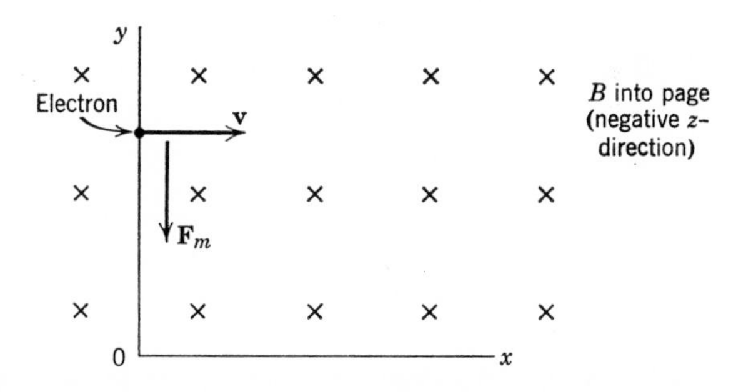

Fig. 5.5. An electron in a uniform magnetic field.

ject to initial conditions. It is always possible to locate the coordinate system so that at $t = 0$

$$\begin{aligned} x &= 0 \\ y &= v_0/\eta B \\ z &= 0 \\ \dot{x} &= v_0 \\ \dot{y} &= 0 \\ \dot{z} &= 0 \end{aligned} \tag{5.39}$$

The first integration of equations 5.36 and 5.37 with respect to time gives

$$\dot{x} = \eta B y + C_1 \tag{5.40}$$

$$\dot{y} = -\eta B x + C_2. \tag{5.41}$$

Using the initial conditions to evaluate the constants,

$$\dot{x} = \eta B y \tag{5.42}$$

$$\dot{y} = -\eta B x \tag{5.43}$$

Substituting equations 5.42 and 5.43 into equations 5.37 and 5.36 we find

$$\ddot{x} = -(\eta B)^2 x \tag{5.44}$$

$$\ddot{y} = -(\eta B)^2 y \tag{5.45}$$

The solutions of these differential equations (found and analyzed in texts on differential equations) are

$$x = A \sin \omega_c t + C \cos \omega_c t \tag{5.46}$$

$$y = D \sin \omega_c t + F \cos \omega_c t \tag{5.47}$$

in which $\omega_c = \eta B$ and A, C, D, and F are constants to be determined. Using the initial conditions it is not difficult to show

$$\begin{aligned} x &= \frac{v_0}{\eta B} \sin \omega_c t \\ y &= \frac{v_0}{\eta B} \cos \omega_c t \end{aligned} \tag{5.48}$$

Equations 5.48 are the parametric equations of a circle of radius $R = v_0/\eta B$ as may be shown by squaring and adding. The angular

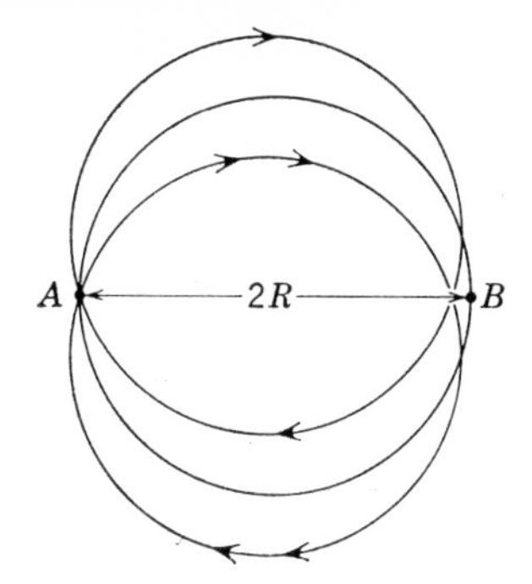

Fig. 5.6. Electron paths in a uniform magnetic field. Electrons with the same speed starting at A will almost meet again at B.

frequency ω of rotation is

$$\omega = \frac{v_0}{R} = \eta B = \omega_c \tag{5.49}$$

The quantity ω_c is commonly called the *cyclotron frequency*. The cyclotron frequency for an electron in a field of 1 gauss (10^{-4} weber/meter^2) is 1.76×10^7 radians/sec or 2.80×10^6 cycles/sec. This circular motion of electrons in magnetic fields finds wide application in electronics.

A uniform magnetic field has focusing properties. Electrons with the same energy which pass through a point in slightly different directions will nearly converge at a point diametrically opposite as shown in Fig. 5.6.

5.4 Magnetic deflection in a cathode-ray tube

A magnetic field applied perpendicular to the direction of the electron beam in a narrow region can deflect the beam in a cathode-ray tube. Consider Fig. 5.7.

Electrons with velocity v_0 enter the magnetic field region and are bent along the arc of a circle of radius

$$R = \frac{v_0}{\eta B} \tag{5.50}$$

From Fig. 5.7 if θ is small,

$$\frac{l}{R} = \sin\theta \approx \theta \tag{5.51}$$

Also if $l \ll L$

$$\theta \approx \frac{y_p}{L} \tag{5.52}$$

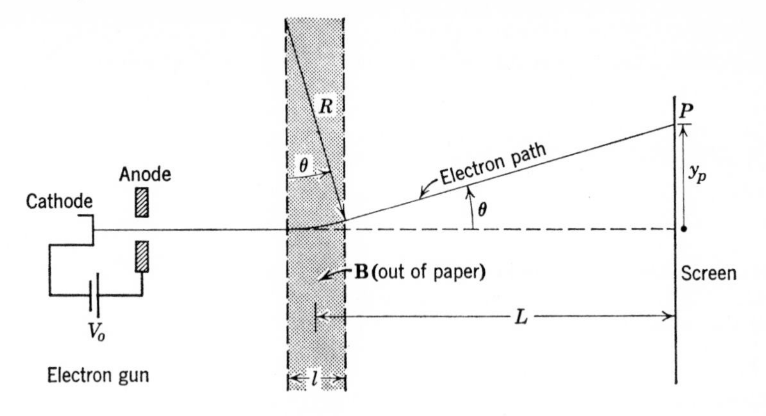

Fig. 5.7. Magnetic deflection in a cathode-ray tube.

and

$$y_p = \frac{Ll}{R} = \frac{Ll\eta B}{v_0} = \frac{Ll\eta B}{\sqrt{2\eta V_0}} \tag{5.53}$$

or

$$\frac{y_p}{B} = Ll\sqrt{\frac{\eta}{2V_0}} \tag{5.54}$$

The ratio y_p/B is called the magnetic deflection sensitivity. Note that the magnetic deflection sensitivity depends on η, whereas the electrostatic deflection sensitivity does not. Magnetic deflection is normally used in television picture tubes. Electrostatic deflection is more commonly used in laboratory cathode-ray oscilloscopes.

5.5 Parallel electric and magnetic fields

Next we consider uniform and parallel electric and magnetic fields as illustrated in Fig. 5.8.

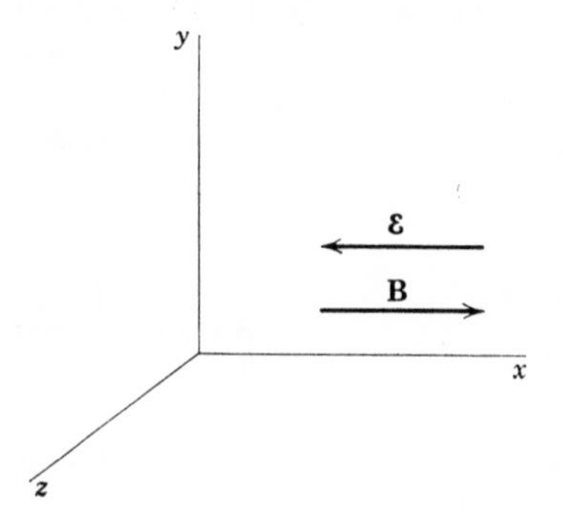

Fig. 5.8. Uniform and parallel electric and magnetic fields.

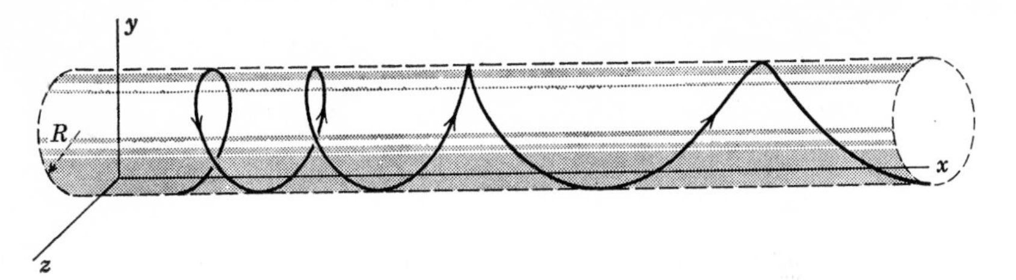

Fig. 5.9. Trajectory of an electron in the parallel fields of Fig. 5.8.

If a charge in this region is either initially at rest or moving in the x-direction, only the electric field will exert a force on the charge. In this case the electric force acts only to change the x-component of velocity; thus the particle moves in a straight line with constant acceleration. However, if initially there is a component of velocity perpendicular to B (v_{y0} and/or $v_{z0} \neq 0$) the projection of the motion in the y-z plane is a circle of radius

$$R = \frac{\sqrt{v_{y0}^2 + v_{z0}^2}}{\eta B} \tag{5.55}$$

The motion in the x-direction is still one of uniform acceleration. Therefore the resultant trajectory is a helix of constant radius R. The pitch of the helix changes quadratically with time as illustrated in Fig. 5.9.

5.6 Crossed electric and magnetic fields

Perpendicular electric and magnetic fields are used in magnetrons and beam-focusing devices. It is important to study the trajectories of charged particles in such fields. Suppose uniform electric and magnetic fields have the directions shown in Fig. 5.10. If an electron starts at rest at the origin, it experiences an electric force upward and acquires a velocity perpendicular to B. The resulting magnetic force bends the path of the electron into the first quadrant of the x-y plane. Since

$$\begin{aligned} \mathcal{E}_x &= 0 \qquad & B_x &= 0 \\ \mathcal{E}_y &= -\mathcal{E} \qquad & B_y &= 0 \\ \mathcal{E}_z &= 0 \qquad & B_z &= -B \end{aligned} \tag{5.56}$$

$$q = -e$$

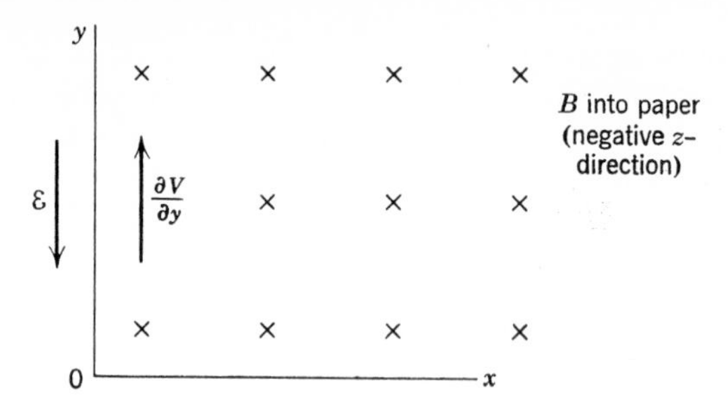

Fig. 5.10. Crossed electric and magnetic fields.

the components of the total force on the electron (see Appendix D) reduce to

$$F_x = ev_yB \tag{5.57}$$

$$F_y = e\mathcal{E} - ev_xB \tag{5.58}$$

$$F_z = 0 \tag{5.59}$$

The y-component of Newton's second law may be written

$$m\ddot{y} = F_y = e\mathcal{E} - eB\dot{x} \tag{5.60}$$

or

$$\ddot{y} = \frac{e}{m}\mathcal{E} - \frac{e}{m}B\dot{x} \tag{5.61}$$

By substituting $\eta = e/m$ and $\omega_c = \eta B$

$$\ddot{y} = \eta\mathcal{E} - \omega_c\dot{x} \tag{5.62}$$

Similarly the x-component of Newton's second law becomes

$$\ddot{x} = \omega_c\dot{y} \tag{5.63}$$

The solution of equations 5.62 and 5.63 must be found subject to the initial conditions. In general the electron need not start at rest. A possible set of initial conditions is

$$\left.\begin{aligned} &\text{at } t = 0 \\ &x = y = 0 \\ &\dot{x} = v_i \\ &\dot{y} = 0 \end{aligned}\right. \tag{5.64}$$

where v_i is the value of the initial x-velocity. The solution of equations

5.62 and 5.63 is somewhat involved. However, by an appropriate substitution we can obtain equations of a form we have previously treated. The coordinate transformation is shown in Fig. 5.11. Here we have a primed system moving in the x-direction with a constant velocity $\mathcal{E}/B$. The x-coordinates transform (from Fig. 5.11) according to

$$x = x' + \frac{\mathcal{E}}{B} t \tag{5.65}$$

Substituting equation 5.65 and its time derivatives into 5.62 and 5.63 we have

$$\begin{aligned} \ddot{y} &= -\omega_c \dot{x}' \\ \ddot{x}' &= \omega_c \dot{y} \end{aligned} \tag{5.66}$$

Equations 5.66 are the same as 5.36 and 5.37 for an electron in a uniform magnetic field. The solution obtained by the methods of section 5.3 and utilizing the boundary conditions 5.64 is that of uniform circular motion. The parametric equations are

$$x' = -R \sin \omega_c t \tag{5.67}$$

$$y = -R \cos \omega_c t + R \tag{5.68}$$

where

$$R = \frac{\mathcal{E}/B - v_i}{\omega_c} \tag{5.69}$$

We complete the transformation indicated in Fig. 5.11 for the simple displacement of the y-coordinate by letting

$$y = y' + R \tag{5.70}$$

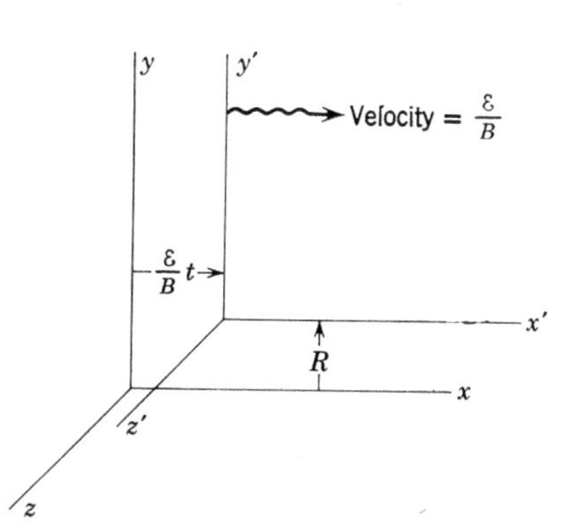

Fig. 5.11. The coordinate transformation used to simplify equations 5.62 and 5.63.

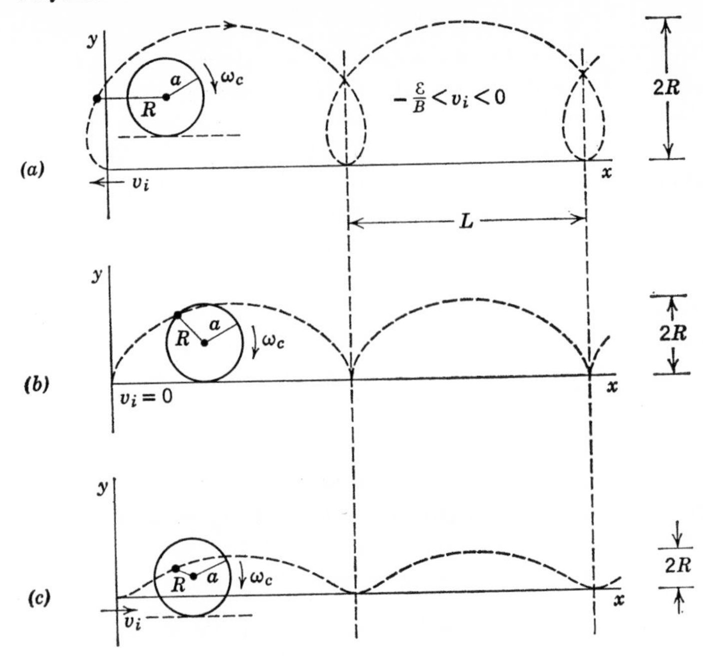

Fig. 5.12. The three classes of cycloids. (*a*) Curtate or epicycloid. (*b*) Common cycloid. (*c*) Prolate or hypocycloid. The radius a and drift speed $\mathcal{E}/B$ of the rolling circle are independent of v_i. The distance of the marker from the center of the circle decreases as v_i increases from negative values.

Hence, the parametric equations of the trajectory in the primed system are

$$x' = -R \sin \omega_c t \tag{5.71}$$

$$y' = -R \cos \omega_c t \tag{5.72}$$

These are the parametric equations of a circle of radius R about the origin in the x'-y' plane of the primed coordinate system. The period of the circular motion is $2\pi/\omega_c$.

The resulting electron motion in the unprimed coordinate system is a combination of circular motion and a uniform translation, which is equivalent to the motion of a marker on the spoke (or its extension) of a rolling wheel. Since the rolling wheel turns with an angular velocity ω_c, and rolls with a speed $\mathcal{E}/B$, its radius a is given by

$$a = \frac{\mathcal{E}}{\omega_c B} \tag{5.73}$$

The speed of the electron relative to the center of the rolling circle is $R\omega_c$.

Figure 5.12 illustrates the three general types of trajectories. Each time the particle reaches the x-axis, the y-component of velocity is zero and the x-component of velocity is v_i. During the time of one complete rotation of the "wheel," the electron advances perpendicular to both the electric and magnetic fields a distance L given by the linear velocity of the wheel, $\mathcal{E}/B$, times the period of rotation.

$$L = \frac{\mathcal{E}}{B} \cdot \frac{2\pi}{\omega_c} = \frac{2\pi\mathcal{E}}{\eta B^2} \tag{5.74}$$

Notice that this advance per cycle is independent of the initial velocity v_i.

In the special case when the initial velocity is equal to $\mathcal{E}/B$, the electric and magnetic forces on the electron are equal and opposite, so that the path is a straight line. This can be seen by equating the forces

$$e\mathcal{E} = ev_iB \tag{5.75}$$

or by setting $v_i = \mathcal{E}/B$ in equation 5.69 to make $R = 0$. This principle is used in mass spectrometers and other devices when a filter to select charged particles with a narrow velocity range that is independent of the charge or mass is desired. Such a device is known as a Wien velocity filter.

The forces acting on the electron at each point of the path of the common cycloid are illustrated in Fig. 5.13. The electric force $\mathbf{F}_e$ is constant and directed upward, but the magnetic force $\mathbf{F}_m$ varies in direction and is proportional in magnitude to the instantaneous speed.

Figure 5.14 shows a representative set of solutions when v_i ranges from a value greater than $2\mathcal{E}/B$ to negative values (initial velocity to

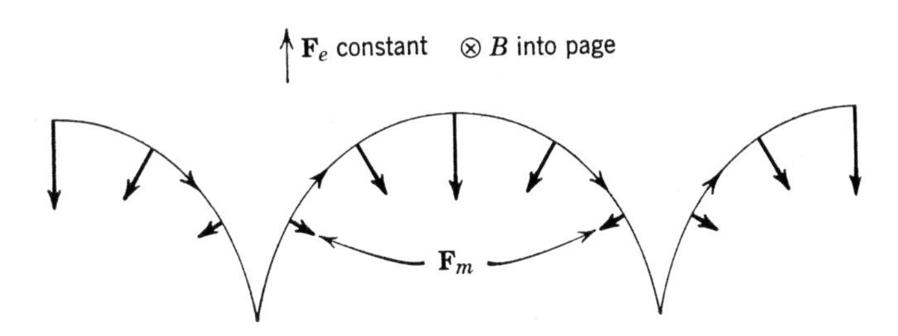

Fig. 5.13. The forces on the electron at various points along a common cycloid trajectory.

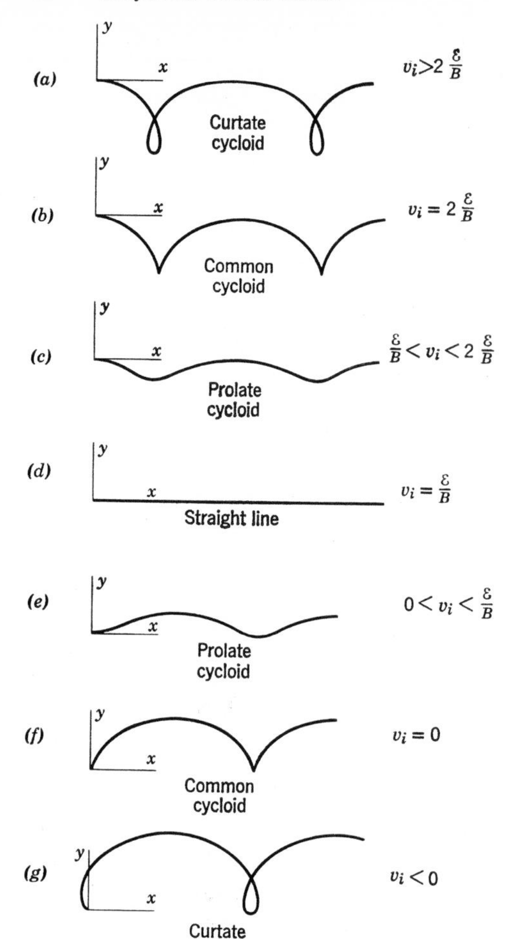

Fig. 5.14. The trajectories for values of v_i greater than $2\ \mathcal{E}/B$ to less than zero.

the left). Notice that the trajectory has the same shape when $v_i = 2\mathcal{E}/B$ and when $v_i = 0$. More generally, pairs of similar trajectories occur for pairs of v_i's greater or less than $\mathcal{E}/B$ by equal amounts. When $v_i > \mathcal{E}/B$, the x-axis is the highest point the electron reaches whereas for $v_i < \mathcal{E}/B$ the x-axis is the lowest point.

5.7 Cycloidal trajectories in a magnetron

Magnetrons are vacuum tube devices which generate or amplify high frequency electromagnetic waves. Crossed electric and mag-

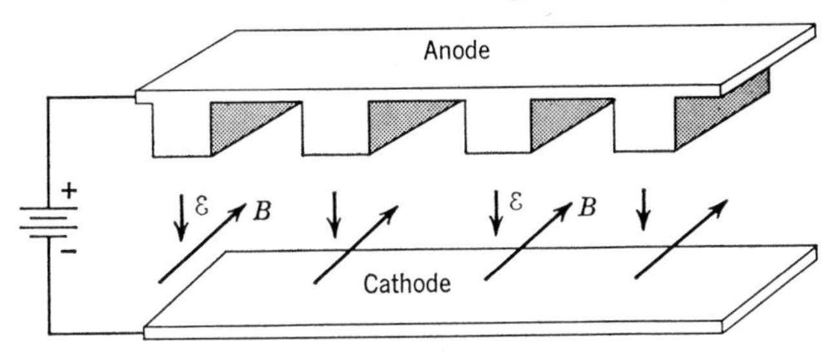

Fig. 5.15. Idealized linear magnetron. The directions of the static (d-c) crossed electric and magnetic fields are shown.

netic fields are used in magnetrons to produce cycloidal trajectories. The trajectories and the mechanism by which amplification occurs are illustrated by considering the idealized linear magnetron sketched in Fig. 5.15.

The serrated anode structure provides resonant circuit elements which are known as cavities. The purpose of these cavities becomes apparent in the following discussion. The physics of cavities is discussed more fully in Chapter 15. Figure 5.16 shows a cross section of this magnetron. High frequency electromagnetic energy is inserted as illustrated by the dotted schematic oscillator circuit in Fig. 5.16. The effect of this oscillator is to produce an alternating potential

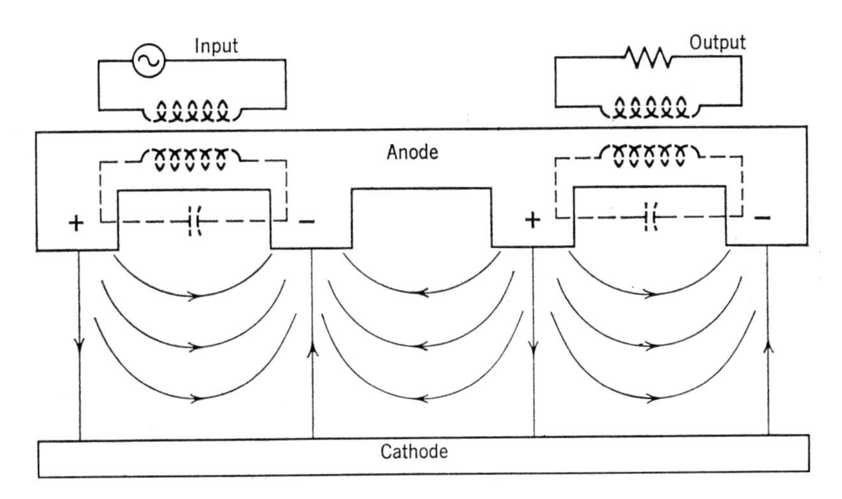

Fig. 5.16. Cross section of linear magnetron showing r-f electric field pattern at one instant of time.

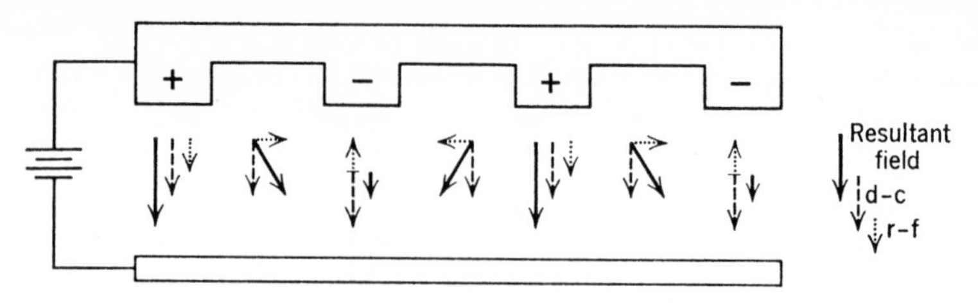

Fig. 5.17. The resultant of the r-f and d-c electric fields at representative points.

difference between adjacent segments of the input anode cavity. The charges on these segments vary in phase with the potential difference. By induction the third segment has a charge opposite to that of the second segment and the fourth opposite to that of the third, etc. Power may be extracted as illustrated schematically by the load circuit to the right. In the absence of electron emission from the cathode, the output energy is less than the input energy because of resistive heating of the anode by the induced a-c currents. Hence, we visualize a wave of potential associated with a wave of induced charge, traveling along the anode structure from left to right with decreasing amplitude. Alternatively, we may imagine that a wave of electric field (an electromagnetic wave) travels from left to right in the space between electrodes. In Fig. 5.16 the lines of the alternating or r-f (radio frequency) electric fields are shown at one instant of time. One half-cycle later the entire pattern is shifted one segment to the right (all field lines reversed). In Fig. 5.17 a steady d-c component of field is added by connecting a battery between cathode and anode. The d-c and r-f fields and their vector sum are shown at representative points.

Next we consider some electron trajectories in a magnetron. In the absence of the r-f field, the path of an electron released with negligible velocity from any point of the cathode is the common cycloid discussed in the previous section. The r-f electric field modifies this path. Figure 5.18*a* portrays the early part of two typical trajectories. The starting times of the electrons are such that they reach the gaps when the magnitude of the r-f field is largest. Electron *B* experiences a net accelerating electric force and gains kinetic energy from the r-f field. Electron *A* experiences a net retarding electric force and loses kinetic energy to the field. If as shown in Fig. 5.18*b*, electron *A* travels to the right at about the same speed as the r-f electric field wave travels to the right, the electron will again experience a retarding force when it reaches the next cavity and will lose more energy to the r-f field. Since the average electric field felt by electron *A* tilts to the right instead of being vertical, the direction of the drift velocity (which is perpendicular to $\mathbf{\mathcal{E}}$ and $\mathbf{B}$ as shown in the previous section) is tilted upward. The problem is somewhat more complex than we have indicated and the cycloidal path may become prolate. However, the average net drift velocity for all cycloids is the same and equal to $\mathcal{E}/B$. The phase of the charge on the segments must remain in near synchronism with the electrons, and therefore the velocity with which the induced charge wave travels from input to output on the serrated structure or circuit must also be on the order of $\mathcal{E}/B$.

The average electric field felt by electron B tilts to the left, so that electron B shifts slightly downward and strikes the cathode, liberating secondary electrons. (In practical magnetrons these secondary electrons may account for more than 90% of the total cathode emission.)

The mechanism by which an electron of type A gives energy to the r-f electromagnetic field may be considered from the viewpoint of induced charges and currents. The negative electrons induce, on the surface of the anode, a positive charge which travels to the right in

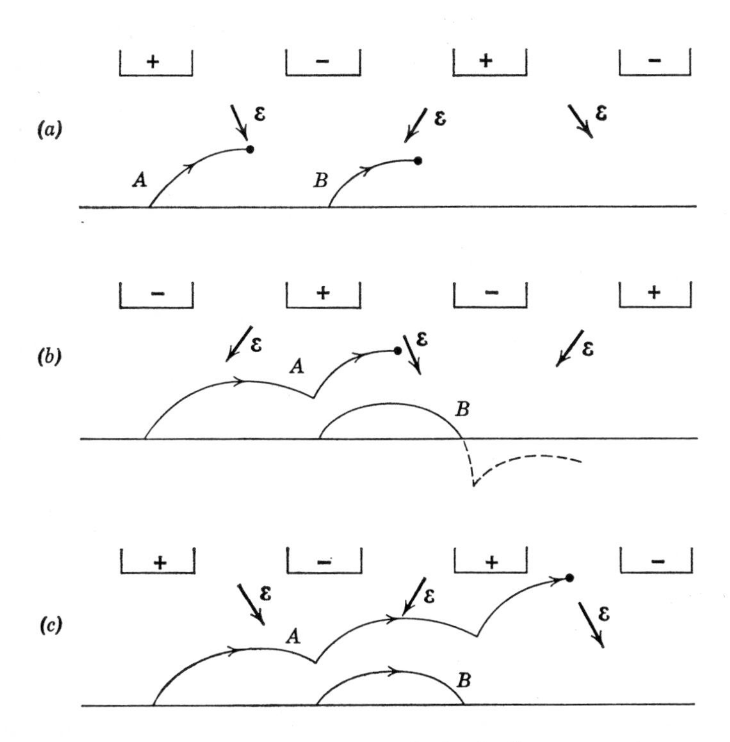

Fig. 5.18. Representative trajectories in the linear magnetron.

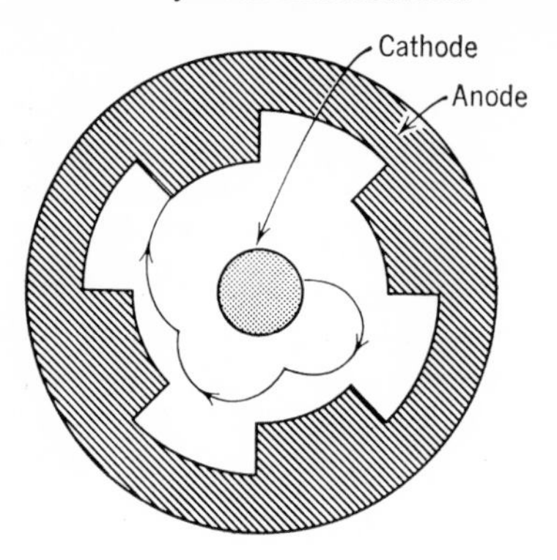

Fig. 5.19. An electron trajectory in a cylindrical magnetron.

step with the electron. Since the electron gets progressively closer to the anode, as shown in Fig. 5.18*c*, the magnitude of the induced charge increases, so that the magnitude of the r-f potential difference between adjacent segments increases. Induced electrode currents are more thoroughly examined in Chapter 7.

Type A electrons give energy to the r-f field; type B electrons extract energy from the r-f field. However, since type B electrons strike the cathode, they are more rapidly removed from consideration than those of type A. Some of the electrons starting with phases in between those of types A and B are either speeded up or slowed down to approach the trajectories of type A or type B electrons. This process produces bunches of electrons centered about type A electrons as they travel along the structure and from cathode to anode. Type A electrons have a constant drift velocity ($\mathcal{E}/B$), and therefore a *constant average kinetic energy* as they travel from cathode to anode. However, in flowing against the retarding r-f electric field, the type A electrons effectively transfer their *d-c potential energy* to the traveling r-f electromagnetic wave. The net effect is a transfer of energy from the d-c battery to the r-f electromagnetic field. In this manner amplification of electromagnetic power is obtained in a magnetron.

Although the physical principles of a magnetron are most readily understood by considering the ideal linear case, practical magnetrons employ cylindrical geometry. Figure 5.19 shows a type A orbit in a cylindrical magnetron.

5.8 Magnetron cut-off

In this section we investigate the behavior of electrons in the space between a cylindrical anode and cathode when a uniform magnetic field parallel to the axis exists (see Fig. 5.20).

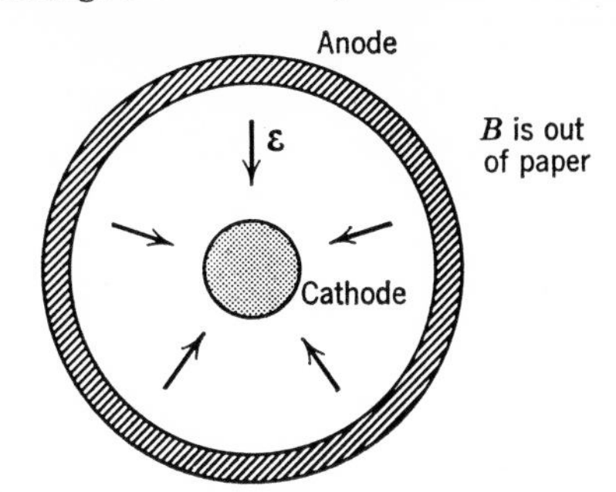

Fig. 5.20. Cylindrical geometry for magnetron cut-off derivation. Anode has radius r_a; cathode has radius r_c.

We make use of the fact that the time rate of change of the angular momentum of a particle is equal to the applied torque. The torque L is defined by

$$\mathbf{L} \equiv \mathbf{r} \times \mathbf{F} \tag{5.76}$$

and if the force $\mathbf{F}$ is in the plane of the paper (see Fig. 5.21*a*)

$$|L| = rF_\theta \tag{5.77}$$

where F_θ is the θ-component of $\mathbf{F}$. The angular momentum P_θ is defined by

$$\mathbf{P}_\theta = \mathbf{r} \times m\mathbf{v} \tag{5.78}$$

and if the velocity $\mathbf{v}$ is in the plane of the paper (see Fig. 5.21*b*)

$$|P_\theta| = rmv_\theta = mr^2\dot{\theta}. \tag{5.79}$$

Hence, equating the torque and the time rate of change of angular momentum

$$rF_\theta = \frac{d}{dt}(mr^2\dot{\theta}) \tag{5.80}$$

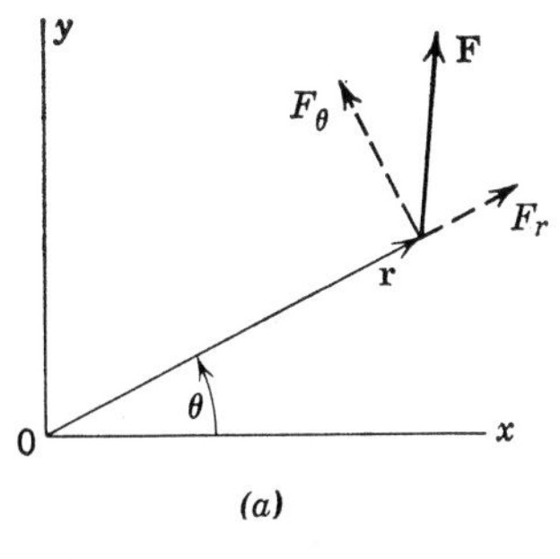

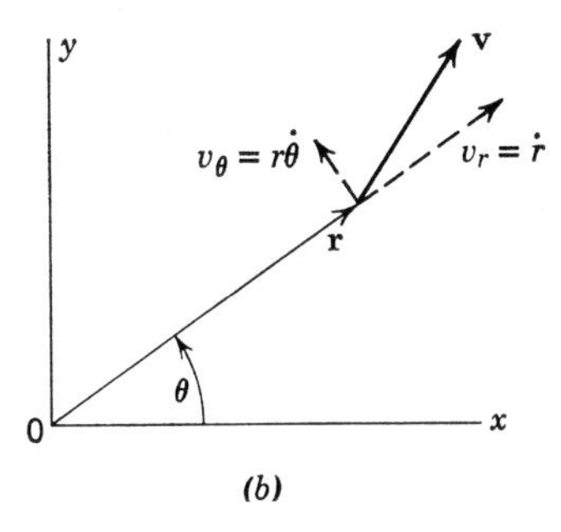

Fig. 5.21. Diagrams for the derivation of the magnetic cut-off equation. (*a*) The force on a particle at $\mathbf{r}$. (*b*) The velocity of a particle at $\mathbf{r}$.

In the problem represented in Fig. 5.20, since the electric field is assumed to be radial, F_θ is the magnetic force due to the radial component $\dot{r}$ of the electron's velocity.

$$F_\theta = e\dot{r}B \tag{5.81}$$

By substituting into equation 5.80

$$er\dot{r}B = \frac{d}{dt}(mr^2\dot{\theta}) \tag{5.82}$$

This equation may be rewritten to give

$$\eta B \frac{d}{dt}\left(\frac{r^2}{2}\right) = \frac{d}{dt}(r^2\dot{\theta}) \tag{5.83}$$

Recalling that $\omega_c = \eta B$ and integrating once with respect to time

$$r^2\dot{\theta} = \frac{\omega_c r^2}{2} + C \tag{5.84}$$

or

$$\dot{\theta} = \frac{\omega_c}{2} + \frac{C}{r^2} \tag{5.85}$$

where C is a constant of integration.

If electrons start at the cathode ($r = r_c$) with zero angular velocity ($\dot{\theta} = 0$), then from equation 5.85

$$C = -\frac{\omega_c r_c^2}{2} \tag{5.86}$$

Using this value of C in equation 5.85,

$$\dot{\theta} = \frac{\omega_c}{2}\left(1 - \frac{r_c^2}{r^2}\right) \tag{5.87}$$

Therefore an electron which leaves the cathode and crosses lines of a uniform axial magnetic field acquires an angular velocity which is equal to half the cyclotron frequency minus a term which is inversely proportional to the square of the distance from the axis of the electrodes. If $r \gg r_c$, then the angular velocity acquired is very nearly equal to half the cyclotron frequency. This has significance in the confinement of electron beams which is discussed in Chapter 15.

Now suppose the anode is maintained at a constant voltage V with respect to the cathode. The angular velocity of an electron when it reaches the anode is determined by equation 5.87 with $r = r_a$. Kinetic energy is associated with this angular velocity, with the kinetic energy coming from the loss of potential energy as the electron falls through the potential difference V. It is important to realize that this energy does *not* come from the *magnetic field*, since there can be no work done by a static magnetic field (the magnetic force is perpendicular to the velocity). If the loss in potential energy is greater than the "angular" part of the kinetic energy, then the rest of the energy will be associated with a velocity in the r-direction and the electron will plunge into the anode. However, if the loss of potential energy is just equal to the acquired "angular" kinetic energy, then the electron will have no radial velocity when it reaches the anode and it will just graze the anode. This condition is called cut-off. The value of V for which cut-off occurs is easily found using conservation of energy and equation 5.87.

If the electron starts at rest at the cathode, where its potential energy will be taken as zero, the statement of conservation of energy when it has reached the anode is

$$\tfrac{1}{2}mv^2 = eV \tag{5.88}$$

But if it just grazes the anode

$$v = r_a\dot{\theta} = r_a \frac{\omega_c}{2}\left(1 - \frac{r_c^2}{r_a^2}\right) \tag{5.89}$$

where we have used equation 5.87.

Eliminating v and solving for the cut-off potential V,

$$V \text{ (at cut-off)} = \frac{r_a^2\omega_c^2}{8\eta}\left(1 - \frac{r_c^2}{r_a^2}\right)^2 \tag{5.90}$$

This condition does not depend on how the potential varies from cathode to anode as long as the electric field is always radial. For example, even when space charge is present equation 5.90 is true, provided the space charge distribution is cylindrically symmetrical.

5.9 Electron optics

We now consider briefly a convenient method of calculating trajectories of charge particles in electric fields to illustrate the techniques of electron optics.

Snell's law for light rays can be written

$$n_1 \sin \theta_1 = n_2 \sin \theta_2 \tag{5.91}$$

where the symbols are defined in Fig. 5.22. The electron optical

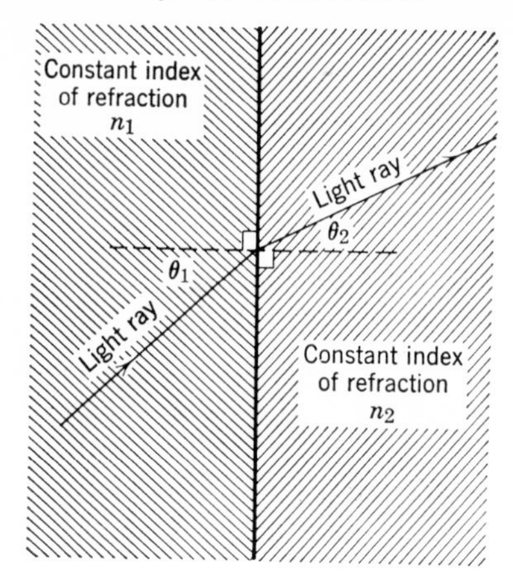

Fig. 5.22. Snell's law (optical).

analogue of Snell's law is shown in Fig. 5.23. We observe that electrons passing from a region of constant potential V_1 to a region of higher potential V_2 have their x-components of velocity increased, whereas their y-components of velocity are unchanged. Consequently, the electrons are deflected towards a normal to the interface between regions of constant potential. If we choose the potential V to be zero where an electron's velocity is zero, we may write

$$v_1 = \sqrt{2\eta V_1} \tag{5.92}$$

$$v_2 = \sqrt{2\eta V_2} \tag{5.93}$$

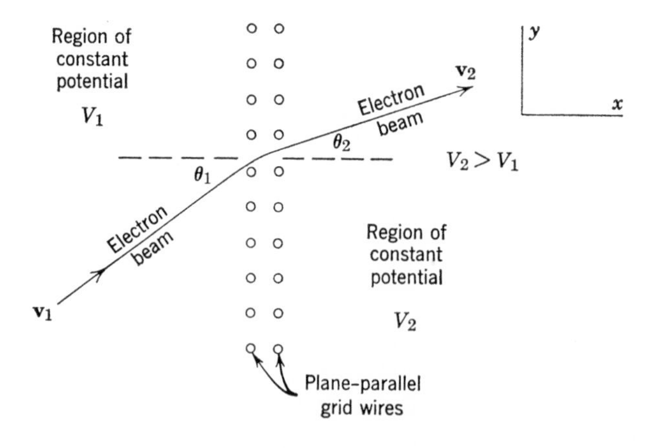

Fig. 5.23. Snell's law (electron optical).

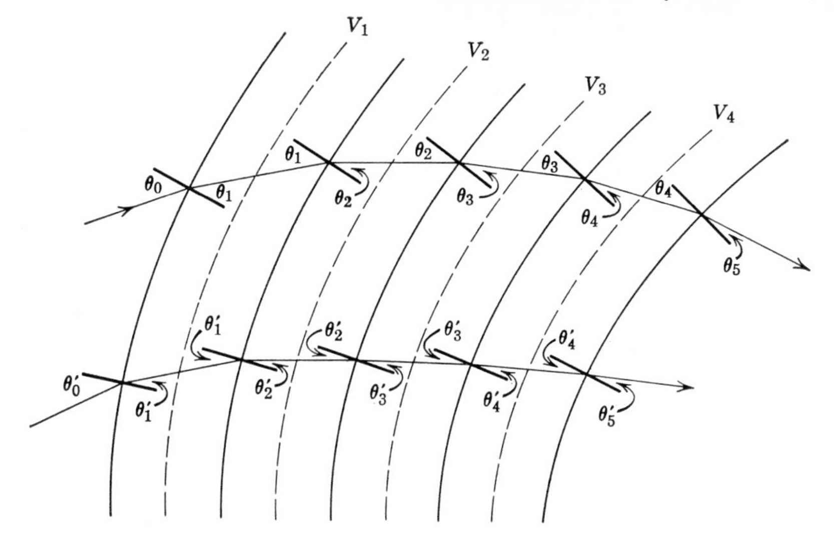

Fig. 5.24. Lines of equal potential and approximate trajectories.

Since only the x-component of velocity is changed, we have

$$v_{y_1} = v_{y_2} \tag{5.94}$$

or

$$v_1 \sin \theta_1 = v_2 \sin \theta_2 \tag{5.95}$$

and using 5.92 and 5.93,

$$\sqrt{V_1} \sin \theta_1 = \sqrt{V_2} \sin \theta_2 \tag{5.96}$$

In equation 5.96 the square root of the potential is seen to be analogous to the index of refraction by comparison with equation 5.91. Equation 5.96 is Snell's law for electron optics and is the basis for plotting electron trajectories in electrostatic lens systems.

To determine a charged particle trajectory, we first determine the equipotential lines of the system. Figure 5.24 shows a portion of the equipotentials of an electron-optical system. To apply Snell's law we consider that the lines of equipotential may be replaced by strips of constant potential. In Fig. 5.24 the dotted lines are the equipotential lines, and the strips of constant potential are bounded by the solid lines drawn approximately parallel to the equipotential lines. Two trajectories are plotted in Fig. 5.24 to show how Snell's law may be utilized at the potential-strip interfaces to plot electron trajectories in static electric fields.

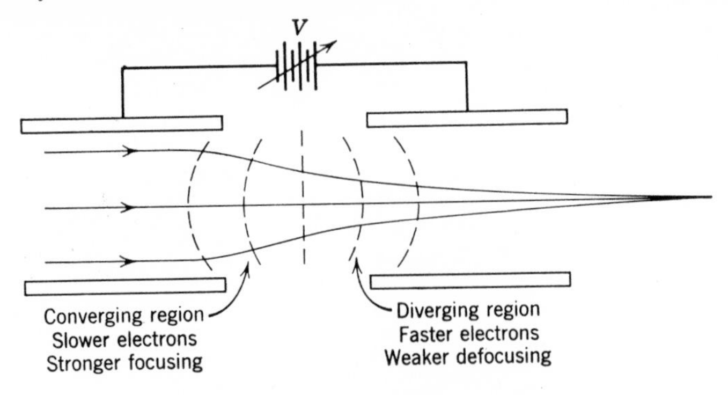

Fig. 5.25. Simple electrostatic lens.

In Fig. 5.25 a simple electrostatic lens system is shown. Here three initially parallel rays of electrons are brought to a focus. The position of the focus is adjusted by varying the potential V between the lens elements.

Electron optics in magnetic fields is more difficult to represent since individual trajectories in magnetic lenses are generally three dimensional. In Fig. 5.26 we show a region containing a constant magnetic field. In the field region the nonaxial electrons have a path which is a segment of a helix. During their helical paths the electrons are redirected toward the axis of symmetry. The location of the focal point depends on the strength of the magnetic field and the velocity of the electrons. In a magnetic lens system, the image rotates with

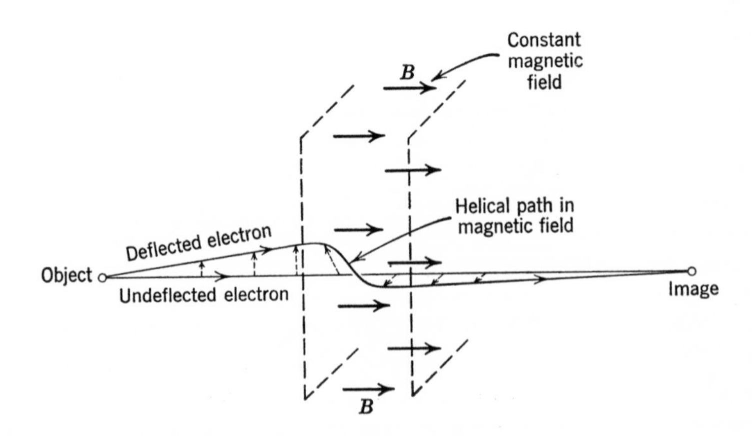

Fig. 5.26. Ideal magnetic lens element.

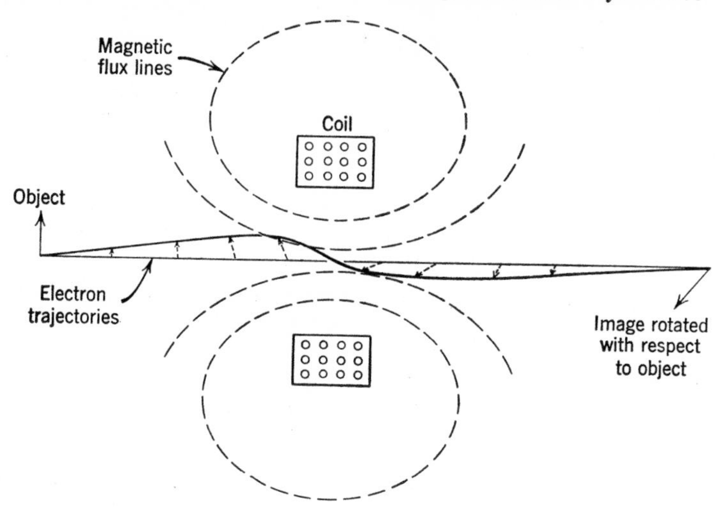

Fig. 5.27. Simple magnetic lens.

respect to the object about the axis of symmetry as the lens is focused by varying the magnetic field. In Fig. 5.27 we show how the idealized magnetic lens of Fig. 5.26 can be approximated in practice.

It will be noticed that in electron optics the "focal lengths" of both magnetic and electrostatic lenses can be varied, whereas in traditional optics, the focal length of a lens is fixed. Unfortunately, electron optics has numerous lens aberration problems as has traditional optics. A treatment of these lens aberrations, however, is beyond the scope of this textbook.

Suggested References

J. R. Pierce, *Theory and Design of Electron Beams*, D. Van Nostrand Company, 1954. Pierce's "Beams" is the basic reference book for workers concerned with the behavior of electrons in electric and magnetic fields. Chapter 3 starts at the level of this textbook, with succeeding chapters more advanced. Chapters 6 and 7 are basic approaches to electron optics.

K. R. Spangenburg, *Vacuum Tubes*, McGraw-Hill Book Company, 1948. Spangenburg's Chapter 13 has a detailed discussion of electron lenses and focal properties. Chapter 15 is devoted to cathode-ray tubes. Chapter 18 discusses magnetrons.

J. C. Slater, *Microwave Electronics*, D. Van Nostrand Company, 1950. This is a relatively advanced treatment of the physics underlying microwave tubes. Chapter 13 contains a good basic description of magnetron principles.

PROBLEMS

5.1. Prove that the transit time for an electron falling from rest through a potential difference of V volts between plane parallel electrodes d meters apart is $\dfrac{2d}{5.94 \times 10^5 \sqrt{V}}$ sec

5.2. What is the time spent by a 1000 volt electron between 2 cm long deflecting plates in a cathode-ray tube?

5.3. If the deflecting plates of a cathode-ray tube are 2 cm long, 0.5 cm apart, and 25 cm from the fluorescent screen, and a deflecting potential of 40 volts produces a 2 cm deflection on the screen, what is the gun voltage?

5.4. An electron is released with zero initial velocity from the lower of a pair of horizontal plates which are 3 cm apart. The accelerating potential between these plates increases from zero linearly with time at the rate of 10 volts per microsecond. When the electron is 2.8 cm from the bottom plate, a reverse voltage of 50 volts is applied.

(*a*) What is the instantaneous potential between the plates just before reversal?

(*b*) With what electrode does the electron collide?

(*c*) What is the time of flight?

5.5. Electrons are projected into a region of constant electric field intensity of magnitude 5×10^3 volts/meter that exists vertically. The electron gun makes an angle of 30° with the horizontal. It ejects the electrons with an energy of 100 ev.

(*a*) How long does it take for an electron leaving the gun to pass through a hole H, at a horizontal distance of 3 cm from the position of the gun? Refer to the figure. Assume the field is downward.

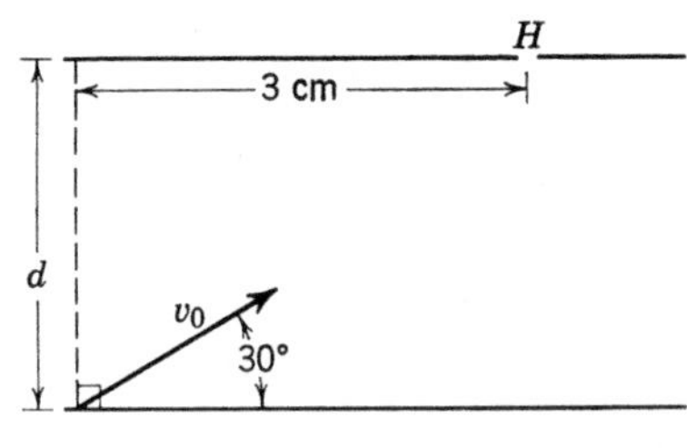

Prob. 5.5

(*b*) What must be the distance d in order that the particles emerge through the hole.

(*c*) Repeat the foregoing for the case where the field is upward.

5.6. In a cathode-ray oscilloscope the accelerating potential V_0 is a constant potential modulated by a sinusoidal potential; $V_0 = V_1 + V_1/2 \cos \omega t$. The horizontal and vertical deflecting plates are both modulated with potentials $V_{\text{vertical}} = V_v \sin f\omega t$ and $V_{\text{horizontal}} = V_h \cos f\omega t$. Consider the resulting vertical deflection D and the horizontal deflection R on the face of the oscilloscope. Plot and describe the resulting pattern on the oscilloscope face when

f is a rational fraction; in particular, consider the trace when $f = 1$, $f = 2$, $f = \frac{1}{2}$, $f = \frac{3}{2}$.

5.7. Prove the last sentence of section 5.5.

5.8. Derive equations 5.48 from 5.46 and 5.47.

5.9. 10^{16} electrons per second pass steadily along a 100-volt electron beam. What is the beam current and the power dissipated when the electrons strike a collector?

5.10. A 1000 ev electron moves perpendicular to a uniform magnetic field of 0.01 weber/meter^2.

(*a*) Find the radius of its path.

(*b*) If the electron velocity were at 5° to the field, what would be the electron's path?

5.11. A cathode-ray tube has deflecting coils producing a uniform magnetic field of 6×10^{-3} weber/meter^2 when the coil current is 1 amp, the field region being 2.5 cm long at 25 cm from the screen. If an alternating current of 0.25 amp (rms) produces a 15-cm long trace on the screen, what is the final anode voltage of the tube?

5.12. An electron is injected into a magnetic field with a velocity of 10^7 meters/sec in a direction lying in the plane of the page and making an angle of 30° with **B** as shown in the figure. What must be the value of **B** in order that the electrons pass through the point Q?

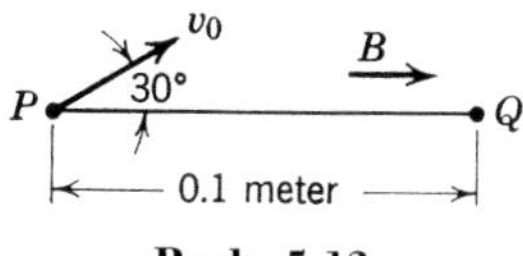

Prob. 5.12

5.13. An electron is released from point O (see figure) with a velocity v_0 parallel to the plates of a parallel-plate capacitor. The distance between the plates is 1 cm, and the applied potential is 100 volts.

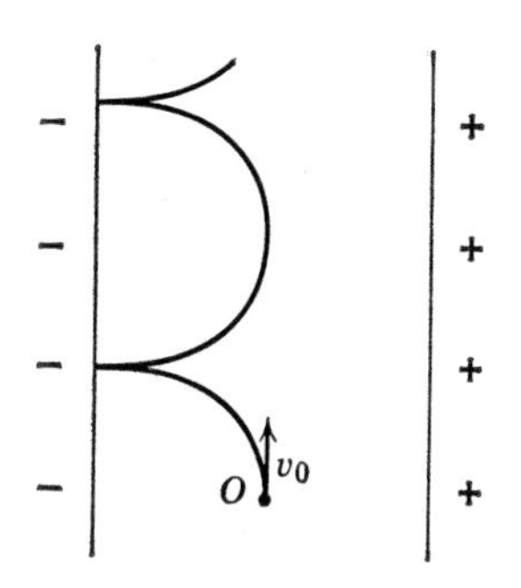

Prob. 5.13

(*a*) What magnitude and direction of magnetic field will cause the electron to move in the cycloidal path indicated? Note that O is midway between the plates and that the electron has zero velocity at the negative plate.

(*b*) What must be the value of v_0 in order that this path be followed.

5.14. In a mass spectrometer, singly charged ions travel from a crossed field region into a uniform magnetic field as shown in the figure. Derive an expression for the mass of the ion in terms of V, B, R, e and d.

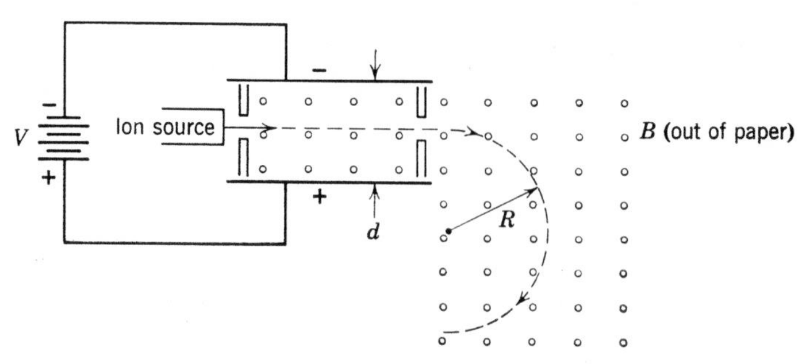

Prob. 5.14

5.15. A uniform magnetic field B exists parallel to the y-axis. A uniform electric field exists parallel to the x-y plane and has components $\mathcal{E}_x$ and $\mathcal{E}_y$. An electron is injected parallel to the z-axis with the initial speed v_{0z}.

(*a*) What must be the value of v_{0z} in order that the electron remain forever in the y-z plane?

(*b*) What are the y and z coordinates of the electron at any time t, if v_{0z} is chosen as in part (*a*)?

(*c*) What is the resultant path?

5.16. In the magnetron of Figs. 5.15 and 5.16, the distance between segment centers is d, the separation between the cathode and anode is s, the magnetic field is B, and the voltage between cathode and anode is V. Calculate the two lowest frequencies the magnetron will amplify. (Obtain an approximate answer by ignoring the r-f electric field.)

5.17. A cylindrical magnetron has a filamentary cathode 0.2 mm in diameter, and a 2-cm diameter anode. If $V_a = 1000$ volts, calculate the cut-off magnetic flux density.

5.18. An electron is injected tangentially into the annular space between two concentric cylinders. Determine the relation that must exist between electron velocity, cylinder radii, and potential difference if the electron is to follow a concentric circular orbit. Calculate the required potential difference if the electron velocity is 10^7 meters/sec and the cylinder radii are 2 and 6 cm.

5.19. Derive an expression analogous to 5.90 for the cut-off voltage of a linear magnetron. Let the separation of cathode and anode in Fig. 5.15 (ignore serrations) be d, and the electron start out with zero velocity.

5.20. Follow the method of section 5.9 to plot the path of the scattering of an α-particle by a heavy fixed nucleus. (The potential due to the nucleus is given by $Q/4\pi\epsilon_0 r$.)

6. classical vacuum devices

In this chapter we apply the concepts of Chapters 4 and 5 to vacuum devices in which electrons are supplied by one of the electrodes. The current-voltage characteristic of the thermionic diode is derived. Multielectrode devices are also considered. The emphasis is on the physical phenomena taking place within the devices, although the use of a triode as an amplifier is discussed.

6.1 Current-voltage relationship in a diode

The simplest electron tube is the two-electrode tube or diode. In its usual form it consists of a thermionically emitting cathode and a collecting electrode, the anode. When the anode potential is higher than the cathode potential, electrons emitted from the cathode are drawn to the anode. When the anode is negative with respect to the cathode, virtually no electrons reach the anode. The diode therefore serves as a one-way current device or rectifier.

When the cathode and anode are closely spaced, parallel plane surfaces, the analysis is particularly simple. We will neglect the fringing fields at the edges of the electrodes and assume that the electric field is everywhere normal to the electrodes. It turns out that the current-voltage relationship which we shall derive also applies to diodes with more complicated geometries. Our diode geometry and potentials are shown schematically in Fig. 6.1.

We are interested in examining how the current i depends on the anode potential V_a and how the potential V depends on the distance x

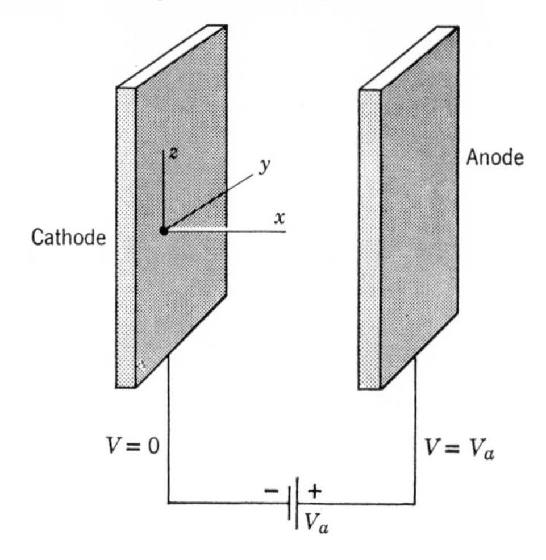

Fig. 6.1. Diode geometry and potentials.

from the cathode under different operating conditions. There are four distinct emission conditions under which a diode may operate.

When the cathode is cold, electrons are emitted at a negligible rate, and the space charge density ρ and the current between the electrodes are zero. Since the charge density is zero and the potential is independent of y and z, Poisson's equation (see Appendix D) becomes

$$\frac{d^2V}{dx^2} = -\frac{\rho}{\epsilon_0} = 0 \tag{6.1}$$

Integration of this equation gives

$$V = \frac{V_a}{d}x \tag{6.2}$$

where we have made use of the boundary conditions at $x = 0$ and $x = d$ indicated in Fig. 6.1. Figure 6.2a shows this linear variation of potential with distance from the cathode for the zero emission case.

If the cathode temperature is raised until a small but significant current flows, a finite negative charge density exists between the electrodes. Examination of Poisson's equation when ρ is negative shows that the curve of V versus x is no longer straight but curves upward as shown in Fig. 6.2b. When ρ is small, the direction of the electric field at the cathode is toward the cathode and is smaller than when ρ is zero. The resultant force on an emitted electron is toward the anode, so that every emitted electron reaches the anode. Operation of the tube under these conditions is said to be temperature-limited, since the current reaching the anode is controlled by the cathode temperature and shows little variation with changes in anode potential.

If the cathode temperature is raised still further, a point can be reached where enough electrons are present just outside the cathode to make the slope of the potential versus distance curve zero at the cathode. This borderline case is shown in Fig. 6.2*c*. Here there is no field acting on the electrons when they are first emitted.

At still higher temperatures the rate of emission is sufficiently large that the potential just outside the cathode is depressed below that of the cathode (see Fig. 6.2*d*). Since the electrons are emitted with a distribution of velocities, only the fast electrons are energetically able to pass the potential minimum and reach the anode. The remaining

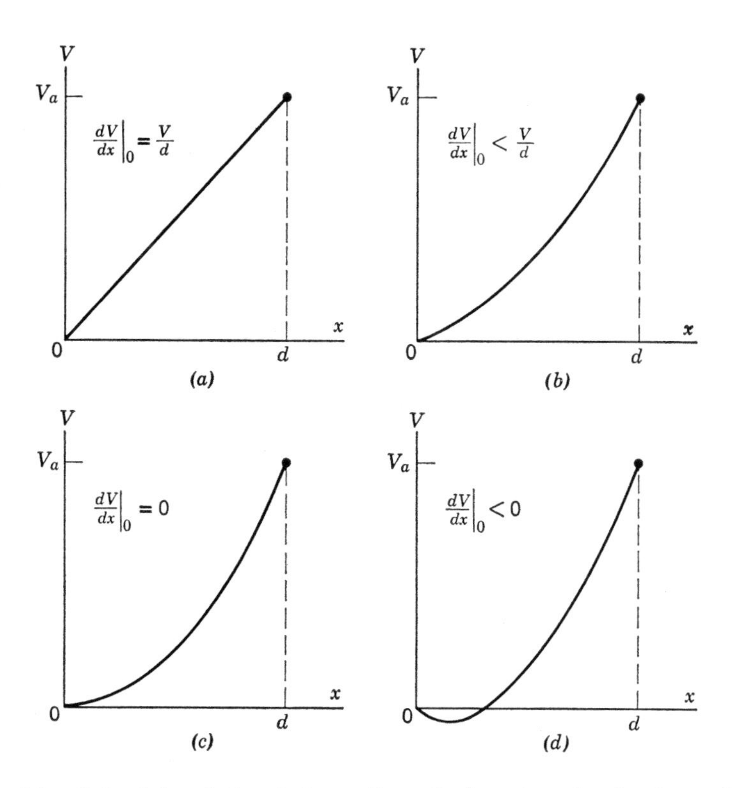

Fig. 6.2. Potential variations between the cathode and anode of a planar diode. (*a*) No electron emission. (*b*) Temperature-limited condition. (*c*) Space-charge-limited condition with zero field at cathode. (*d*) Space-charge-limited condition for finite initial velocity.

electrons are returned to the cathode by the opposing field just outside. The average normally directed energy of an electron upon emission is kT (see equation 4.18) or about $\frac{1}{10}$ ev for a cathode temperature of 1160° K. We would expect, therefore, the depression in potential to be somewhere between zero and a few tenths of a volt, depending on the rate of emission. If the cathode temperature is raised so that emission is increased, more charge develops just outside the cathode and the potential minimum is further depressed, causing more electrons to be returned to the cathode. The fraction of the electrons that passes the potential minimum decreases with increasing temperature in such a way that the net current reaching the anode does not change appreciably with temperature. The anode current under these conditions is said to be *space-charge-limited.* The current reaching the anode is now determined entirely by the *anode potential* and not by the rate of emission from the cathode. Diodes are most often used under space-charge-limited conditions equivalent to Fig. 6.2*d*.

We derive the current-voltage relationship for the space-charge-limited diode by treating the mathematically simpler borderline case of Fig. 6.2*c*. The result is a useful approximation to the rigorous solution. Our derivation utilizes: (1) Poisson's equation, (2) conservation of energy, (3) conservation of current, and (4) the boundary conditions indicated in Fig. 6.2*c*.

Poisson's equation is

$$\frac{d^2V(x)}{dx^2} = \frac{-\rho(x)}{\epsilon_0} \tag{6.3}$$

Conservation of energy may be written

$$eV(x) = \tfrac{1}{2}m[v(x)]^2 \tag{6.4}$$

where $V(x)$ is the potential and $v(x)$ is the velocity. Conservation of current means that the current per unit area or current density J is independent of x. In other words, there is no continuing pile up of electrons anywhere. The current density at a point x may be written in terms of the space charge density $\rho(x)$ and the velocity $v(x)$ (see section 8.3).

$$J = \rho(x)v(x) \tag{6.5}$$

We can eliminate ρ and v by writing

$$\frac{d^2V(x)}{dx^2} = -\frac{\rho(x)}{\epsilon_0} = \frac{-J}{\epsilon_0 v(x)} = \frac{-J}{\epsilon_0\sqrt{2\eta V(x)}} \tag{6.6}$$

If both sides of this equation are multiplied by $2\, dV(x)/dx$ and integrated with respect to x we obtain

$$\left(\frac{dV}{dx}\right)^2 = \frac{-4JV^{1/2}}{\epsilon_0 \sqrt{2\eta}} + C_1 \tag{6.7}$$

From Fig. 6.2*c* the boundary conditions at $x = 0$ are

$$\begin{aligned} V\Big|_{x=0} &= 0 \\ \frac{dV}{dx}\Big|_{x=0} &= 0 \end{aligned} \tag{6.8}$$

Therefore in equation 6.7 C_1 is zero. Taking the square root of equation 6.7 and integrating again, we obtain

$$\tfrac{4}{3}V^{3/4} = 2\sqrt{-J/\epsilon_0}\left(\frac{1}{2\eta}\right)^{1/4} x + C_2 \tag{6.9}$$

From 6.8 C_2 is also equal to zero. Solving equation 6.9 for the current density J yields

$$J = -\tfrac{4}{9}\epsilon_0(2\eta)^{1/2}\,\frac{[V(x)]^{3/2}}{x^2} \tag{6.10}$$

If the experimental values of e, m, and ϵ_0 are substituted in this equation, it is found that

$$J = -2.33 \times 10^{-6}\,\frac{[V(x)]^{3/2}}{x^2}\ \text{amp/meter}^2 \tag{6.11}$$

The minus sign indicates that conventional current is flowing in the $-x$-direction. Here $V(x)$ is the potential in volts at a point x meters away from the cathode. If the applied anode potential is V_a volts, and the distance from the cathode to the anode is d meters, the magnitude of the current density is given by

$$J = 2.33 \times 10^{-6}\,\frac{V_a^{3/2}}{d^2}\ \text{amp/meter}^2 \tag{6.12}$$

Note that equation 6.12 predicts that under space-charge-limited conditions the current density drawn to the anode depends only on the applied potential and not on the cathode rate of emission. The result expressed by the last two equations is known as the Langmuir-Child law or the three-halves power law.

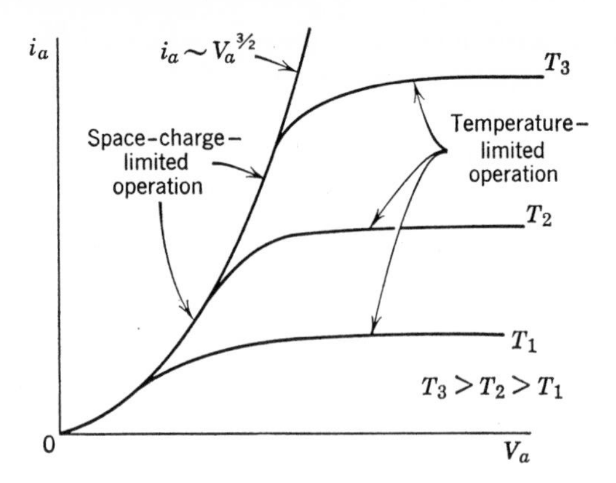

Fig. 6.3. Current-voltage characteristics for a typical diode (cathode temperature T as parameter).

From equations 6.11 and 6.12 it follows that the potential at a distance x from the cathode of a planar diode is given by

$$V(x) = \frac{x^{4/3}}{d^{4/3}} V_a \tag{6.13}$$

This equation describes the curve of potential versus distance shown in Fig. 6.2*c* and closely approximates that of Fig. 6.2*d*. In general, it may be shown that the current drawn by the anode of a diode having arbitrarily shaped electrodes is also proportional to the three-halves power of the applied anode potential when space-charge-limited conditions prevail.

The anode-current versus anode-voltage characteristics of a typical diode are shown in Fig. 6.3 for several cathode temperatures. At any temperature the diode becomes temperature-limited at sufficiently high anode voltages.

6.2 Multielectrode devices

If a grid or mesh of fine wire is placed in front of a thermionically emitting cathode, the current drawn from the cathode under space-charge-limited conditions can be controlled by varying the potential of the grid. When this modification is added to a diode, the tube is called a triode and the additional electrode is called the control grid. A negative d-c or bias voltage is usually applied between the control grid and the cathode. This prevents the control grid from intercepting a significant portion of the current emitted by the cathode. A small a-c voltage may be superimposed on the d-c bias voltage to vary or modulate the anode current, generally with very little a-c power consumption. It should be emphasized that the triode is a space-charge or current-modulating device as distinguished from velocity-modulating devices which are discussed in Chapters 15 and 16.

Additional grids may be inserted between the control grid and anode. These are often held at fixed potentials, but in some instances their control action on the beam may be used to mix (add or multiply) signals from independent sources. A tube with a control grid plus one extra grid is known as a tetrode, and one with a control grid plus two extra grids is called a pentode. In applications where a tube is used to mix signals, as many as four grids may be inserted between the control grid and anode. In this chapter we consider the behavior of grid-controlled tubes when the transit time of electrons from cathode to anode is very small compared with the period of the a-c signal applied to the control grid.

In general, very high frequency tubes are constructed with planar electrodes, whereas cylindrical electrodes are used in tubes that operate at moderate and low frequencies. We confine our discussion to tubes with planar electrodes since their analysis is simplest. The basic principles that apply to tubes with this geometry also apply to those with other geometries.

6.3 Electrostatic field of a triode

Let us consider the electric field in a planar triode when there is no space charge and no current flow. We assume that the spacing of the grid wires is small compared with the cathode-grid distance. This implies that the field near the cathode due to a potential difference between it and the control grid is very nearly uniform over the surface of the cathode. If the grid wire spacing is increased, the field at the cathode becomes different opposite a wire than opposite a gap. A planar triode is indicated schematically in Fig. 6.4.

If space charge is not present, the potential satisfies Laplace's equation (Appendix D), with boundary conditions determined by the applied electrode voltages. We may think of the potential as composed of a linear combination of two independent unit potential functions which we denote as $U_g(x, y, z)$ and $U_a(x, y, z)$. $U_g(x, y, z)$ is the solution of Laplace's equation when the grid is held at $+1$ volt and the cathode and anode are held at zero or ground potential. $U_a(x, y, z)$ is the solution of Laplace's equation when the anode is held at $+1$ volt

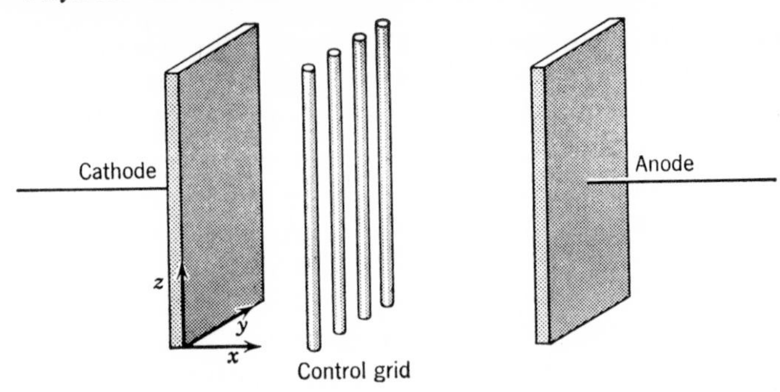

Fig. 6.4. A planar triode.

and the grid and cathode are grounded. Laplace's equation is a linear differential equation and any linear combination of the solutions U_g and U_a must also be a solution. Consider the particular linear combination given by

$$V(x,y,z) = V_g U_g(x,y,z) + V_a U_a(x,y,z) \tag{6.14}$$

This function satisfies the boundary conditions for the case where the

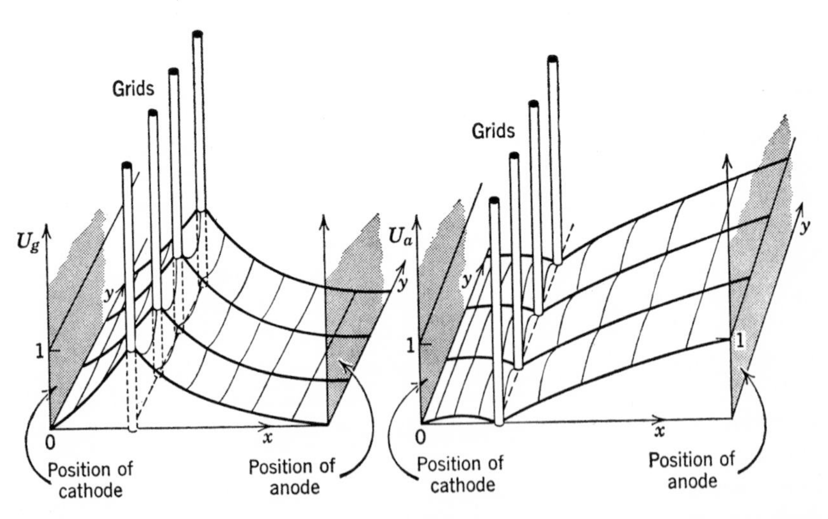

Fig. 6.5. Potential surfaces for the functions U_g and U_a. The cathode, grid, and anode are assumed to be made of the same material so that the effects of different work functions (that is, contact potentials, see section 13.7) need not be considered.

cathode is at ground potential and the grid and anode are at potentials V_g and V_a respectively. Since $V(x, y, z)$ also satisfies Laplace's equation, it must be the potential function that actually exists under these boundary conditions. In Fig. 6.5 we indicate how the functions U_g and U_a depend on position in the space between the cathode and anode. Such graphs are called potential surfaces.

After an electron has been emitted by the cathode, the electric field it sees governs its subsequent motion. An important parameter is the relative effectiveness of the grid and anode in producing electric fields at the cathode. The quantity describing this relative effective-

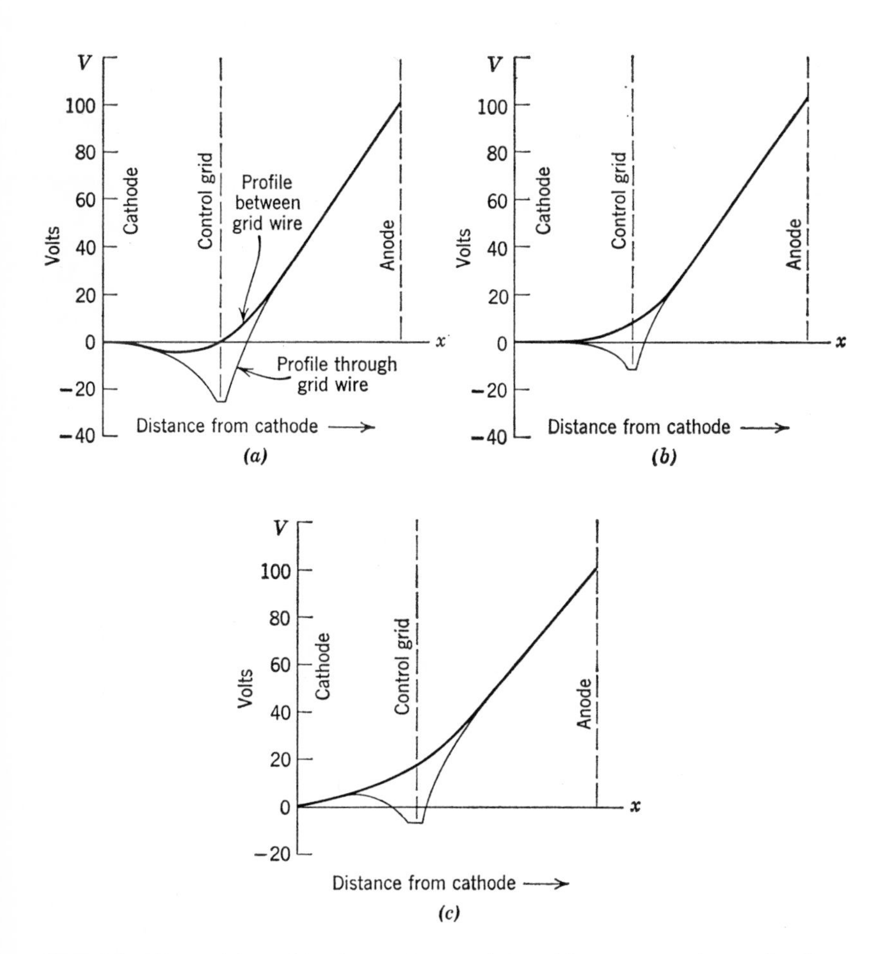

Fig. 6.6. Potential profiles for a planar triode without space charge for three negative values of control grid voltage.

ness is called the *amplification factor* μ and is defined by equation 6.15.

$$\mu \equiv \frac{\left.\dfrac{\partial U_g}{\partial x}\right|_{x=0}}{\left.\dfrac{\partial U_a}{\partial x}\right|_{x=0}} \tag{6.15}$$

The numerator of the right-hand side is seen to be proportional to the force on an electron at the cathode when $V_a = 0$ and $V_g = 1$. Correspondingly, the denominator is proportional to the force on an electron at the cathode when $V_a = 1$ and $V_g = 0$.

In Fig. 6.6 potential profiles are shown for typical linear combinations of the U functions (see equation 6.14). Three negative grid voltages are considered with an anode voltage of 100 volts in each case. In Fig. 6.6*a* the applied grid voltage is such that the potential gradient at the cathode is negative. Under this condition electrons cannot reach the anode and the triode is said to be "cutoff." In Fig. 6.6*b* the potential gradient at the cathode is zero, whereas in Fig. 6.6*c* it is positive, and many electrons can reach the anode.

High amplification factors are obtained when (1) the cathode-to-anode distance is much greater than the cathode-grid distance, and (2) the grid wires are closely spaced.

6.4 Triodes with space charge

Triodes are almost always operated under space-charge-limited conditions since only then is it possible for the grid to control the cathode current. If the cathode emission were temperature-limited, the total emission current would be drawn by the anode and would be independent of anode and grid voltages.

It is found experimentally under space-charge-limited conditions that the total current density drawn from the cathode may be expressed in the form

$$J = k\left(V_g + \frac{V_a}{\mu}\right)^{3/2} \tag{6.16}$$

for a wide range of applied grid and anode voltages. Here k is a constant and μ is the amplification factor. (Vacuum tubes are essentially nonlinear devices. In actuality, the current density may be expanded in powers of V_g and V_a, and 6.16 is the first term in such an expansion.) Since triodes are usually operated with the grid more negative than the cathode, nearly all the current given by equation

6.16 is drawn to the anode. Only the very fast electrons that are emitted with sufficient energy to overcome the grid-cathode potential difference are able to reach the grid. If the grid becomes more positive than the cathode, however, it can draw an appreciable part of the total cathode current. Note that when V_g is more negative than or equal to $-V_a/\mu$, the current is zero or "cut-off." One may experimentally determine μ from the relation

$$\mu = \left| \frac{V_a}{V_g} \right| \qquad \text{(for } J \text{ just equal to zero)} \tag{6.17}$$

By analogy with the diode equation 6.12, equation 6.16 can be written as

$$J = \frac{2.33 \times 10^{-6}}{d_{\text{eff}}^2} (V_{\text{eff}})^{3/2} \tag{6.18}$$

where

$$V_{\text{eff}} = V_g + \frac{V_a}{\mu} \tag{6.19}$$

and d_{eff}, defined by equation 6.18, is called the equivalent diode spacing for the triode. It may be shown that d_{eff} can be expressed in terms of the cathode-grid separation d_g, the cathode-anode separation d_a, and μ.

$$d_{\text{eff}} \approx d_g \left[1 + \frac{1}{\mu} \left(\frac{d_a}{d_g} \right)^{4/3} \right]^{3/4} \tag{6.20}$$

Equation 6.18 merely states that the current density drawn from the cathode of a planar triode is the same as would be drawn by a diode having a cathode-to-anode distance d_{eff}, the equivalent diode spacing of the triode.

Plots of anode current as a function of V_g with V_a as parameter and V_a with V_g as parameter are shown in Figs. 6.7 and 6.8 for a representative triode. The curves for different anode voltages in Fig. 6.7 are similar in shape but displaced from each other horizontally by an amount corresponding to a change in grid voltage equal to $1/\mu$ times the change in anode voltage. The curves in Fig. 6.8 for different values of V_g are similar in shape but displaced horizontally by an amount corresponding to a change in anode voltage equal to μ times the change in grid voltage.

In addition to the amplification factor, two other parameters will be of interest to us. These are the *dynamic plate resistance* r_p defined by

$$r_p \equiv \left. \frac{\partial V_a}{\partial i_a} \right|_{V_g \text{ constant}} \tag{6.21}$$

where i_a is the anode current; and the *mutual conductance or trans-*

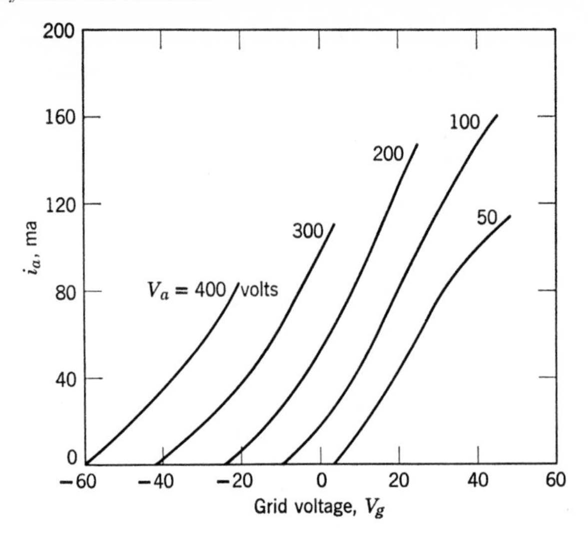

Fig. 6.7. Anode-current versus control grid-voltage characteristics for a triode.

conductance g_m defined by

$$g_m \equiv \left.\frac{\partial i_a}{\partial V_g}\right|_{V_a \text{ constant}} \tag{6.22}$$

Expressed in a similar manner, the amplification factor μ for space-charge-limited operation becomes

$$\mu = -\left.\frac{\partial V_a}{\partial V_g}\right|_{i_a \text{ constant}} \tag{6.23}$$

This last expression follows directly from equation 6.16.

A better understanding of the concept of amplification factor may be derived from a demonstration of the equivalence of 6.15 and 6.23. The potential in a triode without space charge is given by equation 6.14.

$$V = V_g U_g + V_a U_a \tag{6.14}$$

If space charge is present, we must include an additional potential V_s. The potential V_s is due to the electrons only, and not to the electrode voltages. The total potential V_p is then

$$\underset{\text{Poisson's equation}}{\underset{\text{Solution of}}{V_p}} = \underset{\text{Laplace's equation}}{\underset{\text{Solution of}}{V_a U_a + V_g U_g}} + \underset{\text{term}}{\underset{\text{Space-charge}}{V_s}} \tag{6.24}$$

The force F on the electron in a planar triode is obtained from the gradient of the total potential V_p.

$$F = e\frac{\partial V_p}{\partial x} = eV_g\frac{\partial U_g}{\partial x} + eV_a\frac{\partial U_a}{\partial x} + e\frac{\partial V_s}{\partial x} \tag{6.25}$$

The total differential of equation 6.25 is

$$dF = e\,dV_g\frac{\partial U_g}{\partial x} + e\,dV_a\frac{\partial U_a}{\partial x} + d\left(e\frac{\partial V_s}{\partial x}\right) \tag{6.26}$$

The current drawn from the cathode depends on the force on an electron at the cathode. Under space-charge-limited conditions the space-charge density and therefore V_s and $\partial V_s/\partial x$ are functions of the current. If equation 6.26 is applied to the case where the current drawn from the cathode is constant, then F and $\partial V_s/\partial x$ at the cathode must be constant, that is,

$$\begin{aligned} d(F\,|_{x=0}) &= 0 \\ d\left(e\frac{\partial V_s}{\partial x}\bigg|_{x=0}\right) &= 0 \end{aligned} \tag{6.27}$$

Hence, using 6.27, 6.26 may be rearranged to give

$$dV_g\frac{\partial U_g}{\partial x}\bigg|_{x=0} = -dV_a\frac{\partial U_a}{\partial x}\bigg|_{x=0} \tag{6.28}$$

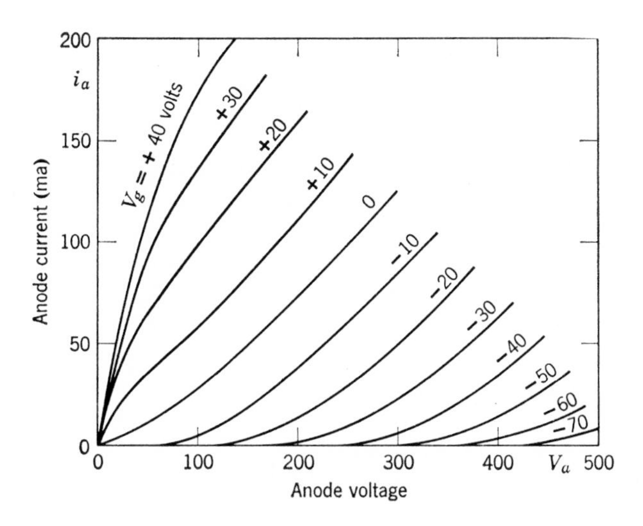

Fig. 6.8. Anode-current versus anode-voltage characteristics for a triode.

and, from 6.15,

$$\mu \equiv \frac{\left.\dfrac{\partial U_g}{\partial x}\right|_{x=0}}{\left.\dfrac{\partial U_a}{\partial x}\right|_{x=0}} = -\left.\frac{dV_a}{dV_g}\right|_{i_a \text{ constant}} = -\left(\frac{\partial V_a}{\partial V_g}\right)_{i_a \text{ constant}} \tag{6.29}$$

Thus the definition of μ in terms of relative forces given by equation 6.15 is equivalent to the electrode potential relation, equation 6.23. Equation 6.15 provides a physical interpretation for μ. Equation 6.23 used in conjunction with experimental characteristic curves such as Fig. 6.8 is convenient for the calculation of μ.

There is a simple relation between μ, g_m, and r_p. To find this relation we treat the anode current as a function of V_a and V_g.

$$i_a = i_a(V_a, V_g) \tag{6.30}$$

Taking the total differential of i_a, we have

$$di_a = \frac{\partial i_a}{\partial V_g} dV_g + \frac{\partial i_a}{\partial V_a} dV_a \tag{6.31}$$

and using 6.21 and 6.22

$$di_a = g_m \, dV_g + \frac{1}{r_p} dV_a \tag{6.32}$$

If di_a is zero, or i_a is a constant,

$$g_m r_p = \left.\frac{-dV_a}{dV_g}\right|_{i_a = \text{constant}} = \mu$$

$$\mu = g_m r_p \tag{6.33}$$

An expression for g_m in terms of current density may be found from the defining equation by multiplying equation 6.18 by the cathode area A and differentiating with respect to V_g. Thus in MKS units

$$g_m = \frac{3}{2} \frac{(2.33 \times 10^{-6})}{d_{\text{eff}}^2} \left(V_g + \frac{V_a}{\mu}\right)^{1/2} A \tag{6.34}$$

$$g_m = \frac{3}{2} \frac{(2.33 \times 10^{-6})^{2/3} J^{1/3}}{d_{\text{eff}}^{4/3}} A \tag{6.35}$$

$$g_m = \frac{2.64 \times 10^{-4}}{d_{\text{eff}}^{4/3}} J^{1/3} A \tag{6.36}$$

The amplification factor μ depends principally on the electrode geometry but not on the cathode area or anode current. On the other hand, the transconductance g_m is directly proportional to the cathode area and to the one-third power of the current density. Equations 6.36 and 6.20 show that high transconductance is obtained when the cathode-grid spacing is small. Since $r_p = \mu/g_m$, the dynamic plate resistance is inversely proportional to the cathode area and inversely proportional to the one-third power of the current density.

Measured values of μ for presently available triodes generally lie between 2.5 and 100. Values of g_m lie between 200 and 50,000 μa/volt (micromhos). Values of r_p generally fall between 1000 and 50,000 ohms, with typical values around 5000. The parameters μ, g_m, and r_p are important in describing the behavior of triodes in circuits.

The equations developed in this section should bring about a realization that a triode under normal operating conditions has a general current-voltage relation which is similar to the three-halves power law for diodes. This is a consequence of space-charge-limited operation.

6.5 Amplification by triodes

We now consider briefly the way triodes can amplify an a-c voltage. Figure 6.9 is a schematic diagram showing a triode in a simplified amplifier circuit. The major elements of this circuit are the triode, a generator providing an input a-c signal voltage e_g, a grid bias battery E_{cc}, an anode or plate supply battery E_{bb}, and a load resistor R_L.

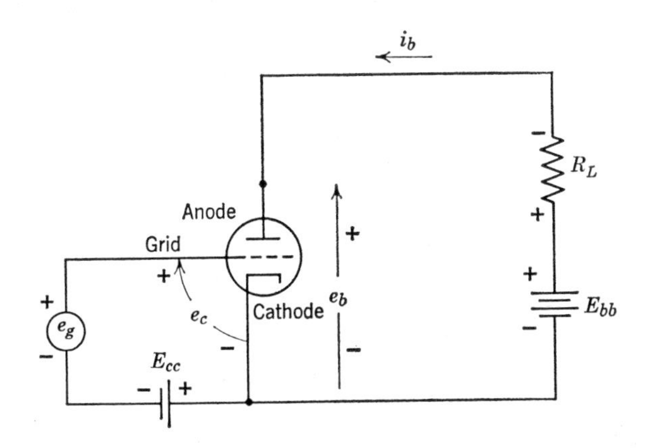

Fig. 6.9. The basic circuit of a triode used as an amplifier. (The voltage e_c is the potential of the grid relative to the cathode. In normal operation e_c is a negative number.)

Here we have introduced the symbols e and E for potential difference in order to conform with conventions adopted for circuit applications of vacuum tubes. Lower case letters are used to designate the instantaneous values of time-varying quantities defined in Fig. 6.9. Also the subscript b is introduced to represent anode current and voltage.

Because of the presence of the load resistor R_L, the potential e_b between the plate and the cathode depends upon both the magnitude of the battery supply voltage E_{bb} and the magnitude of the anode current i_b. Application of Kirchhoff's law to the anode circuit of Fig. 6.9 gives

$$E_{bb} = e_b + i_b R_L \tag{6.37}$$

or

$$i_b = -\frac{e_b}{R_L} + \frac{E_{bb}}{R_L} \tag{6.38}$$

This is the equation of a straight line on an i_b versus e_b graph with a slope of $-1/R_L$ and an i_b intercept of E_{bb}/R_L. Such a line is called a load line.

The load line represents one relation between two variables i_b and e_b and by itself is insufficient to determine i_b and e_b. The plate characteristics (Fig. 6.8) provide the additional needed relation. We therefore have two relations between i_b and e_b. One is

$$i_b = i_b(e_b, e_c) \tag{6.39}$$

the plate characteristics of Fig. 6.8. The other is the load line, equation 6.38. Once e_c, the total grid-cathode voltage, is specified, a simultaneous solution of these two relations yields the values of i_b and e_b.

It is most convenient to perform the solution graphically. The intersection of the load line with the characteristic curve for a specific e_c gives the values of i_b and e_b for that value of e_c. This is shown in Fig. 6.10. If the grid input signal voltage e_g is zero, e_c equals the bias voltage E_{cc}, and the current i_b and potential e_b are called the operating or quiescent current I_b and voltage E_b. As e_c changes, different characteristic curves must be used and the solution slips along the load line as indicated in Fig. 6.10 by the intersection of the load line with the dotted curves, e_{c1} and e_{c3}. Suppose the input signal voltage e_g is varied so as to cause e_c to vary between e_{c1} and e_{c3}. The input voltage change Δe_c and the resulting change in plate voltage Δe_b are indicated in Fig. 6.10. The voltage amplification or gain K is defined by

$$K \equiv \frac{\Delta e_b}{\Delta e_c} \tag{6.40}$$

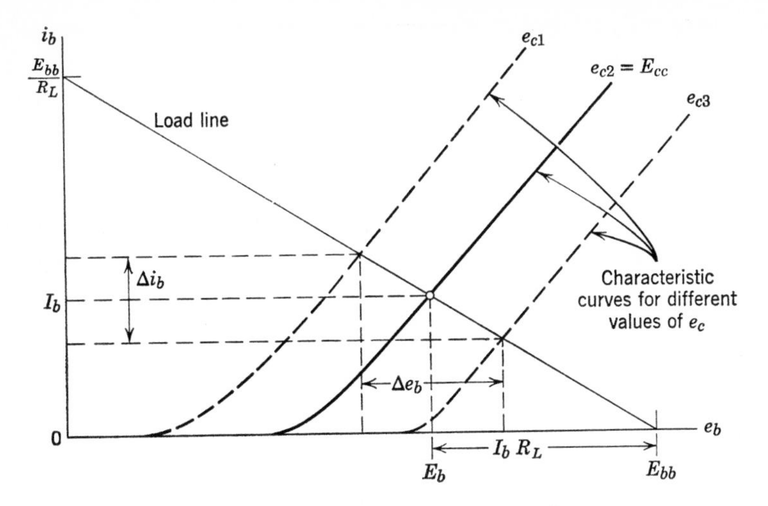

Fig. 6.10. Load line intersection with representative characteristic curves.

Note from 6.38 that the gain is also given by

$$K = -\frac{\Delta i_b}{\Delta e_c} R_L \tag{6.41}$$

If the triode were only capable of amplifying voltages, it would have no significant advantage over a transformer. The real usefulness of the triode and other multielectrode devices lies in their ability to amplify a-c power, that is, to control a large a-c power output with a small expenditure of a-c input power. The input power of a triode is small because its grid current is usually negligibly small. The power gain of a triode results from the conversion of the energy stored in the plate supply battery via the kinetic energy of electrons to a-c output energy in the load circuit of the amplifier. The details of this energy conversion are discussed in Chapter 7.

Example. Determine the voltage amplication K of the amplifier circuit of Fig. 6.9 with a 6J5 triode, $E_{cc} = -8$ volts, $E_{bb} = 360$ volts, and $R_L = 20{,}000$ ohms.

The load line is drawn on the 6J5 triode characteristics of Fig. 6.11 by finding the intercepts $E_{bb} = 360$ volts, and $E_{bb}/R_L = 360/20{,}000 = 18$ ma. We can also draw the load line from the intercept $i_b = 0$, $e_b = E_{bb} = 360$ volts, and the slope of the load line which is $-1/R_L$. The intersection of this load line with the curve of $E_{cc} = -8$ volts yields a quiescent current of 6.4 ma and a plate voltage of 232 volts. If, for example, e_g is ± 6 volts, e_c changes from the quiescent value of -8 volts to -2 volts and to -14 volts. When $e_c = -2$ volts, i_b is 10.9 ma and $e_b = 142$ volts. When $e_c = -14$ volts, $i_b = 2.6$ ma

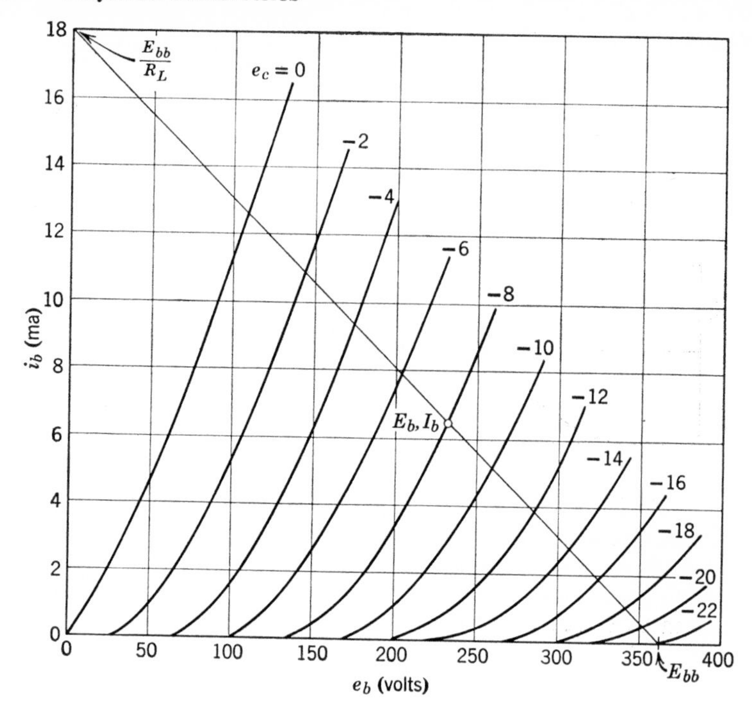

Fig. 6.11. Plate characteristics of a 6J5 triode.

and $e_b = 308$ volts. A change of grid voltage of 12 volts has produced an output voltage change across the load resistor of 166 volts. The varying component of the output voltage is $^{166}/_{12} = 13.8$ times as great as the input signal, representing a voltage amplification of 13.8. Another way of finding the output voltage change across the 20,000 ohm load is to multiply the current change $(10.9 - 2.6 = 8.3$ ma) times 20,000 which also gives 166 volts.

The magnitude of the voltage gain of the triode amplifier in terms of the tube parameters μ, g_m, r_p can be found graphically by considering Fig. 6.12. In this figure two characteristic curves for grid voltages differing by $\Delta e_c = 1$ volt and intersected by the load line are shown. The horizontal distance between the two characteristic curves is μ (equation 6.23), since μ is the change in e_b for a 1-volt grid change when i_b is constant. The magnitude of the voltage gain $|K|$ is the change in e_b for a 1-volt grid change *in the amplifier circuit.* Graphically $|K|$ is the horizontal distance between the two points of intersection of the characteristics with the load line. From the definition of r_p (equation 6.21) the slope of the characteristic curve is $1/r_p$.

Examination of Fig. 6.12 shows that

$$\frac{h}{\mu - |K|} = \frac{1}{r_p} \tag{6.42}$$

and

$$\frac{h}{|K|} = \frac{1}{R_L} \tag{6.43}$$

Eliminating h and solving for $|K|$, we have

$$|K| = \frac{\mu}{1 + r_p/R_L} \tag{6.44}$$

or since $\mu = g_m r_p$,

$$|K| = \frac{g_m}{\dfrac{1}{r_p} + \dfrac{1}{R_L}} \tag{6.45}$$

Here we have only calculated the magnitude of the gain. Since an increase in e_c causes a reduction in e_b, the gain K is a negative number. Hence,

$$K = \frac{-\mu}{1 + \dfrac{r_p}{R_L}} = \frac{-g_m}{\dfrac{1}{r_p} + \dfrac{1}{R_L}} \tag{6.46}$$

The above discussion indicates how the tube parameters enter into a description of the triode operation in a circuit.

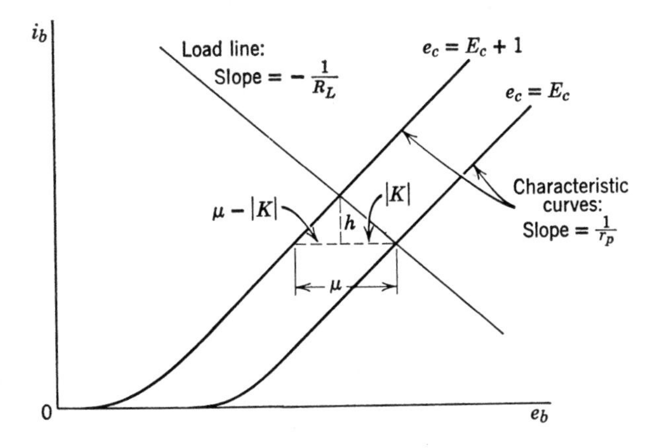

Fig. 6.12. Graphical construction for determining the gain of a triode amplifier.

6.6 Tetrodes

The high frequency performance of a triode is in part limited by the capacitance between the grid and the anode. One manifestation of this capacitance is that some of the a-c energy in the anode circuit is fed back into the grid circuit and may lead to unwanted oscillations. In addition the effective input capacitance (that is, the ratio of the change in charge on the grid to the change in the grid potential) is increased by this feedback effect. If, when charge is added to the grid, the potential of the anode or plate were to remain constant, then the input capacitance would be the sum of the grid-cathode capacitance C_{gk} and the grid-plate capacitance C_{gp}. However, in an amplifier circuit the anode voltage V_a decreases by $|K|$ times the change in grid voltage. This reduction in plate voltage tends by induction to decrease the grid voltage and an additional charge ($C_{gp}\,\Delta V_a = |K|C_{gp}\,\Delta V_g$) must be put onto the grid to counteract this effect. Thus, under actual operating conditions, when the plate voltage changes with grid voltage, the input capacitance is increased by the term $|K|C_{gp}$ and becomes

$$C_{\text{in}} = C_{gk} + C_{gp} + |K|C_{gp} = C_{gk} + (1 - K)C_{gp} \tag{6.47}$$

Since $|K|$ may be fairly large, a small capacitance between the grid and anode may cause appreciable shunting of the input signal. This is known as the Miller effect.

The gain-dependent term in the input capacitance can be avoided by inserting a coarse mesh, shielding electrode known as a screen grid between the control grid and the anode. Since the screen grid shields the control grid from the anode, C_{gp} is negligible. Furthermore, since the screen grid in an operational circuit is held at constant potential, there are no gain-dependent capacitance terms, and the input capacitance becomes

$$C_{\text{in}} = C_{gk} + C_{gs} \tag{6.48}$$

where C_{gs} is the control grid-screen grid capacitance. A tube which contains a cathode, control grid, screen grid, and anode is called a tetrode.

A set of anode-current versus anode-voltage characteristics for a typical tetrode is shown in Fig. 6.13. The curves are shown for two values of control grid voltage e_{c1}, e_{c2}, with the screen grid held at a fixed positive potential E_s. When the anode voltage e_b becomes sufficiently high (say, greater than e_1 in Fig. 6.13), secondary emission

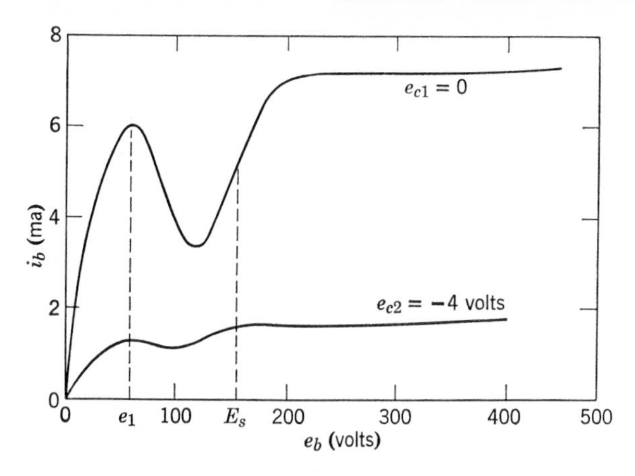

Fig. 6.13. Plate characteristics for a tetrode.

from the anode occurs. When e_b is also less than the screen voltage ($e_1 < e_b < E_s$), the secondary electrons are attracted to the screen and the net anode current may decrease with an increase in anode voltage as shown by the dips in Fig. 6.13. For very high anode voltages ($e_b > E_s$), the secondaries are returned to the anode and cause no reduction in the anode current. Furthermore, for $e_b > E_s$ the anode-current is relatively independent of anode voltage e_b. The total current drawn from the cathode under these conditions is determined almost entirely by the screen grid and control grid voltages. Because of the secondary emission dip in the plate characteristics, tetrodes are useful as amplifiers only over a limited range of anode voltages.

The screen grid has the effect of making the amplification factor of a tetrode much higher than that of a triode because it electrostatically shields the anode from the cathode, thus reducing the anode's effectiveness in controlling current. The transconductances of commercial tetrodes and triodes lie in about the same range, since this parameter is determined largely by the geometry of the control grid-cathode system. However, there is some reduction in the transconductance of tetrodes over that of triodes because of screen grid interception. Because of the tetrode's high μ, and because $\mu = g_m r_p$, the dynamic plate resistance r_p of a tetrode is very high. This is demonstrated by the fact that the anode current curves in Fig. 6.13 are relatively independent of anode voltage for anode voltages appreciable greater than the screen grid voltage, E_s. For anode voltages lower than screen grid voltages, the slope of the curves varies widely and actually indicates a negative plate resistance for some anode voltages. A negative resistance is one where the current decreases as the applied voltage increases. This property can be useful, although the negative resistance regions of ordinary tetrodes are often too narrow and unstable for practical use.

6.7 Pentodes

The pentode is possibly the most widely used of all electron tubes for amplification. Its advantages include (1) high gain per stage, (2) extremely small control grid to anode capacitance, and (3) anode-current versus anode-voltage characteristics that do not show the secondary-emission dips of the tetrode characteristics.

By inserting a third grid known as a suppressor grid between the screen grid and anode and keeping this suppressor grid at cathode potential, the exchange of secondary electrons between the screen grid and anode is practically eliminated. The electrode arrangement and potential profiles for a planar pentode are shown in Fig. 6.14. It can be seen that most of the secondary electrons emitted from the screen grid will be returned to that electrode since the potential

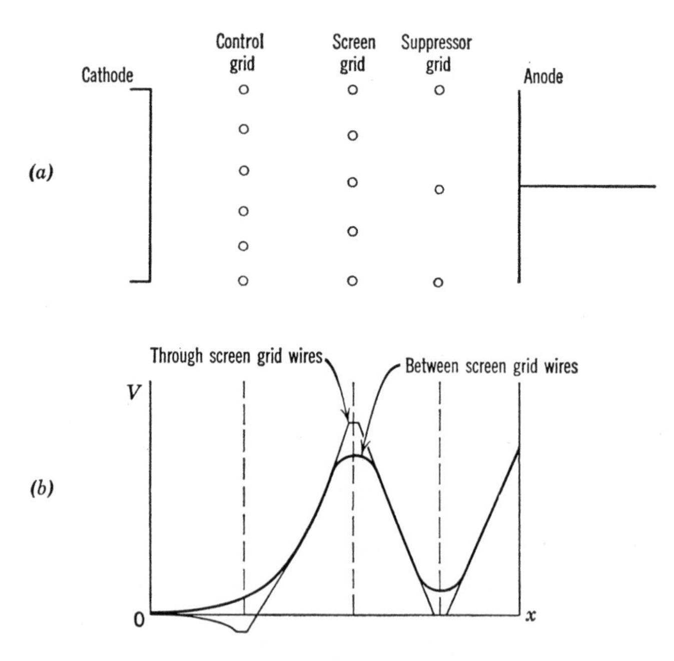

Fig. 6.14. Electrode arrangement (*a*) and potential profiles (*b*) for a pentode.

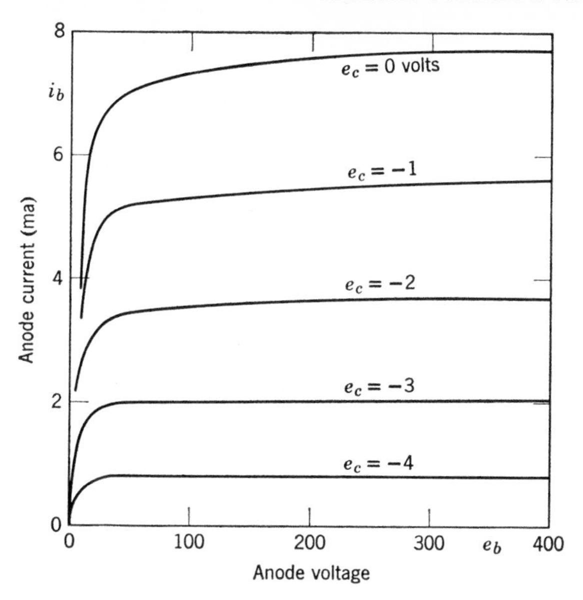

Fig. 6.15. Anode-current versus anode-voltage curves for a pentode.

decreases on both sides of it. Secondary electrons emitted from the anode will be returned to the anode for the same reason. Since there is no exchange of secondary electrons between the screen and anode over a wide range of anode voltages, the dips seen in the tetrode characteristics (Fig. 6.13) are not present in the pentode characteristics (Fig. 6.15).

The screen grid current in pentodes is normally about one-quarter of the anode current. Since the suppressor grid is at cathode potential, it does not intercept a significant part of the beam current. Its wires are spaced relatively far apart so that the potential at points between its wires is always appreciably greater than zero. Thus the electrons that pass through the screen grid are mainly deflected through openings between suppressor grid wires and travel on to strike the anode. The suppressor grid adds to the effectiveness of the screen grid in shielding the anode from the control grid and cathode, so that pentode amplification factors tend to be very high.

Anode-current versus control grid voltage curves (the transfer characteristics) for a typical pentode are shown in Fig. 6.16 for different screen grid voltages. These curves are analogous to those shown for a triode in Fig. 6.7. The pentode curves are relatively

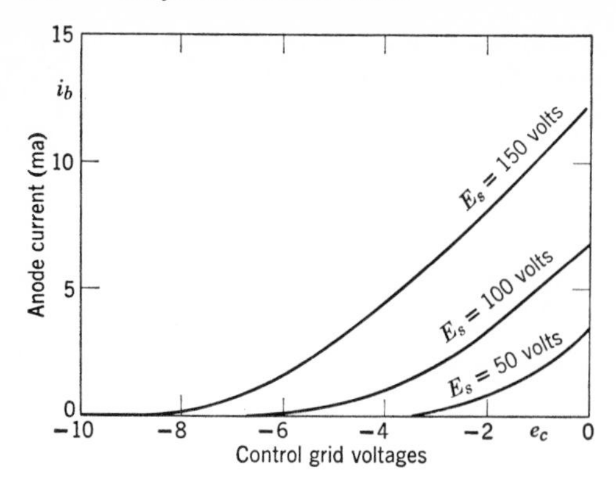

Fig. 6.16. Anode-current versus grid-voltage curves for a pentode.

independent of changes in anode voltage; the field at the cathode is determined principally by the control and screen grid voltages.

The transconductance g_m of a pentode is determined largely by the geometry of the control grid-cathode system, as with the triode and tetrode. Because of screen grid interception, g_m is reduced by the ratio of the anode current to the total cathode current. The amplification factor and dynamic plate resistance tend to be so high that they lose significance in circuit analysis and consequently are not as important as the transconductance. For example, when r_p is large, the equation for the voltage gain of a simple vacuum tube amplifier (6.46) becomes

$$K = -g_m R_L \tag{6.49}$$

Some pentodes are made with a nonuniform spacing between control grid wires. This construction has the effect of making the amplification factor higher in regions where the grid wires are close together and lower where they are further apart. If the grid is made increasingly negative with respect to the cathode, the anode current from different regions of the cathode emitting surface is cut off at different negative grid voltages. Regions of higher amplification factor (small grid-wire separation) are active when higher current is drawn from the cathode. The amplification factor measured for the tube as a whole increases with anode current. The greater effectiveness of the control grid in controlling the anode current at high anode currents results in a transconductance for those tubes that increases more rapidly than the one-third power of the current drawn from the cathode. By varying the negative d-c bias voltage applied to the grid, the transconductance can be varied, and the gain of the amplifier stage in which the tube is used can be controlled. These tubes are called "variable μ" or "remote cut-off" tubes and are used extensively in amplifiers where automatic gain control is needed. The technique of varying the grid wire spacing may be applied to triodes and tetrodes as well as to pentodes.

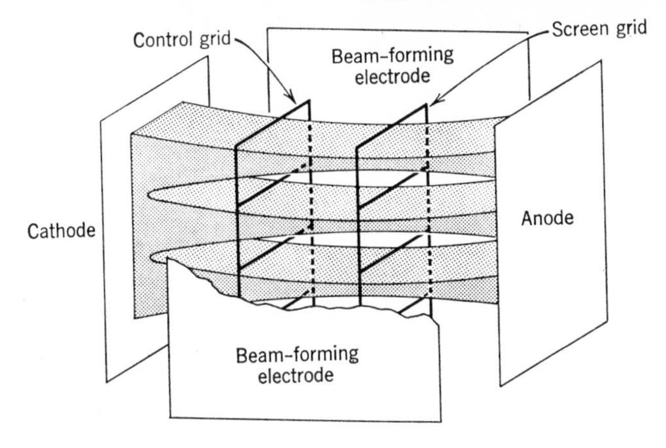

Fig. 6.17. Schematic representation of a beam power tube.

6.8 Beam power tubes

A tetrode can be constructed to have characteristics similar to those of a pentode if electrodes of special design are utilized. If the anode is placed at a relatively large distance from the screen grid, the depression in potential due to the beam space charge will eliminate the need for a suppressor grid. A tetrode of this type is called a beam power tube. The construction of such a tube is shown in Fig. 6.17.

A high space charge density between the screen and anode is achieved by the combination of beam-forming electrodes and alignment of the control grid and screen grid wires to focus the electrons into narrow streams. This confinement of the beam and the resultant high space charge density produces a significant potential depression between the screen and anode. This depression functions as a suppressor grid.

Beam power tubes have characteristic curves similar to those of pentodes. Undesirable secondary emission effects are eliminated, except at very low anode voltages. These tubes are very useful as power amplifiers.

6.9 Phototubes and photomultiplier tubes

Vacuum tubes which employ photoemission rather than thermionic emission are known as phototubes. Simple phototubes generally have a large cathode area and a wire anode as shown in Fig. 6.18. The surface of the cathode is coated with a low work function material such as cesium oxide ($W \approx 1$ ev). Light shining on the cathode produces an anode current that is proportional to the incident light flux. Typical characteristic curves are illustrated in Fig. 6.19. The phototube current is independent of the anode voltage over a wide range for a constant light flux on the surface.

In phototubes much larger anode currents can be obtained by secondary emission multiplication. Electrons from a photocathode are directed at a succession of secondary emitting electrodes called dynodes (Fig. 6.20).

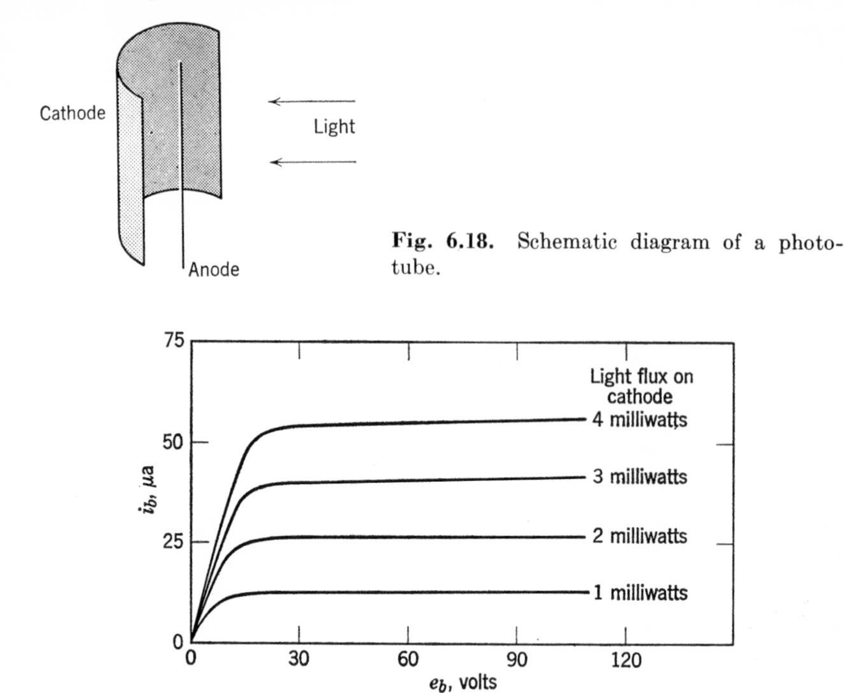

Fig. 6.18. Schematic diagram of a phototube.

Fig. 6.19. Current-voltage characteristics for a typical vacuum phototube.

The current multiplication at each dynode is the secondary emission ratio s, so for n dynodes the over-all current multiplication is s^n. For example, if $s = 3.5$ and there are ten dynodes, the current multiplication is about 280,000. A tube with such an arrangement of photocathode, dynodes, and anode is called a photomultiplier. Photomultipliers are useful for meas-

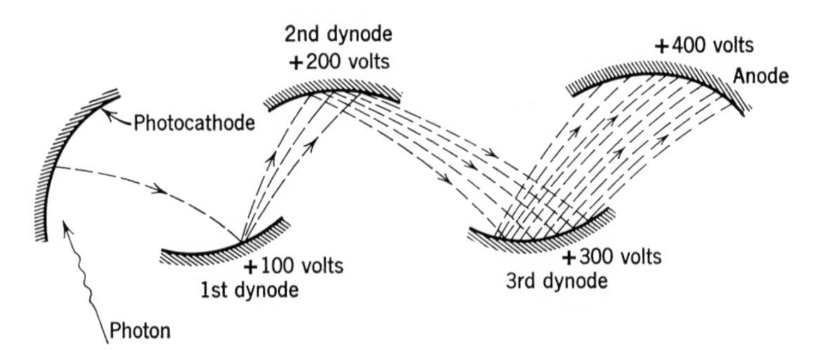

Fig. 6.20. A three-stage photomultiplier tube.

uring light of low intensity such as that from stars or from scintillations in crystals caused by nuclear radiations.

6.10 Image orthicons

Image orthicons are complex vacuum tubes in which electronic techniques are employed to amplify optical images. Figure 6.21 shows the basic components contained within the vacuum envelope of an image orthicon. An optical image is focused on the photocathode. Electrons released from this photocathode are accelerated through a potential difference of 400 to 700 volts and focused on the target, a thin film having high resistivity. Secondary electrons emitted by the target are collected by the target mesh to create an intensified, positively charged electrostatic image in the target. Modern high-sensitivity image orthicons may use secondary emission ratios as high as 10 to 14 at the target. After the image is formed on the target, a low-energy electron beam scans the backside of the target, losing electrons to the positively charged portions of the image. The nonabsorbed electrons are reflected back to a secondary emission multiplier for additional amplification. It should be noted that the current out of the secondary emission multiplier is proportional to the "darkness" of the image, that is, the brighter the image element the smaller the amplified reflected beam. The dissected image may then be amplified further by low-noise amplifier techniques and electronically reassembled elsewhere by standard television circuitry.

Modern high-sensitivity image orthicons can resolve two lines less than 0.1 mm apart and are 100 to 1000 times more sensitive than the fastest photographic emulsions. Photocathodes are available for the infrared and ultraviolet as well as the visible spectrum. The high sensitivity of modern image orthicons coupled with the capability of electronic image processing assure an increasingly important role for image orthicons in the technology of the future, particularly in astronomy, medicine, and nuclear physics.

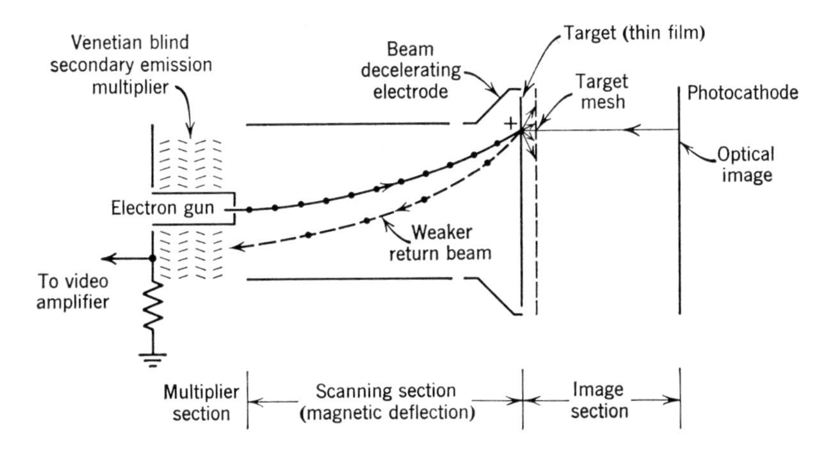

Fig. 6.21. Image orthicon components.

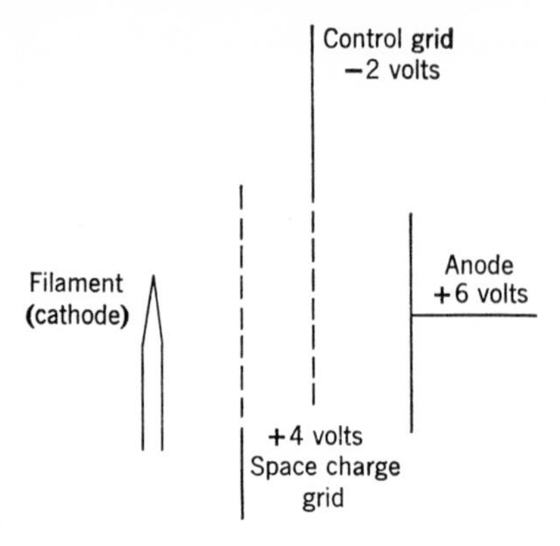

Fig. 6.22. Electrode arrangement in an electrometer tube.

6.11 Electrometer tube

An electrometer tube is a vacuum tube which can be used in specialized amplifier circuits to measure extremely small currents. This is accomplished by passing the feeble current to be measured through an external grid-cathode resistance of the order of 10^{11} ohms to achieve a significant grid-voltage change. The unique feature of an electrometer tube is that the internal grid current is

Table 6.1. Causes and cures of grid current

Source of grid current	Countermeasure
(1) Finite surface resistance of insulation between electrodes	(1) Separate grid and cathode leads
(2) Positive ions evaporated from filament attracted to negative control grid	(2) Insert positive space charge grid between cathode and control grid
(3) Positive ions formed in residual gas in tube	(3) Keep all voltages below 8 volts
(4) Atmospheric ions outside tube attracted to grid connection	(4) Evacuate container for tube and circuit elements
(5) Photoelectric emission from the grid due to:	(5)
(*a*) Light from hot filament	(*a*) Use low work function filament coating
(*b*) Soft x-rays from plate	(*b*) Keep plate voltage below 6 volts
(*c*) Room light	(*c*) Place tube in black box or turn off lights
(6) Thermionic emission from grid	(6) Use high work function material for grid and cool it

made extremely small to achieve a sufficiently large effective internal grid-cathode resistance so that the external resistance is not shunted. To understand how the grid current is minimized we list in Table 6.1 the various sources of grid current together with the appropriate countermeasures.

The arrangement of electrodes in an electrometer tube is shown in Fig. 6.22. Electrometer tubes are used to measure currents from ionization chambers and photocells as small as 10^{-16} amp. It should be noted that the reduction of internal grid currents to extremely low values means that electrometer tube amplifiers have extremely large current and power gains.

Suggested References

W. W. Harman, *Fundamentals of Electron Motion*, McGraw-Hill Book Company, 1953. In Chapter 5, the Langmuir-Child space charge treatment is extended to multigrid devices. This text covers much of the "vacuum" electronics presented in our textbook at a somewhat more detailed level, and presents a basic physical approach to the phenomena.

K. R. Spangenburg, *Vacuum Tubes*, McGraw-Hill Book Company, 1948. Chapters 7 through 11 present a more detailed treatment on our level of the basic concepts presented here. Chapter 19 discusses the photoelectric tube and Chapter 20 discusses some of the special tubes mentioned in this textbook.

S. Seely, *Electron-Tube Circuits*, McGraw-Hill Book Company, 1958. This text begins the study of vacuum-tube circuits where our text leaves off. Load lines and simple amplification concepts are discussed in the early chapters.

W. G. Dow, *Fundamentals of Engineering Electronics*, Second Edition, John Wiley and Sons, 1952. A detailed analysis of all aspects of grid controlled tubes is presented in Chapters 1, 2, 5, 6 and 7.

PROBLEMS

6.1. Show that in a space-charge-limited diode with plane parallel electrodes the electric field at the plate is four-thirds of its value when no current is flowing.

6.2. For a space-charge-limited diode find the variation with distance from the cathode of (*a*) the velocity of an electron, (*b*) the potential V, (*c*) the current density J, (*d*) the space charge density ρ, and (*e*) the electric field $\mathcal{E}$.

6.3. A parallel-plane diode is operated at a plate voltage of 10 volts. Calculate the velocity of an electron halfway between cathode and plate when (*a*) the current is space-charge-limited, and (*b*) temperature-limited (ignore initial velocities). (*c*) At what distance from the cathode is the potential 5 volts in each case if the anode-cathode spacing is 1 cm?

6.4. A parallel-plane diode has a plate-cathode separation of 1 cm and a cathode area of 16 cm². Assuming space-charge limitation and a plate voltage of 100 volts, find (*a*) the current density, (*b*) the total current, (*c*) the number of electrons in the plate-cathode space, and (*d*) the average density of electrons.

6.5. Consider a space-charge-limited planar diode. Assume that the electrons are emitted with zero initial velocity, and neglect fringe effects at electrode edges. (*a*) What is the ratio of the total charge in transit between the electrodes to (*i*) the total charge on the plate (*hint:* use Gauss' law), (*ii*) to what it would be if the same current could be drawn without any space-charge limitations. (*b*) How does the power dissipated in the anode of a space-charge-limited diode vary with changes in anode voltage?

6.6. Show that the cathode-plate electron transit times for space-charge-limited and space-charge-free planar diodes with the same plate voltage are in the ratio 3:2.

6.7. Calculate the space-charge density at the anode and at the cathode of a planar diode with plates 5 mm apart at a potential difference of 300 volts. Assume that space-charge-limited conditions exist. What is the significance of the calculated space-charge density at the cathode? (*Hint:* Consider the electron velocity and current density at the cathode.)

6.8. From a consideration of equation 6.13, Poisson's equation, and the conservation of energy, show that although the space charge density at the cathode of a space-charge-limited diode is infinite, the current density is finite. (See Problem 6.7.)

6.9. Show by direct substitution that the linear combination $V(x, y, z) = V_gU_g + V_aU_a$ is a solution of Laplace's equation for the boundary conditions $V_k = 0$, $V_g = V_g$, $V_a = V_a$.

6.10. Verify that for the special case of Fig. 6.6*b*

$$\mu = \left|\frac{V_a}{V_g}\right|.$$

6.11. Calculate the plate voltage V_{eff} of the equivalent diode for a planar triode whose grid-cathode spacing is 0.03 cm and current density is 0.02 amp/cm^2, assuming that the "equivalent plate" is at the grid. If $V_g = -3$ volts, $V_a = +150$ volts on the triode, what is the value of μ?

6.12. Calculate the cathode-grid transit time for an electron in the triode of Problem 6.11.

6.13. If the normal operating anode current of a triode is changed from 8 ma to 1 ma, by what factor is the dynamic plate resistance changed?

6.14. The plate current of a triode is given by $i_a = i_a(V_a, V_g)$. When V_a and V_g change to $V_a + \delta V_a$ and $V_g + \delta V_g$, then i_a becomes $i_a + \delta i_a$. Use Taylor's theorem for a function of two variables to show that $\delta i_a = g_m \delta V_g + \delta V_a / r_p$, provided that *either* δV_g and δV_a are small *or* the characteristics are free from curvature.

6.15. A particular triode is normally operated with an anode voltage of 50 volts and a d-c grid bias of -2 volts. If these voltages are changed to 100 volts and -4 volts respectively, by what factors are (*a*) the anode current, and (*b*) the transconductance changed?

6.16. Two different triodes are used in parallel in an amplifier. Evaluate the r_p and g_m of the combination in terms of the parameters of the individual tubes.

6.17. The potential minimum of a particular space-charge-limited planar diode is depressed V_m volts below the potential of the cathode. A fraction F of the emitted electrons is able to overcome the potential minimum and reach the anode. Show that the potential V_m can be expressed in the form $V_m = -\frac{kT}{e} \ln F$.

6.18. For the tube characteristics shown in Fig. 6.11, find the approximate values of μ, g_m, and r_p for the quiescent conditions illustrated.

6.19. See whether equation 6.44 is true for the conditions illustrated in Fig. 6.11.

6.20. Find the quiescent conditions for a plate supply voltage of 200 volts, a 40-kilohm load, and a bias supply $E_{cc} = -4$ volts for the tube of Fig. 6.11.

6.21. Find μ, g_m, r_p under the conditions of Problem 6.20.

6.22. Solve Problem 6.19 for the conditions of Problem 6.20.

6.23. The beam of an electron gun (see figure) is directed at electrode A which intercepts all the electrons. (Neglect secondary electrons.) If the voltage V_1 is increased by a factor of 4, by what factor is the *power* dissipated in electrode A increased in each of the cases listed:

(*a*) V_2 fixed and cathode emission is temperature limited before and after V_1 changes.

(*b*) V_2 fixed and cathode emission is space-charge limited before and after the change.

(*c*) Electrode A connected directly to the accelerating electrode so its voltage is also increased by a factor of 4, space-charge-limited emission both before and after change.

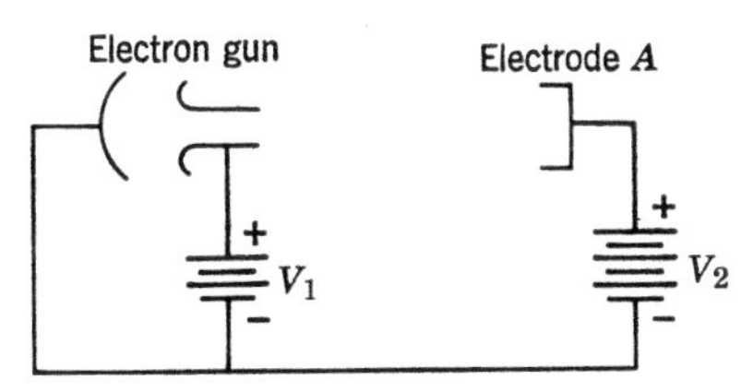

Prob. 6.23

6.24. A beam-power tetrode has a plate resistance of 200,000 Ω. If the screen is connected to the anode and the tube is operated as a triode, the plate resistance is 10,000 Ω. Assume zero screen-grid current (no interception). What is the screen grid-to-anode transconductance if the screen grid is used as the controlling electrode and the regular control grid is maintained at a constant bias voltage? (Note that for small variations in applied potentials equation 6.31 becomes for a tetrode

$$di_a = \frac{\partial i_a}{\partial V_g} dV_g + \frac{\partial i_a}{\partial V_s} dV_s + \frac{\partial i_a}{\partial V_a} dV_a$$

where the subscript s refers to the screen grid.

6.25. A constant light flux illuminates the photocathode of a photomultiplier with 10 secondary emission multiplication stages. By what factor is the output current increased if (*a*) the secondary emission ratio is increased from 3 to 4?

(*b*) the number of multiplication stages is increased from 10 to 12 and the secondary emission ratio is 3?

6.26. Suppose that the grid of a planar triode could be located at the potential minimum. Assuming then that the potential at all points in the plane of grid wires is equal to the grid potential, show that the g_m of such a tube in terms of the cathode temperature T and the anode current i_a is:

$$g_m = \frac{e}{kT}\, i_a$$

(*Hint:* Use the results and concepts of Problem 6.17.)

7. induced currents, a-c power, and equivalent networks

In this chapter the currents that flow in the circuits external to a vacuum tube as a result of electronic motion within the tube are considered. These induced currents are important in the application of tubes as circuit elements. An electron accelerating or decelerating under the influence of an electric field gains or loses kinetic energy. The source that provides the field loses or gains an equal amount of energy. Using the concepts of induced current and energy exchange we consider power amplification in a triode.

After studying the external electrode currents, we consider these currents in an external circuit. We introduce a method for the analysis of circuits using grid-controlled tubes. It is found that a grid-controlled tube driven by a small a-c signal may be simulated by a simple equivalent network containing an ideal voltage generator or ideal current generator as an active element. An equivalent network can be substituted for the tube for the purpose of analysis, and the a-c currents that flow in the various circuit elements can be determined by Kirchhoff's laws.

7.1 Currents induced by electron motion

Let us consider what happens when a charge moves from one electrode to another. In Fig. 7.1 we show an isolated charge q in transit

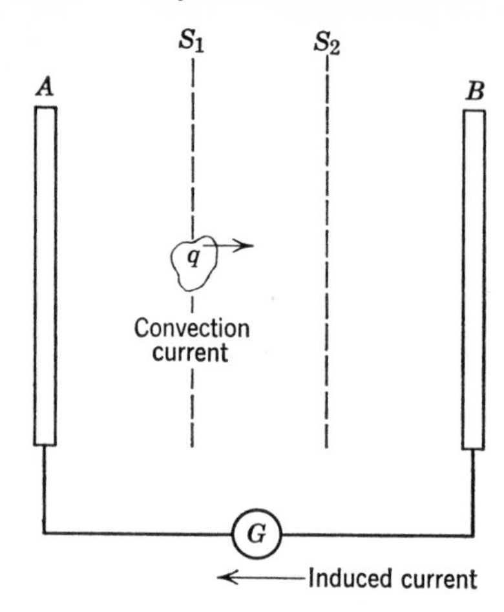

Fig. 7.1. Currents between two electrodes, A and B.

between planar electrodes A and B which are connected through a galvanometer. Because of this interconnection, charge cannot pile up on either electrode. It might be thought that no deflection of the galvanometer will occur until the charge strikes electrode B and flows back to A through the galvanometer. This is not the case. In reality, charge flows through the galvanometer while q is in transit between the electrodes, and the current through the galvanometer stops when the charge strikes electrode B. The current through the galvanometer is known as the *induced current*. In the space between the electrodes, the current through an imaginary surface S_1, through which the charge is in the process of passing, is called the *convection current*. Convection currents both in space and in wires are the currents normally discussed in this text.[1] The induced current is equal to the rate of change of the charge induced on either electrode by the moving charge.

When an electron travels in the vicinity of a conductor, charges must be induced on the conductor such that the electric field within the conductor is zero at all times. The surface charges quickly and continually rearrange themselves to maintain this condition as the electron moves. Figure 7.2 illustrates the electric lines of force originating on a single electron and terminating on induced positive

[1] For completeness we point out that at other surfaces of the interelectrode space, such as S_2, where there is no charge, there is a kind of current existing. This is known as a *displacement current* and results from the time rate of change of the electric field at S_2. This rate of change of field is called a current because it plays the same role as convection current in Maxwell's equations.

charges on the surfaces of parallel plane conductors. The lines of force of the static electric field are not included. Note that there are more lines terminating on the conductor nearer the electron. In all cases the total effective positive charge ($q + q'$ in Fig. 7.2) induced on both electrodes equals e, the magnitude of the charge of the electron.

The magnitude of the induced charge q' on the anode may be computed by equating the work done in transferring the induced positive charge from cathode to anode through the external circuit to the energy gained by the electron in its movement from the cathode toward the anode. The battery V_0 effectively transfers a positive charge q' from *cathode to anode* as the electron moves from $z = 0$ to an arbitrary position z. The electron is acted on by a uniform electric field V_0/d,

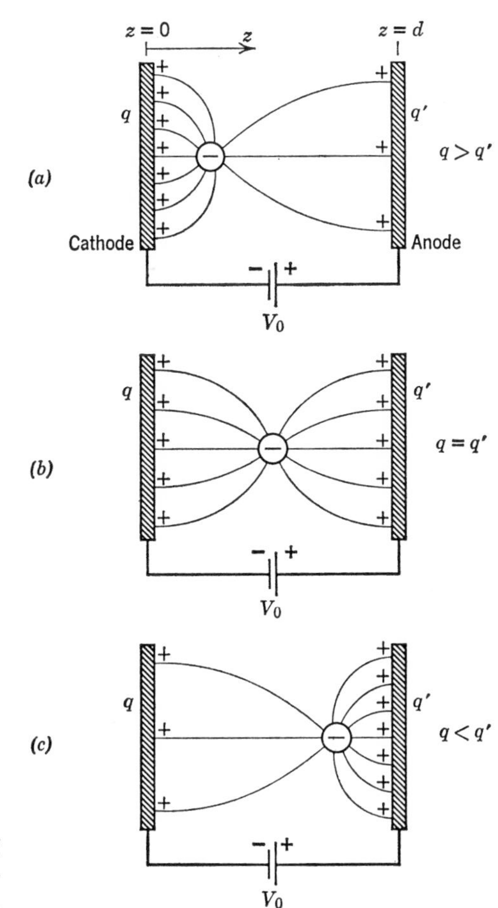

Fig. 7.2. The electric lines of force associated with an electron between parallel electrodes.

and a total work of

$$W = Fz = \frac{eV_0 z}{d} \tag{7.1}$$

is done on the electron. The battery does work $V_0 q'$ in transferring the induced charge; the induced charge in turn sets up fields which do the same amount of work on the electron so that

$$V_0 q' = \frac{eV_0 z}{d} \tag{7.2}$$

or

$$q' = \frac{ez}{d} \tag{7.3}$$

Thus we see that the induced charge on the anode grows linearly with distance as the electron moves from cathode to anode. The current associated with the changing induced charge is

$$i = \frac{dq'}{dt} = \frac{e}{d}\frac{dz}{dt} = \frac{ev}{d} \tag{7.4}$$

This relationship is a fundamental one in the field of high-frequency devices. It is limited, however, to plane-parallel electrodes in the absence of space charge. The total induced current produced by a large number of (noninteracting) electrons is the sum of all the individual contributions.

It is to be noted that the induced current i in equation 7.4 is independent of the electrode potentials and therefore is the same current that flows when the battery is not present and the conductors are joined by a wire.

We next find a general relationship for the induced current flowing into an arbitrarily shaped electrode by considering that the electron gains an energy $e\,\Delta V$, where ΔV is the change in potential due to its position change while an induced charge $\Delta q'$ flows to the electrode. If we let V_0 be the potential difference between the electrodes, then

$$V_0\,\Delta q' = e\,\Delta V \tag{7.5}$$

or

$$\Delta q' = e\frac{\Delta V}{V_0} = e\,\Delta U_1 \tag{7.6}$$

Here $U_1 \equiv V/V_0$ is a dimensionless function of position. It is numerically equal to the potential function when a potential difference V_0 of one volt is applied between the electrodes. U_1 is the same sort of unit potential function that was described in section 6.3. Dividing 7.6 by Δt and going to the limit, the induced current is

$$i = \frac{dq'}{dt} = e\,\frac{dU_1}{dt} \tag{7.7}$$

U_1, a function of position, is also an implicit function of time because the position of the electron changes with time. Thus

$$\frac{dU_1}{dt} = \frac{\partial U_1}{\partial x}\frac{dx}{dt} + \frac{\partial U_1}{\partial y}\frac{dy}{dt} + \frac{\partial U_1}{\partial z}\frac{dz}{dt} = -\boldsymbol{\mathcal{E}}_1 \cdot \mathbf{v} \tag{7.8}$$

where $\boldsymbol{\mathcal{E}}_1$, the negative gradient of U_1, is a vector function of position. $\boldsymbol{\mathcal{E}}_1$ has the dimensions of meters^{-1} and is numerically equal to the electric field when $V_0 = 1$ volt. Then using 7.8 in 7.7

$$i = -e\boldsymbol{\mathcal{E}}_1 \cdot \mathbf{v} \tag{7.9}$$

for an electron in transit between electrodes. This reduces to equation 7.4 for plane parallel electrodes.

Equation 7.9 must be modified if a continuous distribution of charge is present, so that

$$i = \int_{\text{volume}} \rho \boldsymbol{\mathcal{E}}_1 \cdot \mathbf{v}\, d\tau \tag{7.10}$$

From equation 6.5, $\mathbf{J} = \rho\mathbf{v}$, so we may write

$$i = \int_{\text{volume}} \mathbf{J} \cdot \boldsymbol{\mathcal{E}}_1\, d\tau \tag{7.11}$$

$\mathbf{J}$ is the current density at the volume element $d\tau$, and the integral is taken over the region occupied by the space charge. This result is still valid if the electrodes are joined by an impedance instead of a conductor.

Example. We illustrate the preceding discussion by considering the currents that flow in the three-electrode system shown in Fig. 7.3.

An electron, starting from rest at electrode 1, accelerates in a uniform field to the grid from time t_0 to t_1, but from t_1 to t_2 moves in the region between the grid and electrode 3 at constant velocity. The induced current into the grid increases uniformly with time between t_0 and t_1, but is constant from t_1 to t_2 because v is constant (see equation 7.4).

While the electron is to the left of the grid, a total charge of e flows through the battery from the negative to the positive terminal, and the battery expends eV of energy in moving the induced charge. The electron gains this amount of kinetic energy from the field. The kinetic energy of the electron is converted into heat upon striking electrode 3. Thus the energy expended by the battery is finally converted into heat energy in electrode 3. The positive induced charge which flows to electrode 3 through the external circuit while the electron is in transit is canceled when the electron strikes this electrode. Note that the net charge (area under the i_2 versus t curve) flowing to the grid is zero.

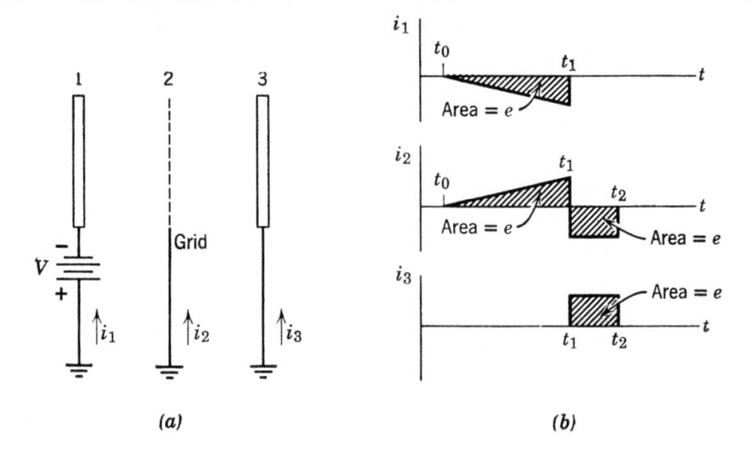

Fig. 7.3. Currents in a three-electrode system. (*a*) Three planar electrodes. (*b*) Current versus time for each electrode for a single electron in transit.

7.2 Current and power in external impedances

We now consider the effect of an external load resistance connecting two electrodes between which a d-c beam of electrons is passing. Figure 7.4 illustrates a beam of electrons passing through a grid and striking electrode P. If dN/dt electrons per second pass through the grid and strike electrode P, an induced current $I_0 = (dN/dt)\, e$ will flow from ground through the load resistance R to meet the arriving electrons. A voltage drop of $I_0 R$ is developed in the resistance by the induced current. The power dissipated in the resistance by this

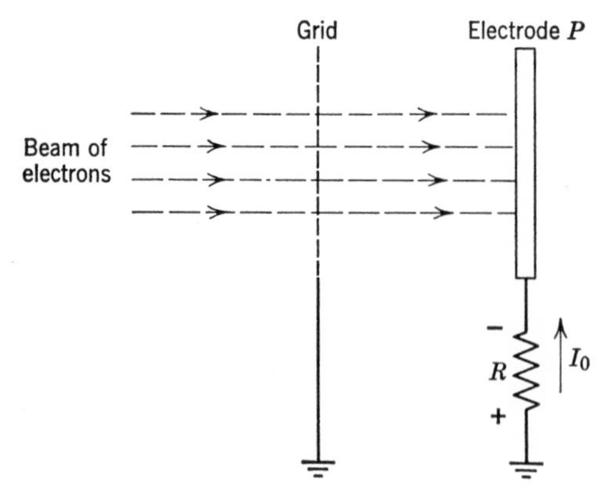

Fig. 7.4. Parallel electrodes connected by an external load resistance.

current is $I_0{}^2R$. This power is supplied by the kinetic energy of the electrons in the beam.

Since each electron in the beam faces a decelerating electric field due to I_0R, it loses an amount of kinetic energy eI_0R during its flight from the grid to electrode P. (It is evident that I_0R must be smaller than the voltage to which the electrons have been accelerated in order that they reach P.) For dN/dt electrons per second the total power lost by the electrons in the interelectrode region is

$$eI_0R\frac{dN}{dt} = I_0{}^2R \tag{7.12}$$

which is equal to the heat power dissipated in the resistance by the induced current. The remaining part of the electrons' kinetic energy is transformed into heat energy when they strike electrode P.

The present considerations are just as valid if R is replaced by a complex impedance Z. It is important to stress that in the model developed here the voltage iZ which develops across Z is not caused by the electrons which strike P and flow through Z. The induced currents flow only *while charge is in transit between the electrodes.* The positive charge that flows through Z is canceled when the individual electrons strike electrode P.

7.3 The extraction of power from a modulated beam

The control of energy or the conversion of one form of energy to another is of basic importance to our present-day technology. In this section we demonstrate how a change in beam current in an electron tube can provide a large change in energy in an external load. Since a change in beam current may require only a small expenditure of energy, as was seen in Chapter 6 for a triode, this process can provide the all-important control or amplification feature. Beam currents are often modulated periodically. In such cases the average power in a load in the presence of modulation is greater than the average power in the absence of modulation. This difference in power is called the a-c power. Since energy must be conserved and very little of the a-c power ordinarily comes from the a-c input signal, most of the a-c power must come from another source. In this case the source of energy is a battery or a d-c power supply which conveys power to the load via the kinetic energy of the beam as described in section 7.2.

We now consider the simple case in which the beam current I_0 of Fig. 7.4 has a sinusoidal modulation at an angular frequency ω. This may be obtained by varying the number of electrons passing the grid per unit time. The instantaneous current i may be written

$$i = I_0 + I_1 \sin \omega t \tag{7.13}$$

where I_1 is the amplitude of the current modulation. The total instantaneous power developed in the resistance R is

$$P = i^2R = (I_0 + I_1 \sin \omega t)^2 R \tag{7.14}$$

When this power is averaged over a cycle, we obtain

$$\bar{P} = I_0^2 R + \frac{I_1^2 R}{2} \tag{7.15}$$

Note that this power is greater than the power I_0^2R in the absence of the current modulation. The a-c power $I_1^2R/2$ resulting from the sinusoidal modulation is obtained at the expense of the kinetic energy of the electrons. To see qualitatively why the load power in the presence of modulation is greater, consider two half-cycles. When i is greater than I_0, the number of electrons passing through the grid and the voltage drop across R are greater than average. Thus more than half of the electrons lose more kinetic energy than under d-c conditions. In the other half-cycle, less than half of the electrons lose less kinetic energy than under d-c conditions. As a result of the modulation the average kinetic energy with which electrons bombard the collecting electrode is reduced because of the a-c power transferred to the load.

An important feature is that the *induced current* flowing through an external impedance Z is independent of the magnitude of the impedance provided that the electron velocity is not appreciably changed by the retarding voltage iZ. In many devices this condition is satisfied. The induced electrode current is determined only by the current crossing between the electrodes. Modulating the beam causes an a-c power to be developed which varies linearly with the resistance (see equation 7.15). Since we can modulate the beam in a manner that consumes very little power, then, at the *expense of the kinetic energy* of the electrons and hence the d-c voltage supply, we can develop a large *a-c power in an output resistance.* This is an important method for amplifying a-c power.

In Chapters 15 and 16 we discuss klystrons, traveling-wave tubes, and other esoteric devices. Although these tubes differ in the means used to attain current modulation of the beam and the types of load in which the power is developed, they each provide a-c power amplification by the principles previously discussed. In klystrons and traveling-wave devices the energy of a d-c power supply provides the kinetic energy of the electrons, which is partly converted into useful

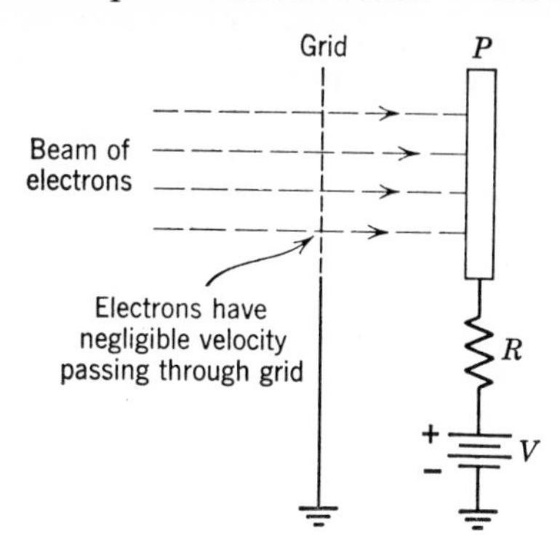

Fig. 7.5. Electrodes connected by d-c supply and load resistance in series.

a-c power. On the other hand, in magnetrons (discussed in Chapters 5 and 16) the potential energy of the electrons, also obtained from a d-c power supply, provides a-c output power.

Let us reconsider the triode in the light of the present discussion. In a triode amplifier, the d-c supply is in series with the external impedance as shown in Fig. 7.5. The electrons have negligible velocity while passing through the grid and are accelerated toward electrode P by the battery. The induced currents pass through the battery as well as the series resistance, and power is transferred as before. The average power I_0V of the battery goes into the d-c power I_0^2R in the load resistance, the a-c power output $I_1^2R/2$, and the average power dissipated by the kinetic energy of the electrons as they strike electrode P. Thus

$$I_0V = I_0^2R + \frac{I_1^2R}{2} + \bar{P}_{\substack{\text{dissipated}\\\text{with}\\\text{modulation}}} \tag{7.16}$$

When no modulation is present, or $I_1 = 0$,

$$I_0V = I_0^2R + \bar{P}_{\substack{\text{dissipated}\\\text{without}\\\text{modulation}}} \tag{7.17}$$

Substituting 7.17 into 7.16, we may write

$$\bar{P}_{\substack{\text{dissipated}\\\text{with}\\\text{modulation}}} = \bar{P}_{\substack{\text{dissipated}\\\text{without}\\\text{modulation}}} - \frac{I_1^2R}{2} \tag{7.18}$$

Thus, the power dissipated as heat in the anode is reduced in the presence of modulation by the a-c power term. In fact, the anodes of high-power vacuum tubes which are operated near their plate-dissipation limits may melt if the current modulation is removed.

7.4 Equivalent networks

Now that we have discussed the physics of induced current flow in circuits external to a tube, we are ready to consider the representation of a tube as a circuit element. In the previous chapter it was pointed out that the current drawn from the cathode of a grid-controlled tube could be expressed as a function of the potentials of the grid and anode relative to the cathode and the tube parameters g_m and r_p. Equation 6.32 states

$$di_a = g_m\, dV_g + \frac{dV_a}{r_p} \tag{6.32}$$

In the special case in which the applied anode and grid voltages are modulated sinusoidally, the anode current will also be modulated sinusoidally. Using the notation of Chapter 6, where E_{cc} was the grid-cathode voltage with zero input signal and I_b and E_b were the corresponding "quiescent" anode current and voltage, we may write, for sinusoidal modulation at angular frequency ω

$$\begin{aligned} V_g &= E_{cc} + e_g \sin \omega t \\ i_a &= I_b + i_p \sin \omega t \\ V_a &= E_b + e_p \sin \omega t \end{aligned} \tag{7.19}$$

Here i_p, e_g, and e_p are constants representing the peak values of the modulation terms. Taking the differentials of equations 7.19 with respect to time, we find

$$\begin{aligned} dV_g &= e_g\omega \cos \omega t\, dt \\ di_a &= i_p\omega \cos \omega t\, dt \\ dV_a &= e_p\omega \cos \omega t\, dt \end{aligned} \tag{7.20}$$

Substituting these differentials into 6.32 and canceling common terms, we obtain

$$i_p = g_m e_g + \frac{e_p}{r_p} \tag{7.21}$$

Equation 7.21 is valid only if e_g, i_p, and e_p are small enough so that g_m and r_p may be considered constant over the entire range of variation of the voltages and currents. This is known as a small signal approximation. As written in 7.21 e_g, i_p, and e_p are peak values. They can equally well represent rms quantities.

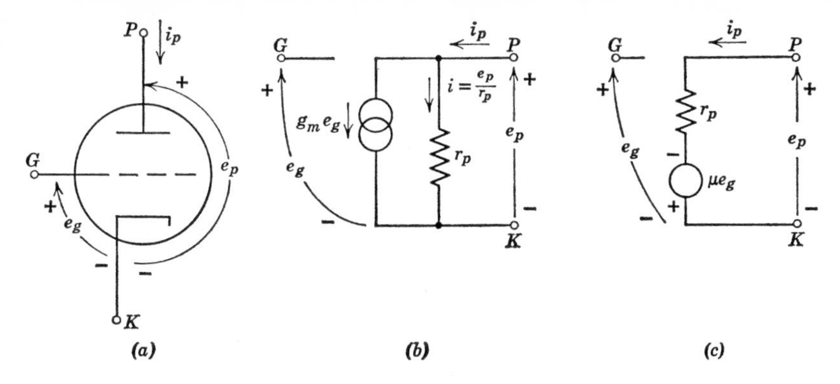

Fig. 7.6. Representations of a triode. (*a*) Schematic. (*b*) Ideal current-generator equivalent network. (*c*) Ideal voltage-generator equivalent network.

Equation 7.21 may be represented by either of two simple equivalent networks. These are shown in Fig. 7.6*b* and 7.6*c*. Figure 7.6*b* has as an active element an ideal current generator $g_m e_g$ (infinite parallel internal impedance) and Fig. 7.6*c* has as an active element an ideal voltage generator μe_g (zero series internal impedance). Note that in each case the output of the active element is proportional to the a-c grid-cathode voltage e_g.

Applying Kirchhoff's current law to Fig. 7.6*b*, i_p may be written as the sum of the current $g_m e_g$ through the generator and the current e_p/r_p through r_p. Thus the network of Fig. 7.6*b* does indeed represent equation 7.21. Kirchhoff's voltage law applied to Fig. 7.6*c* states that the sum of the voltages around the plate circuit loop is zero.

$$e_p - i_p r_p + \mu e_g = 0 \tag{7.22}$$

This is a simple rearrangement of 7.21.

We may conclude that the small signal a-c behavior of a circuit containing a triode may be analyzed by replacing the triode by either of the equivalent networks shown in Fig. 7.6. The same equivalent networks may be used for tetrodes and pentodes provided the screen and suppressor grids are held at constant potentials. Since μ and r_p tend to be extremely high for tetrodes and pentodes, the current-generator network is usually used for these tubes because it does not involve μ.

In a tube there are interelectrode capacitances between all pairs of electrodes, as suggested in section 6.6. The three interelectrode

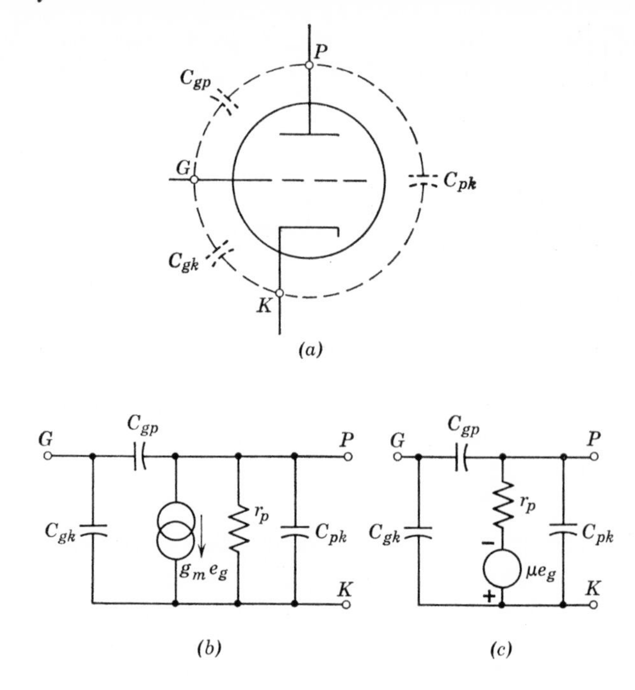

Fig. 7.7. Representations of a triode when interelectrode capacitances are included.

capacitances of a triode are represented in Fig. 7.7*a* and are included in the equivalent networks in Fig. 7.7*b* and *c*. The equivalent networks of Fig. 7.7 more completely represent the behavior of a triode than those of Fig. 7.6. The networks of Fig. 7.7 can be used, for example, to derive the expression for the input capacitance C_{in} of a triode (Miller effect) which we found earlier by physical arguments (see equation 6.47).

7.5 Equivalent network treatment of a simple triode amplifier

We now use the equivalent networks to reexamine the simple triode amplifier, previously discussed in section 6.5. In Fig. 7.8 the triode amplifier circuit is shown in (*a*), the ideal current-generator representation in (*b*), and the ideal voltage-generator representation in (*c*). Note that in the equivalent circuit representations of the amplifier, the emfs of the batteries E_{cc} and E_{bb} are not indicated, since only a-c voltages and currents are considered. The internal resistances of these batteries are assumed negligible, and are not shown. Interelectrode capacitances are ignored so that this analysis is only valid at low or moderate frequencies.

The gain K of the amplifier shown in Fig. 7.8*a* is given by the ratio of the a-c output voltage e_p to the a-c input voltage e_g. From Fig. 7.8*b* or *c* it can be seen by using Kirchhoff's laws to find e_p in terms of e_g that the voltage gain is

$$K = \frac{e_p}{e_g} = \frac{-\mu R_L}{r_p + R_L} = -\frac{g_m r_p R_L}{r_p + R_L} \tag{7.23}$$

In amplifiers employing tetrodes and pentodes, r_p is normally large compared with R_L. The gain is then given by

$$K_{\text{pentodes}} \approx -g_m R_L \tag{7.24}$$

Equations 7.23 and 7.24 are seen to be the same as those found in the previous chapter by graphical means (equations 6.44, 6.45, and 6.49).

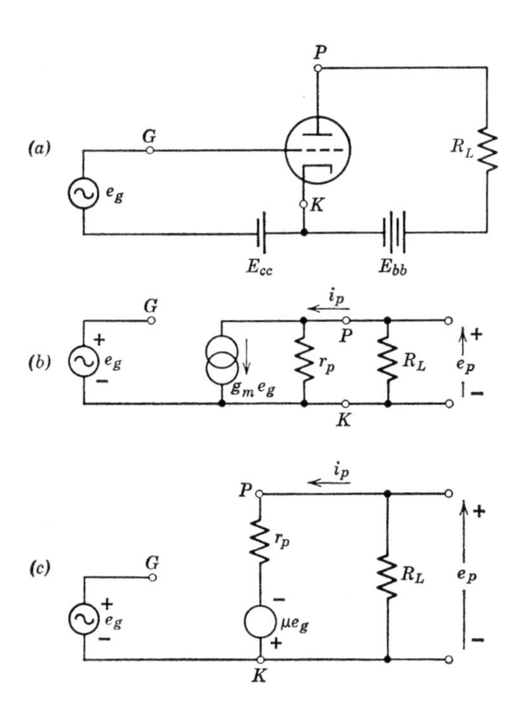

Fig. 7.8. Triode amplifier and equivalent networks.

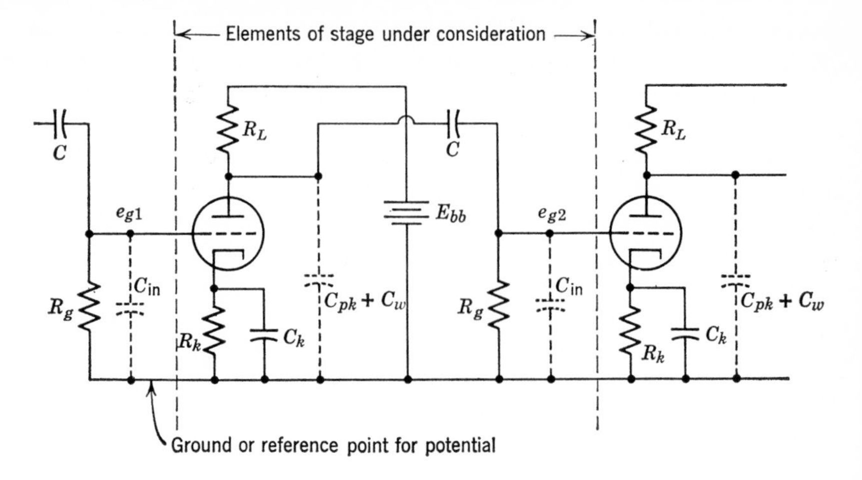

Fig. 7.9. Triode amplifier stage.

The gain is negative, indicating that the polarity of the signal voltage is reversed in going through an amplifier stage.

7.6 Frequency response of a triode amplifier stage

In this section we discuss how the gain of one stage of a simple multistage triode amplifier depends on frequency and introduce a figure of merit for vacuum tubes known as the gain-bandwidth product. Figure 7.9 shows a single stage of a simple multistage capacitance-coupled triode amplifier. We note that the grid bias in this amplifier

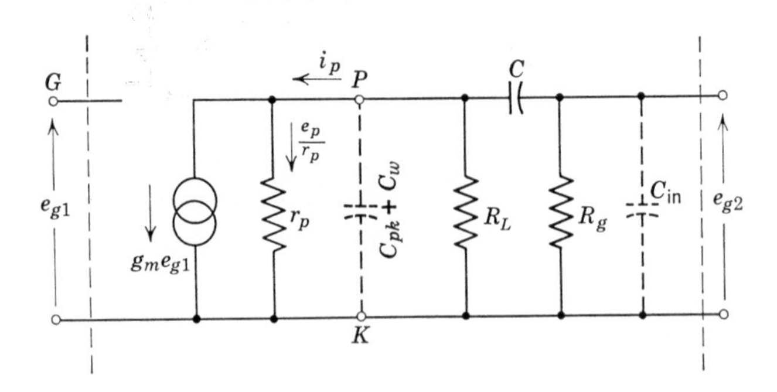

Fig. 7.10. An equivalent circuit for the triode amplifier stage of Fig. 7.9.

stage is applied to the cathode by the d-c plate current I_b through R_k; C_k must be large enough to shunt all a-c signals of interest past R_k. The grid is coupled to ground through the resistance R_g and the average grid potential is zero. The resistance R_g is generally large to minimize the power drawn from the previous stage. An equivalent circuit for this amplifier stage is shown in Fig. 7.10. Since C_k is assumed to short-circuit R_k for all frequencies, C_k and R_k are omitted from the equivalent circuit.

In Fig. 7.11 the magnitude of the voltage gain of this stage, defined as the ratio of e_{g2} to e_{g1} (see Fig. 7.9), is plotted as a function of the angular frequency ω of the a-c signal. The high-frequency cut-off frequency f_H and the low-frequency cut-off frequency f_L represent those frequencies at which the magnitude of the voltage gain of the amplifier stage drops to $1/\sqrt{2}$ of the mid-frequency voltage gain K_m. Figure 7.12 summarizes the equivalent-circuit simplifications in the various frequency ranges and presents formulas for the upper and lower cut-off frequencies. For simplicity it is assumed that $R_g \gg R_p$, where R_p is the equivalent resistance of r_p and R_L in parallel.

$$R_p \equiv \frac{r_p R_L}{r_p + R_L} \tag{7.25}$$

The gain at low frequencies is reduced by the voltage-divider action of $1/\omega C$ and R_g. The gain at high frequencies is reduced by the shunting of the load resistor by: the input capacitance of the next stage C_{in},

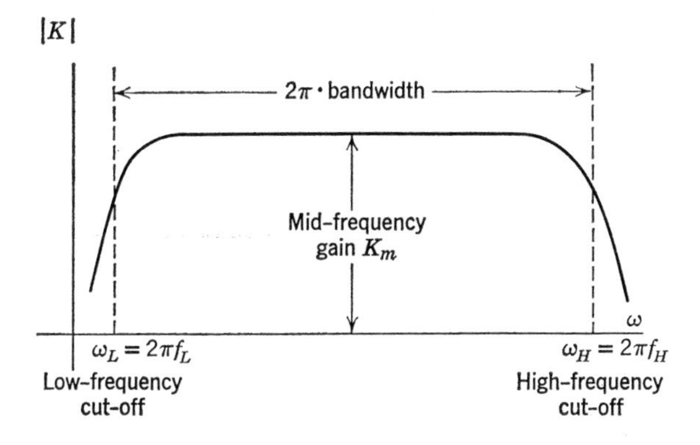

Fig. 7.11. Voltage gain of a single stage as a function of frequency.

Frequency Range	Simplified Equivalent Circuits	Assumptions	Voltage Gain
Low frequencies	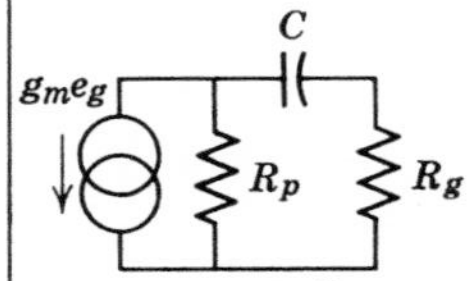 $g_m e_g$, C, R_p, R_g; $R_p \equiv \frac{r_p R_L}{r_p + R_L}$	$\frac{1}{\omega C_{\text{in}}} \gg R_g$ $R_g \gg R_p$ $\frac{1}{\omega(C_{pk} + C_w)} \gg R_p$	$\lvert K_L \rvert \approx \frac{\lvert K_m \rvert}{\sqrt{1 + (\omega_L/\omega)^2}}$ where: $\omega_L \equiv \frac{1}{R_g C}$
Mid-frequencies	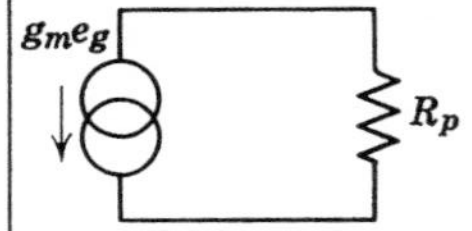 $g_m e_g$, R_p	$\frac{1}{\omega C} \ll R_g$ $\frac{1}{\omega C_{\text{in}}} \gg R_g$ $R_g \gg R_p$ $\frac{1}{\omega(C_{pk} + C_w)} \gg R_p$	$K_m \approx -g_m R_p$
High frequencies	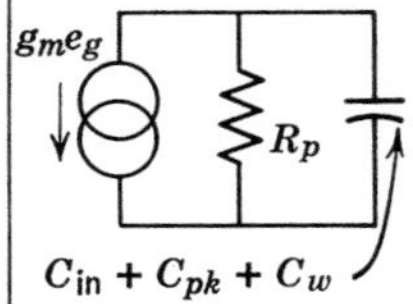 $g_m e_g$, R_p, $C_{\text{in}} + C_{pk} + C_w$	$R_g \gg \frac{1}{\omega(C_{\text{in}} + C_{pk} + C_w)}$ $R_g \gg R_p$ $\frac{1}{\omega C} \ll \frac{1}{\omega C_{\text{in}}}$	$\lvert K_H \rvert \approx \frac{\lvert K_m \rvert}{\sqrt{1 + (\omega/\omega_H)^2}}$ where: $\omega_H \equiv \frac{1}{R_p(C_{\text{in}} + C_{pk} + C_w)}$

Fig. 7.12. Summary of the analysis of the frequency dependence of the gain of a single stage.

the plate to cathode capacitance C_{pk}, and the wiring capacitance C_w of the stage under consideration.

The bandwidth B of this amplifier stage is by definition $f_H - f_L$, which is approximately equal to f_H, since f_L is relatively small. The gain-bandwidth product of our simple amplifier stage is then

$$K_m B = K_m(f_H - f_L) \approx K_m \frac{\omega_H}{2\pi} = \frac{g_m R_p}{2\pi} \cdot \frac{1}{R_p(C_{\text{in}} + C_{pk} + C_w)} \tag{7.26}$$

$$K_m B \approx \frac{1}{2\pi} \cdot \frac{g_m}{C_{\text{in}} + C_{pk} + C_w}$$

For a triode the dominant capacitance term in 7.26 is C_{in} which is given by

$$C_{\text{in}} = C_{gk} + (1 - K_m)C_{gp} \tag{6.47}$$

The gain-bandwidth product can be increased by introducing a screen grid to reduce C_{in} and C_{pk}. Thus pentodes are more suitable than triodes for amplifiers in which a constant gain over a wide range of frequencies is desired (wide-band amplifiers). For pentodes C_{gp} is small and the capacitance C_{in} is independent of the gain K_m and therefor the gain-bandwidth product is independent of the external load resistor. Thus for pentodes the gain-bandwidth product simplifies to

$$K_m B \approx \frac{g_m}{2\pi C} \tag{7.27}$$

where C is the effective capacitance of the tube. Since the gain-bandwidth product depends mainly on the tube parameters, it is a useful figure of merit for a tube. Equation 7.27 indicates that we can design a stage to have high gain and small bandwidth or small gain and large bandwidth. From the definition of ω_H given in Fig. 7.12, it is evident that large bandwidth is associated with small R_p and vice-versa.

7.7 High-frequency effects

At very high frequencies the usefulness of grid-controlled tubes is severely limited by effects in addition to those considered in section 7.6. Equivalent networks become too complex for convenient use in analysis.

At frequencies above about 50 Mc, the inductive reactance associated with electrode leads can cause the a-c voltage between the electrodes to be significantly less than the a-c voltage applied to the external tube terminals. Furthermore, the inductance associated with the cathode lead may bring about significant coupling between the control-grid circuit and the anode circuit, since the voltage drop across this inductance is common to both circuits. Thus tubes designed for very high-frequency operation are constructed with very short leads which are well separated.

In the vicinity of 1000 Mc radiation losses from electrodes and leads become important. It may be necessary to confine the leads and electrodes within the r-f current-carrying circuit. The lead inductance and high-frequency losses are reduced by using planar electrodes and disc-shaped leads. These leads join onto the electrodes on all sides and pass radially out through the envelope of the tube.

At frequencies above 1000 Mc, further limitations arise because the transit times of electrons between electrodes become comparable with the period of the a-c signal. In this case the grid potential changes significantly while the electron is in transit, and the grid becomes less effective in modulating the current. This transit-time limitation occurs at lower frequencies for tetrodes and pentodes than for triodes. Fortunately, at very high frequencies different modulating techniques exist in which transit time effects are beneficial. Some of these techniques are discussed in Chapters 15 and 16.

Suggested References

K. R. Spangenburg, *Vacuum Tubes,* McGraw-Hill Book Company, 1948. Section 16.4 considers induced currents and carries out the analysis for the diode and triode electrodes, elaborating on transit time. Sections 16.1 to 16.3 describe the onset of high-frequency limitations.

W. J. Kleen, *Electronics of Microwave Tubes,* Academic Press, 1958. This is an advanced text and a basic reference for microwave tubes such as we consider in our Chapters 15 and 16. However, Kleen's Chapter 3 uses the induced current concept to treat diode and triode electrode currents.

S. Seely, *Electron-Tube Circuits,* McGraw-Hill Book Company, 1958. Seely begins with a careful definition of equivalent circuits for vacuum tubes and continues with the circuit aspects, although a physical feeling for the circuits is sometimes difficult to extract from the mathematical details.

PROBLEMS

7.1. Draw the voltage-generator a-c equivalent circuits of the circuits shown.

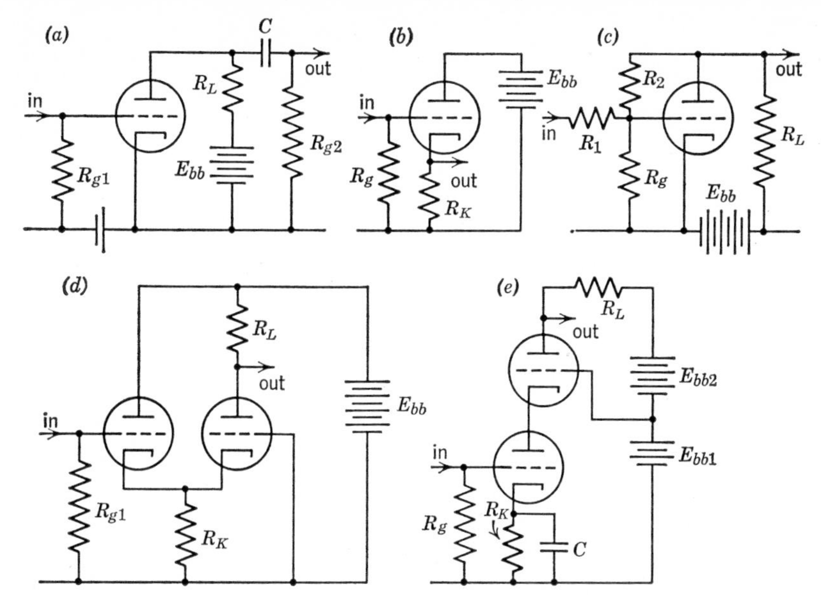

Prob. 7.1

7.2. Repeat Problem 7.1, using the current-generator equivalent circuit for the tubes.

7.3. A single-stage amplifier has a load resistance of 20,000 ohms. Calculate the gain for (*a*) a triode with $g_m = 2$ ma/volt and $r_p = 10{,}000$ ohms, and (*b*) a pentode with $g_m = 2$ ma/volt.

7.4. The amplifier of Problem 7.3 is coupled to another stage through a 0.005 μf capacitor and a grid leak of 1 megohm. If the total effective capacitance across the load is 50 $\mu\mu$f, calculate the frequencies at which the gain has decreased by $1/\sqrt{2}$ with the triode and the pentode.

7.5. An a-c signal of 2 volts rms at 2000 cps is applied to a triode for which $\mu = 20$, $r_p = 7500$ ohms. If the plate load is a pure resistance of 15,000 ohms, find

(*a*) the a-c plate current.
(*b*) the a-c output voltage.
(*c*) the gain of the amplifier.
(*d*) the a-c power in the load resistor.

7.6. Repeat Problem 7.5 for a pure inductive load of reactance 15,000 ohms.

7.7. A pentode amplifier has a load made up of a 250 μh inductor, a 0.0001 μf capacitor, and a 20,000 ohm resistor, all in parallel. If g_m of the pentode is 5 ma/volt, calculate the frequencies at which the amplifier has

(*a*) maximum gain,
(*b*) gain $1/\sqrt{2}$ of the maximum.
(*c*) What is the maximum gain?

7.8. Draw the equivalent circuit, including interelectrode capacitances, for a simple triode amplifier feeding a resistive load, and derive an expression for the equivalent input impedance (a-c grid voltage/a-c grid current).

7.9. A high gain 6SF5 triode with $\mu = 100$, $r_p = 66{,}000$ ohms, $C_{gp} = 2.4$ $\mu\mu$f, $C_{gk} = 4.0$ $\mu\mu f$, and $C_{pk} = 3.6$ $\mu\mu f$, is used as a simple amplifier at 30 kc/sec.

(*a*) Find the input capacitance and resistance of the tube for a load resistor of 100,000 ohms.

(*b*) Repeat for a load impedance $Z_L = 60{,}000 + 60{,}000j$ ohms.

7.10. Repeat Problem 7.9 for a medium gain 6J5 triode with $\mu = 20$, $r_p = 7700$ ohms, $C_{gp} = 3.4$ $\mu\mu$f, $C_{pk} = 3.4$ $\mu\mu$f, $C_{pk} = 3.6$ $\mu\mu$f, for plate loads of

(*a*) 20,000 ohms.

(*b*) $10{,}000 + 10{,}000j$ ohms.

7.11. In the arrangement shown, a single electron leaving the cathode and accelerated toward plate *A* passes through the hole in *A* with 20 ev kinetic energy, and travels through *G* to strike plate *C*.

(*a*) Sketch the current that flows from ground toward *G* as the electron goes from *A* to *C*. Indicate the relative values of the induced current at the time when the electron is at *A*, *G*, and *C*.

(*b*) When the electron has struck plate *C*, where can the 20 ev of kinetic energy the electron had when it passed through *A* be found?

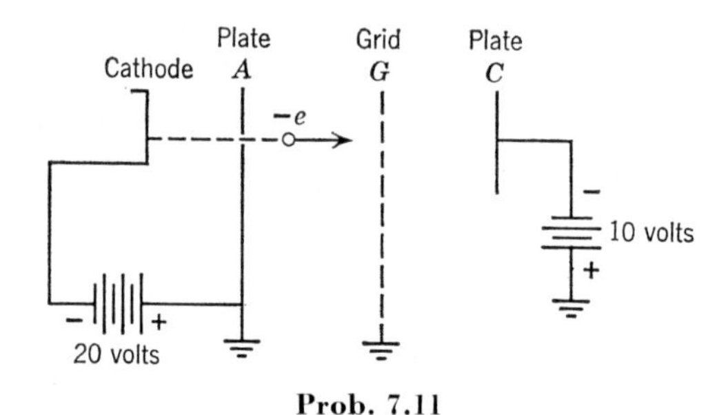

Prob. 7.11

7.12. Consider a simple 6J5 triode amplifier with a load resistance of 20,000 Ω and $E_{bb} = 300$ volts. Using the characteristic curves of Fig. 6.11, a grid bias of −8 volts, and the input signal *amplitude* of 8 volts, compute:

(*a*) The average power the plate must dissipate in the presence of the input signal.

(*b*) The average power the plate must dissipate in the absence of the input signal.

7.13. Show that the convection current due to an electron arriving at the anode is equal to the induced current due to the electron given by equation 7.4.

8. assemblies of particles

Before beginning a study of the electronics of gases and semiconductors it is helpful to develop some of the concepts that arise when the behavior of systems containing large numbers of particles is considered. We introduce the continuity equation and describe some important special cases of it. Definitions of current density, mobility, and conductivity are made, and a simple theory of mobility presented. Finally we consider diffusion and derive the Boltzmann and Einstein relations.

8.1 The continuity equation

The purpose of a continuity equation is to describe the time rate of change of the numerical density of particles in a volume element in space. A change in numerical density may result from flow toward or away from the volume element and/or creation or annihilation of particles in the element. We first treat the flow contribution to the change in numerical density.

Consider a region in space containing a large number of particles. The general motion of such an assembly of particles may be treated as an over-all average drift velocity superimposed upon random thermal velocities. For many problems, such as the flow of a fluid, the random thermal velocities can be neglected and the average drift velocity can be used to represent the velocity of every particle in a volume element. The average drift velocity need not be the same at every point in space. In general, however, the average drift velocity varies gradually enough

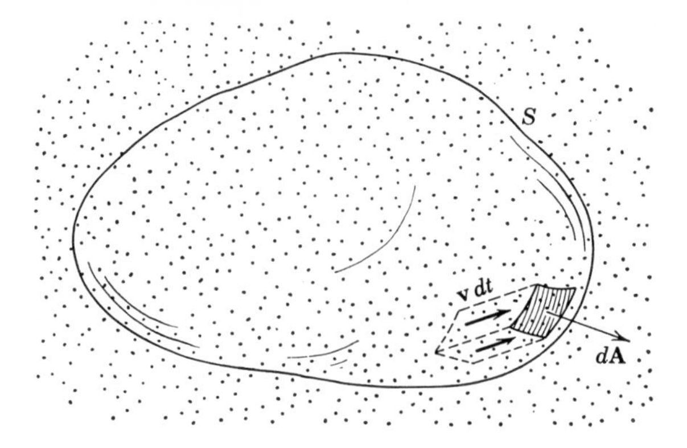

Fig. 8.1. Particles crossing the surface element dA of the closed surface S.

from point to point so that all the particles near any point move with essentially the same average drift velocity.

Now let us consider a closed surface S in the region and calculate the rate of flow of particles into or out of the volume bounded by this surface. In Fig. 8.1 we picture an element of area $d\mathbf{A}$ on the surface S. The particles which will cross the surface element $d\mathbf{A}$ during the next interval of time dt must all lie within a parallelepiped with base $d\mathbf{A}$ and slant height $\mathbf{v}\,dt$. The volume of the parallelepiped containing the particles which will cross $d\mathbf{A}$ in the next interval dt is $\mathbf{v} \cdot d\mathbf{A}\,dt$ (using the scalar product notation). Multiplying this volume by the number of particles per unit volume n near the element $d\mathbf{A}$ yields the number crossing this element in time dt. Thus the number of particles crossing $d\mathbf{A}$ *per unit time* is $n\mathbf{v} \cdot d\mathbf{A}$. The product $n\mathbf{v}$ is sometimes called the flux density of particles.

If $\mathbf{v}$ is directed outward, then the flow of particles through $d\mathbf{A}$ contributes to a decrease in the number of particles inside S. If $\mathbf{v}$ is directed inward, the flow through $d\mathbf{A}$ contributes to an increase in the number of particles inside S. In general, particles may flow inward through parts of the surface S and outward through other parts of the surface. The quantity $n\mathbf{v} \cdot d\mathbf{A}$ is positive when $\mathbf{v}$ is directed outward from the surface and negative when $\mathbf{v}$ is directed inward. Thus the sum of terms $n\mathbf{v} \cdot d\mathbf{A}$ for every element $d\mathbf{A}$ of the closed surface gives the net rate at which particles flow outward. That is,

$$\text{Rate of outward flow across } S = \sum_{\substack{\text{all} \\ d\mathbf{A}}} n\mathbf{v} \cdot d\mathbf{A} = \int_S n\mathbf{v} \cdot d\mathbf{A} \quad (8.1)$$

The number of particles inside S may be written as $\bar{n}V$ where $\bar{n}$ is the average numerical density of particles and V is the volume enclosed by S. The rate at which the number of particles inside S decreases is numerically equal to the rate at which particles flow out through the surface *for the special case of no net creation or annihilation of particles inside* V. That is,

$$\frac{\partial(\bar{n}V)}{\partial t} = -\int_S n\mathbf{v} \cdot d\mathbf{A} \qquad \text{no net creation or annihilation} \tag{8.2}$$

The minus sign in 8.2 occurs because $\bar{n}V$ decreases when the integral or flow term is positive. If there is a net creation or annihilation of particles, the net rate of creation can be expressed as $\bar{C}V$, where $\bar{C}$ is a function representing the average net rate of creation per unit volume. If $\bar{C}$ is negative, it represents a net annihilation. For the general case, the rate of change of the number of particles inside S is

$$\frac{\partial(\bar{n}V)}{\partial t} = -\int_S n\mathbf{v} \cdot d\mathbf{A} + \bar{C}V \tag{8.3}$$

If we divide equation 8.3 by V and let V become infinitesimally small, the averages $\bar{n}$ and $\bar{C}$ may be replaced by their values n and C at a point. The first term on the right of equation 8.3 (divided by V) becomes by definition the divergence of $n\mathbf{v}$ (see Appendix C). Hence we may write

$$\frac{\partial n}{\partial t} = -\nabla \cdot (n\mathbf{v}) + C \tag{8.4}$$

This partial differential equation, a combination of geometrical and kinematical concepts, is known as the continuity equation. It has applications in the fields of fluid flow, ionization of gases, production and motion of electrons and holes in semiconductors, flow of electrons in vacuum tubes, and production and flow of neutrons in a reactor. In fact, we have already used the continuity concept in our treatment of the space-charge-limited diode when we employed the conservation of current. The continuity equation is merely a mathematical statement of the common sense notion that a region can gain or lose particles by flow, creation, and annihilation.

8.2 Special cases of the continuity equation

Steady states

Many physical problems are concerned with finding solutions in which the value of a physical quantity is constant in time at every point in space. Such solutions are called steady-state solutions. A steady-state solution of the continuity equation is one for which the density n is constant in time at every point in space (that is, $\partial n/\partial t = 0$). However, the density n may still vary from place to place. For a steady-state problem the continuity equation reduces to

$$\nabla \cdot (n\mathbf{v}) = C \tag{8.5}$$

which simply states that the net rate of outward flow equals the net rate of creation.

Conservation

Certain physical quantities such as charge cannot be created or destroyed. In a continuity equation dealing with such quantities, the net rate of creation per unit volume C must always equal zero and we say that the physical quantity is conserved. Thus, when conservation occurs, the continuity equation becomes

$$\frac{\partial n}{\partial t} = -\nabla \cdot (n\mathbf{v}) \tag{8.6}$$

Although net charge is never created or destroyed, it is often convenient to imagine that charged particles can be individually created or destroyed. For example, in the pair-production process a positron and an electron (net charge 0) are created from a gamma ray (uncharged).

Simultaneous steady state and conservation

For the twin conditions of steady state and conservation, the continuity equation reduces to

$$\nabla \cdot (n\mathbf{v}) = 0 \tag{8.7}$$

Any of the forms of the continuity equation must, of course, be solved in accordance with proper boundary conditions.

8.3 Current density

When the continuity equation is applied to charge, the particle density n must be replaced by the charge density or charge per unit volume ρ, and the rate of flow of particles per unit area $n\mathbf{v}$ must be replaced by the rate of flow of charge per unit area $\rho\mathbf{v}$, which by definition is the current density $\mathbf{J}$.

$$\mathbf{J} \equiv \rho\mathbf{v} \tag{8.8}$$

Since charge is always conserved, the continuity equation for charge may be written

$$\frac{\partial \rho}{\partial t} = -\nabla \cdot \mathbf{J} \tag{8.9}$$

Equation 8.9 is directly analogous to 8.6, and is an important equation of electricity and magnetism.

Example. Deduce from the continuity equation for charge the equation that expresses the conservation of current under steady-state conditions for a diode with cylindrical symmetry.

The continuity equation 8.9 becomes

$$\nabla \cdot \mathbf{J} = 0 \tag{8.10}$$

Furthermore, because of the cylindrical symmetry and the nature of the problem, electrons in a cylindrical diode flow along radii and $\mathbf{J}$ is a vector entirely in the radial direction. From Appendix C we can express the divergence of a radially directed vector in cylindrical coordinates in terms of partial derivatives, so that 8.10 becomes

$$\frac{1}{r}\frac{\partial}{\partial r}(rJ) = 0 \tag{8.11}$$

or

$$rJ = \text{constant} \tag{8.12}$$

This result may be compared with the corresponding equation for a planar diode, J = constant.

Using equation 8.12, conservation of energy, Poisson's equation, and appropriate boundary conditions, the potential in a cylindrical diode can be evaluated as a function of radius, and the constant in 8.12 evaluated in terms of the anode-cathode potential difference.

8.4 Mobility and conductivity

Currents in free space are best described through a detailed treatment of particle trajectories of the type carried out in Chapter 5. In free space the kinetic energy of charged particles may change continually and may increase to large values. On the other hand, when charged particles move through a solid, liquid, or gas, collisions occur and the kinetic energies of the charged particles cannot increase indefinitely. In a classical picture, the particles lose energy to the atoms of the medium in these collisions. In a wave-mechanical picture, the electron waves are reflected by nonperiodic potential energy gradients and lose energy to the recoiling atoms.

A detailed description of the individual trajectories of a large number of particles is hopelessly complicated. As we noted earlier, however, it is often possible to describe the flow of charged particles in terms of an average drift velocity $\mathbf{v}_D$. In many situations it is found that, at constant temperature, the average drift velocity is proportional to and in the same or opposite direction as the applied electric field. Then

$$\mathbf{v}_D = \pm\mu\boldsymbol{\mathcal{E}} \tag{8.13}$$

Equation 8.13 is the defining equation for the constant of proportionality μ, which is called the mobility. The plus sign holds for positive charges, the minus sign for negative charges. If we replace $\mathbf{v}$ in equation 8.8 by $\pm\mu\boldsymbol{\mathcal{E}}$ and ρ by $\pm|\rho|$ then

$$\mathbf{J} = |\rho|\mu\boldsymbol{\mathcal{E}} \tag{8.14}$$

The conductivity σ of a medium (the reciprocal of the resistivity) is defined as the ratio of current density to the applied electric field.

$$\sigma \equiv \frac{\mathbf{J}}{\boldsymbol{\mathcal{E}}} \tag{8.15}$$

Using 8.14, σ may be expressed in terms of the mobility of the charges in the medium

$$\sigma = |\rho|\mu \tag{8.16}$$

In metals at constant temperature, $\mathbf{J}$ is directly proportional to $\boldsymbol{\mathcal{E}}$, so that σ is a constant. This experimental fact is known as Ohm's law. Equation 8.15 is a more fundamental form of Ohm's law than the more familiar $V = IR$ because the resistance R depends not only upon the metal but also upon the shape of the particular metal sample involved. In 8.15, σ depends only on the metal and not upon its shape.

8.5 Simple classical theory of mobility

In the absence of an applied electric field, the charge carriers in a solid, liquid, or gas bounce around randomly among the atoms of the medium as suggested in Fig. 8.2*a*. For zero field the paths of the charged particles between collisions are straight lines, provided forces act only during collisions. When an electric field is applied to the medium, the particles accelerate in the direction of the field, the paths become curved, and a net drift velocity develops as shown in Fig. 8.2*b*. If $\bar{t}$ is the average time between collisions, the average change in velocity in the direction of the applied field between collisions is given by

$$\overline{\Delta\mathbf{v}} = \mathbf{a}\bar{t} = \frac{\mathbf{F}\bar{t}}{m} = \frac{q\boldsymbol{\mathcal{E}}}{m}\,\bar{t} \tag{8.17}$$

We assume that the velocities immediately after the collisions are

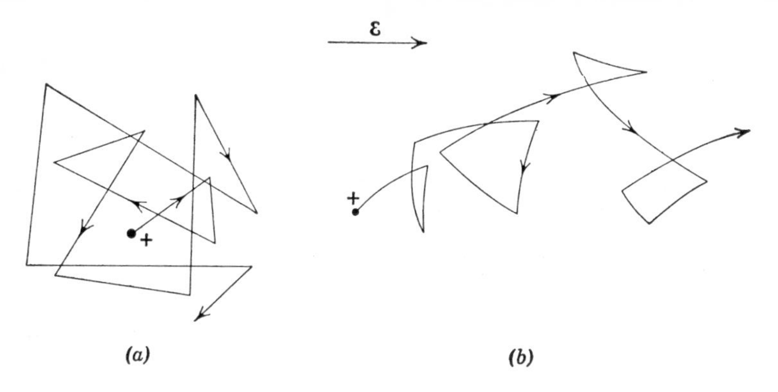

Fig. 8.2. Charged particle trajectories in a medium. (*a*) No electric field (*b*) Applied electric field.

randomly distributed and average to zero (in other words, the scattering is spherically symmetric). The average behavior is that a particle starts out after a collision with zero velocity and attains a final velocity $(q\mathcal{E}/m)\bar{t}$ before the next collision. The average drift velocity $\mathbf{v}_D$ between collisions is half the final velocity, so that

$$\mathbf{v}_D = \frac{q\mathcal{E}}{2m}\,\bar{t} \tag{8.18}$$

Using equation 8.13 the mobility is given by

$$\mu = \frac{q\bar{t}}{2m} \tag{8.19}$$

There are two criticisms of this simple theory. First, the average velocity after the collisions is not zero. That is, the probability for forward scattering in the direction of drift is slightly greater than that for backward scattering. Second, the average time between collisions $\bar{t}$ depends on direction. For forward directions $\bar{t}$ is shortest because the average velocity of the charge carriers is greatest in that direction and forward scattered carriers are apt to encounter scattering atoms more quickly. These two effects tend to cancel and the prediction of the simple theory, that $\mathbf{v}_D$ is proportional to $\mathcal{E}$, is borne out remarkably well experimentally.

8.6 Diffusion

Diffusion is the name for the net flow of randomly moving particles from regions of high concentration or density of particles to regions of lower concentration. Although it is possible to work out theories of diffusion based on the details of the collisions and the distribution of velocities, we shall simply state an empirical law governing diffusion. It is found experimentally that under most circumstances the flux density of particles $n\mathbf{v}$, due to diffusion, is proportional to the maximum directional derivative or "gradient" of the numerical density of the particles. Furthermore, since the flow is from high concentration to low concentration, the direction of the flux density is opposite to that of the gradient; thus in vector notation

$$n\mathbf{v} = -D\nabla\mathbf{n} = -D \text{ grad } \mathbf{n} \tag{8.20}$$

Here D is a constant of proportionality known as the diffusion constant. In nonvector notation and for flow in the x-direction only equation 8.20 becomes

$$nv_x = -D\frac{\partial n}{\partial x} \tag{8.21}$$

Equation 8.20, which describes diffusion, can be combined with the continuity equation 8.4 to give (for the case of flow due to diffusion only)

$$\frac{\partial n}{\partial t} = \nabla \cdot (D\nabla n) + C \tag{8.22}$$

If the flux density is in the x-direction only, the divergence is simply the partial derivative with respect to x (see Appendix C), so

$$\frac{\partial n}{\partial t} = \frac{\partial}{\partial x}\left(D\frac{\partial n}{\partial x}\right) + C \tag{8.23}$$

Furthermore, since D is a constant

$$\frac{\partial n}{\partial t} = D\frac{\partial^2 n}{\partial x^2} + C \qquad \text{(flux in } x\text{-direction only)} \tag{8.24}$$

In equation 8.22, D may be brought out in front of the operators since it is a constant. The divergence of a gradient $(\nabla \cdot \nabla)$ is abbreviated ∇^2 in Appendix C and called the Laplacian operator. Thus, in three dimensions,

$$\frac{\partial n}{\partial t} = D\nabla^2 n + C \tag{8.25}$$

Equations 8.22 through 8.25 are all statements of the continuity equation when the flow of particles is due to diffusion alone.

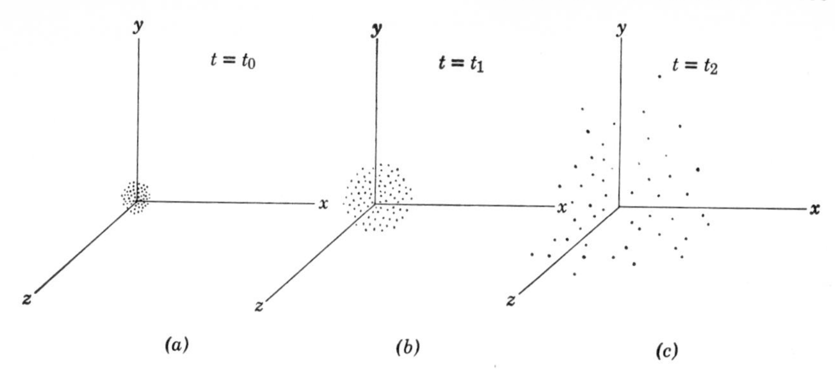

Fig. 8.3. The diffusion of particles away from the origin at three different times $t_0 < t_1 < t_2$.

Example. Suppose a cloud of neutral particles is initially confined to a small region of space within a gas. At $t = 0$ the neutral particles are allowed to begin to diffuse through the gas. Show that the numerical density of particles n depends on position and time as $n = A/t^{3/2}\, e^{-r^2/4Dt} + B$, where A and B are constants and D is the diffusion constant.

We need to show that n satisfies equation 8.25 with the creation term set equal to zero. Because of the spherical symmetry in this problem, $\nabla^2 = 1/r^2\, \partial/\partial r\, (r^2\, \partial/\partial r)$ (see Appendix C). Substitution of the above expression for n into both sides of 8.25 yields an identity which the reader may verify by carrying out the differentiations.

In Fig. 8.3 we portray the spatial distribution of the diffusing particles at three instants of time.

8.7 The Boltzmann and Einstein relations

In this section we derive an expression for the diffusion constant D for charged particles moving among scattering atoms in terms of the mobility and the temperature. The result itself will be used later and the method of deriving it illustrates the use of the diffusion equation, Maxwell-Boltzmann statistics, and the concepts of flux density and mobility. Although a particular physical model is used in this derivation, the final result, being a relation among certain constants, has general validity and may be used in a wide range of problems.

In our model we imagine a rectangular box extending from $x = 0$ to $x = x_0$, containing a cloud of positively charged particles of charge q, free to move among *uniformly distributed scattering atoms* at an absolute temperature T. Furthermore, a uniform electric field $\boldsymbol{\mathcal{E}}$ in the negative x-direction tends to make the charged particles "pile

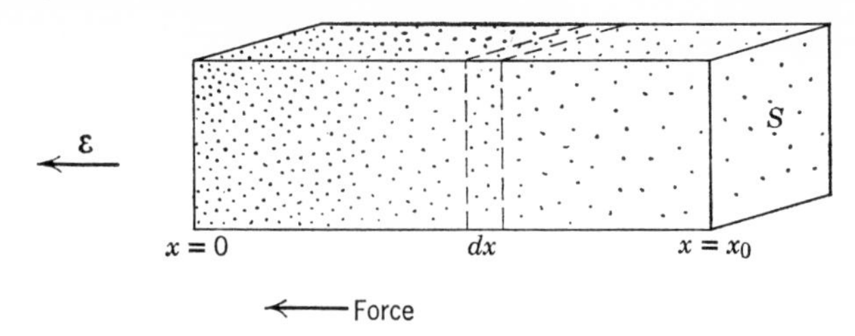

Fig. 8.4. The distribution of free charged particles in a uniform field (scattering atoms not shown).

up" at the $x = 0$ end of the box. In an equilibrium situation diffusion of particles away from $x = 0$ due to the high concentration there just balances the piling-up effect of the electric field, resulting in a distribution of charged particles as suggested in Fig. 8.4. If we arbitrarily call the potential energy of a charged particle zero when the particle is at $x = 0$, and neglect the potential energy due to the space charge itself, the potential energy of a particle at x may be written

$$U = q\mathcal{E}x \tag{8.26}$$

This is verified by taking the negative gradient of U which equals $-q\mathcal{E}$, the force.

From equation 3.44 the average number of particles in each quantum state of a system at temperature T obeying Maxwell-Boltzmann statistics is given by

$$P_{\mathrm{MB}} = Ae^{-E/kT} \tag{8.27}$$

where E is the energy of a state and A is a constant, not to be confused with the cross-sectional area S of the box. The energy of each particle in the system under discussion is made up of both kinetic energy K and potential energy U.

$$E = K + U = K + q\mathcal{E}x \tag{8.28}$$

The total number of particles dN contained in a volume element $S\,dx$ may be found from equation 3.4 by summing P_{MB} over all quantum states available to the particles in the volume element. This summation is equivalent to a sum over all the kinetic energies available to the particle in $S\,dx$ because the potential energy $q\mathcal{E}x$ is essentially the same for every particle in the volume element.

$$dN = \sum_{\substack{\text{all energy} \\ \text{states in } S\,dx}} P_{\mathrm{MB}} = \sum_i Ae^{-(K_i+q\mathcal{E}x)/kT} = e^{-q\mathcal{E}x/kT}\sum_i Ae^{-K_i/kT} \tag{8.29}$$

If the temperature is the same for each volume element and if each element is the same size, the factor $\sum_i Ae^{-K_i/kT}$ is the same for each volume element. Thus the *density* of particles in each element is proportional to $e^{-q\mathcal{E}x/kT}$ and may be written

$$n(x) = n_0 e^{-q\mathcal{E}x/kT} \tag{8.30}$$

where the constant of proportionality n_0 may be interpreted as the density at $x = 0$.

Equation 8.30 is a specific example of an important general relationship known as the *Boltzmann relation.* It is usually written in the form

$$n = n_0 e^{-U/kT} \tag{8.31}$$

The Boltzmann relation governs the equilibrium distribution of particles obeying Maxwell-Boltzmann statistics in a potential energy field.

If equilibrium exists, the flux density of particles nv_D passing any plane perpendicular to the x-axis from right to left due to the drift velocity in the electric field must equal the flux density $-D\,\partial n/\partial x$ from left to right due to diffusion.

$$nv_D = -D\frac{\partial n}{\partial x} \tag{8.32}$$

Since $v_D = \mu\mathcal{E}$,

$$n\mu\mathcal{E} = -D\frac{\partial n}{\partial x} \tag{8.33}$$

Differentiating equation 8.30

$$\frac{\partial n}{\partial x} = -\frac{q\mathcal{E}n_0}{kT}e^{-q\mathcal{E}x/kT} = -\frac{q\mathcal{E}n}{kT} \tag{8.34}$$

Substituting 8.34 into 8.33 and canceling common factors, we have

$$D = \frac{kT\mu}{q} \tag{8.35}$$

This equation is known as the Einstein relation. It is to be emphasized that, although equation 8.35 was derived using a physical system in equilibrium, it is applicable even in nonequilibrium situations. The Einstein relation will be used in Chapter 14 in computing the reverse saturation current of a p-n junction diode.

PROBLEMS

8.1. The birth rate on a certain South Sea island is proportional to the product of the number of men times the number of women, with a constant of proportionality B. The death rate is proportional to the total population with a constant of proportionality D. Assume there is no net immigration or emigration from the island and that the population is always 60% women.

(*a*) Show, using the continuity equation, that the total population N will remain constant if

$$N = \frac{D}{0.24B}$$

(*b*) Show that the population is unstable; that is, if larger than $D/0.24B$ it will continue to grow and if smaller it will continue to decrease.

(*c*) What are the units of B and D?

8.2. The current density in a semiconductor due to electrons is the sum of the diffusion current density and the drift current density. The carriers are generated thermally at a constant rate, and are lost by recombination (see Chapter 9) at a rate n/τ per unit volume, n being the number of electrons per unit volume and τ the mean lifetime of the carriers. Show that the continuity equation takes the form (in one dimension)

$$\frac{\partial n}{\partial t} = -\frac{n - n_0}{\tau} + D\frac{\partial^2 n}{\partial x^2} - \mu\frac{\partial(n\mathcal{E})}{\partial x}$$

where n_0 is the electron density at thermal equilibrium and in the absence of an electric field.

8.3. Solve the equation in Problem 8.2 for the special case of a steady state with no electric field. (The solution will contain two constants of integration.)

8.4. Consider a semiconductor of infinite length running from $x = 0$ to $x = \infty$ with no applied electric field. The excess electron density over the equilibrium value, $n - n_0$, is sometimes called the *injected concentration* N, and has the value $N(0)$ at $x = 0$. Show that then $N(x) = n - n_0 = N(0)e^{-x/L}$, where $L = \sqrt{D\tau}$ = *diffusion length*. (See Problem 8.2.)

8.5. Show that L in Problem 8.4 may be interpreted as the average distance that an injected carrier travels before disappearing by recombination (compare with the mean life of a radioactive atom).

8.6. Again let $\mathcal{E} = 0$, but assume that the injected concentration of Problem 8.4 varies sinusoidally with frequency $\omega/2\pi$, so that $N(x,t) = N(x)e^{j\omega t}$. Show then that the continuity equation becomes

$$\frac{\partial^2 N}{\partial x^2} = (1 + j\omega\tau)\frac{N}{L^2}.$$

8.7. Show that the a-c solution of the continuity equation with steady state and zero field may be obtained from the d-c solution (Problem 8.3) by replacing L by $L\,(1 + j\omega\tau)^{-1/2}$.

8.8. Carry out the differentiations suggested in the solution of the example in section 8.6.

8.9. When carbon is placed in iron it will diffuse through it. At 300° K and 1000° K the diffusion constants are 10^{-9} cm^2/sec and 10^{-6} cm^2/sec respectively. Assume that the iron is in the form of a long thin cylindrical rod. If the carbon is initially placed in a very small region at one end of the rod so that the carbon density in this region is initially very high, the solution to equation 8.24 is

$$n = n_0 t^{-\frac{1}{2}} e^{-x^2/At}$$

(*a*) Verify that the suggested solution satisfies the equation and evaluate the constants.

(*b*) How long will it take before the carbon density at 1 cm from the end is 10% of the density at the end at the two temperatures indicated.

8.10. A crystal of germanium has 10^{22} free electrons per meter^3. The electron mobility μ is 0.38 meter^2 volt-sec. What is the conductivity σ?

8.11. A pulse of electrons is injected into a bar of germanium, and reach a collector 1.5 cm away 4.6 μsec later, the electric field along the bar being 100 volts/cm. What is the drift mobility of the electrons?

8.12. A proposed digital computer memory is a germanium bar 2 cm long, with 5 volts applied between the ends. Information is stored by injecting electron pulses at one end which drift to a collector 1.75 cm along the bar. If one pulse per microsecond arrives, how many pulses can be stored in the bar at any given time? What is an obvious disadvantage of this device?

8.13 A germanium bar 0.05 cm long with 5 volts across the ends has electron pulses injected at one end, collected at the other, amplified, and then reinjected at the first end. If the electron mobility is 0.38 meter^2/volt-sec, at what frequency does the device oscillate?

8.14. When an electron is placed in a magnetic field, there are only two allowed directions of electron spin. Owing to the spin interaction with the magnetic field these two directions have different energies associated with them. The direction with the greater energy has an energy $2\mu_B B$ more than the other. μ_B is the Bohr magneton and is $\approx 10^{-19}$ erg/gauss. Let B be 3000 gauss. For an electron gas with 10^{23} electrons, calculate the number in each energy level at 2° K. (*Note:* the fact that the "spin populations" are not the same for both levels is employed in various amplifiers which go under the general heading of "masers"; see Chapter 16.)

8.15. Sometimes it is convenient to speak of a negative absolute temperature. Imagine a collection of 10^{23} electrons initially at 2°K subject to a strong d-c magnetic field such that the energy separation between the two resultant levels is the same as for Problem 8.14. If the magnetic field is now instantaneously reversed in direction (before any spins have a chance to "flip"), more electrons will have their spins oriented in the direction of smaller energy. Using the Boltzmann relation, compute the effective temperature of the spin system.

8.16.* (*a*) Calculate the potential as a function of radius in a cylindrical diode in terms of the anode-cathode potential difference and the radii of the anode and cathode under space-charge-limited conditions.

(*b*) Calculate the dependence of the anode current on anode-cathode voltage for this cylindrical diode.

* Spangenburg, *Vacuum Tubes*, McGraw-Hill Book Company, 1948, p. 173.

9. gaseous processes

In Chapter 9 physical phenomena associated with the motion of charged particles in gases are studied. Ionization and its reverse process, recombination, are discussed. The related concepts, mean free path, and collision cross section are developed. Townsend, glow, and arc discharges are described and distinguished. Positive ion sheaths are examined and estimates are made of sheath thicknesses. The gaseous devices described in Chapter 10 utilize these concepts.

9.1 Ionization

Whenever a neutral atom loses one or more electrons, ionization has occurred. The resulting charged atom is called a positive ion. Also electrons may attach themselves to neutral atoms or molecules to produce negative ions. The forces which hold additional electrons to neutral atoms are weak and negative ions can easily lose their excess electrons. Figure 9.1 is a plot of the energy required to remove an outermost electron from a neutral atom as a function of atomic number Z. It will be noticed in Fig. 9.1 that the closed shell atoms (helium, neon, etc.) require the greatest energies for ionization and that the alkali metal atoms (lithium, sodium, etc.) having only a single electron in their outermost partly filled shells are most easily ionized. Atoms with low ionization energies form solids with low work functions. The principal sources of ionization energy are photon energy ($h\nu$), thermal energy (kT), and collision energy ($\frac{1}{2}mv^2$). We now examine each of these energy sources in some detail.

Electrons may be emitted from the individual atoms of a gas when photons of greater energy than the ionization energy bombard the

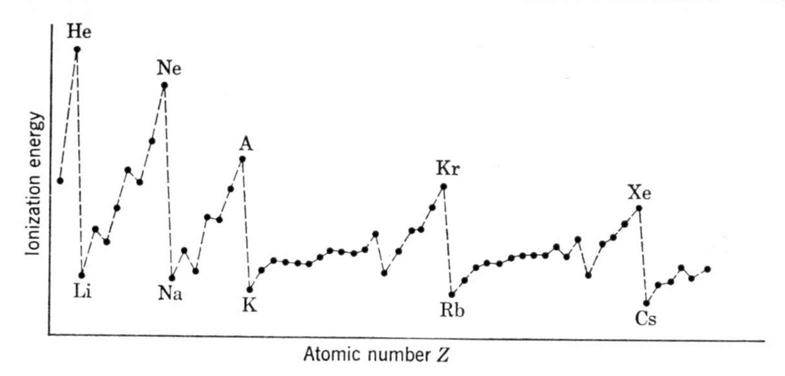

Fig. 9.1. Ionization energy for neutral atoms versus atomic number.

atoms. This process is energetically similar to that of photoemission from solids discussed in section 4.1. The ions which are created photoelectrically in a gas are free to participate in gaseous conduction when electric fields are applied. For example, the energy for the ionization of the atoms in the earth's ionosphere is supplied by photons from the sun.

In gases, very high temperatures are required for thermal ionization. If significant thermal ionization is to be present, the average kinetic energies of molecules (kT) must be of the order of the ionization energy. If the ionization energy is 10 ev, temperatures of the order of 10^5 °K are required for significant thermal ionization. At room temperatures, since $kT \approx 1/40$ ev, very little thermal ionization occurs. Since the individual kinetic energies of gas atoms are distributed over a wide range (Maxwell-Boltzmann statistics), thermal ionization appears gradually with increasing temperature and does not have a threshold energy as does photoionization. Thermal ionization is an important process in the sun's outer atmosphere or corona where the temperature is several million degrees centigrade.

When fast moving charged particles bombard neutral atoms, ionization or excitation may readily occur. In this case long-range Coulomb forces act between the charged projectile and the bound electrons and the probability for ionization is very large. When fast moving, neutral particles are used, only short-range forces act and the probability of ionization is small. Experimentally it is found that when a fast-moving charged particle slows down in passing through a gas, one ion pair is produced on the average for every 30 ev of energy lost by the particle. This empirical fact applies to the passage of any charged particle through almost any gas and allows one to calculate the initial energy of a charged particle from a measurement of the number of ions it produces in coming to rest.

9.2 Recombination

Recombination is the process wherein positive ions and electrons combine to form neutral atoms or molecules. It is the reverse process to ionization.

The capture of an electron by a heavy ion is very unlikely without a third body participating in the collision. In Chapter 2 we learned that bound particles may possess only discrete values of energy and momentum. Free particles, on the other hand, may have any values of energy and momentum. It is easy for a bound particle, which has received sufficient energy, to find one of the infinite number of suitable unbound states. On the other hand, it is difficult for a free particle to lose energy and jump into one of the few bound states available. A third body can provide the necessary adjustability in energy and momentum to give the recombination process a significant probability. Containing walls may serve as third bodies for recombination. An electron may attach itself to a wall and an ion can later capture it to become a neutral atom. Another recombination mechanism may occur at moderately low temperatures. Under these conditions some electrons may be moving slowly enough to attach themselves to neutral atoms or molecules to form heavy negative ions. Subsequently, these negative ions may collide with positive ions and the electrons may be transferred to the positive ions to complete the recombination process. If the electron is captured in a state other than the lowest energy available state, one or more photons may be emitted as the electron drops into lower energy states. In any case, direct electron-positive ion recombination is a relatively rare phenomenon, and ions and electrons make many collisions before recombination occurs.

We now consider how the numerical density of ions may change with time in the presence of recombination for situations where there is no net flow of ions or electrons ($\nabla \cdot n\mathbf{v} = 0$). If n_p is the number of positive ions per unit volume and n_n the number of electrons per unit volume, the number of recombinations per unit volume per second will be proportional to the product of n_n and n_p. The recombination coefficient R is defined in such a way that Rn_pn_n is the number of recombinations per unit volume per second. If q is the rate at which positive ion-electron pairs are being produced per unit volume, then

$$\frac{dn_n}{dt} = q - Rn_nn_p \tag{9.1}$$

If the gas or liquid is uncharged, then

$$n_n = n_p = n \tag{9.2}$$

and equation 9.1 becomes the basic differential equation for recombination

$$\frac{dn}{dt} = q - Rn^2 \tag{9.3}$$

It should be noted that equation 9.3 is an example of the continuity equation in which there is no flow into or out of the volume under consideration and where the net rate of creation per unit volume C on the right-hand side of equation 8.4 equals the difference between the rates at which ions are formed and lost by recombination.

Example. Calculate the time dependence of the numerical density of electrons n_n in a neutral, flow-free, partially ionized gas after the source of ionization has been removed. At the instant the source of ionization is removed,

$$t = 0, \qquad n_n = n_p = n_0, \qquad \text{and } q \text{ becomes zero} \tag{9.4}$$

Integration of equation 9.3, with q set equal to zero and subject to the initial conditions 9.4 yields

$$n = \frac{n_0}{1 + n_0 Rt} \tag{9.5}$$

9.3 Bohr theory of stopping power

The theory for the collisional ionization of gases by fast-moving charged particles was first presented by Bohr. This Bohr theory computes the stopping power of a medium for a fast-moving charged particle, that is, the loss of energy due to ionization per unit length of path dE/dx. dE/dx is often called the space rate of energy loss of a charged particle. From this space rate of energy loss and the average energy lost (30 ev) per ion pair produced, the number of ion pairs per unit length of path may be estimated theoretically. Conversely, a measurement of the number of ion pairs produced per unit length of path provides a useful means of identifying fast-moving charged particles in cloud chambers, bubble chambers, photographic emulsions, and other particle-track detectors. We now present a simplified treatment of this classical theory.

The derivation is performed in two steps. First, the loss of kinetic energy by a fast-moving charged particle in a collision with a single electron is calculated by considering the momentum transfer in the collision. Second, we calculate the total number of collisions which occur per unit length of path to obtain the total energy per unit length of path lost to the electrons in the medium. The loss of energy to nuclei is small and is neglected in our derivation. We assume that

1. The displacement of an electron during a "collision" is small compared

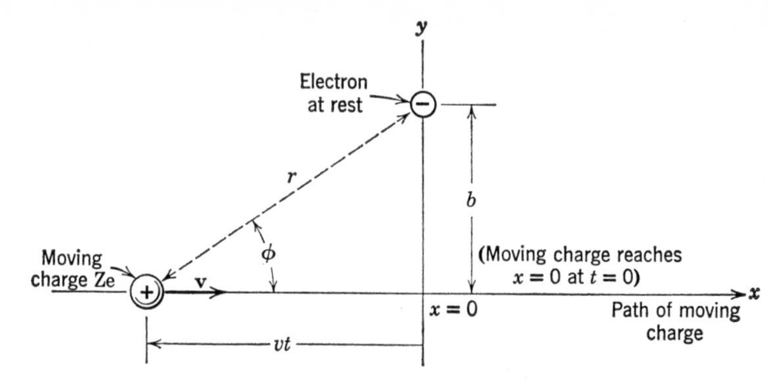

Fig. 9.2. Collision geometry-Bohr stopping power theory.

to the impact parameter b (see Fig. 9.2). This assumption requires that the fast moving charged particle moves past an electron very quickly.

2. The mass of the fast-moving charged particle is much greater than the mass of an electron, so the charged particle moves essentially in a straight line through the medium.

We first compute the y-component of momentum p_y which a free electron receives during a collision. The magnitude of the force on the electron is given by Coulomb's law

$$F = \frac{Ze^2}{4\pi\epsilon_0 r^2} \tag{9.6}$$

The y-component of the momentum p_y given to the electron in the collision equals the time integral of the y-component of force F_y, hence

$$p_y = \int_{\substack{\text{duration}\\ \text{of passage}}} \frac{Ze^2}{4\pi\epsilon_0 r^2} \sin\phi \, dt \tag{9.7}$$

After utilizing the geometry of Fig. 9.2 to express r and dt in terms of ϕ and $d\phi$, we obtain

$$p_y = \frac{Ze^2}{4\pi\epsilon_0 bv} \int_0^{\pi} \sin\phi \, d\phi = \frac{2Ze^2}{4\pi\epsilon_0 vb} \tag{9.8}$$

The x-component of momentum p_x given to the electron in the collision is approximately zero since for each x-component of the Coulomb force when $\phi < \pi/2$ there is an equal and opposite x-component of force when $\phi > \pi/2$.

The kinetic energy ΔE_c given to the electron per collision is

$$\Delta E_c = \frac{p_y^2}{2m} = \frac{Z^2e^4}{8\pi^2\epsilon_0^2 mb^2v^2} \tag{9.9}$$

Equation 9.9 tells how much energy a single electron will acquire as a result of the passage of a heavy fast-moving charge Ze at a distance of b from the electron.

We now compute the energy ΔE lost by the charged particle to electrons in moving a distance Δx. A single collision of the type previously discussed is considered to take place in a very short distance compared with Δx. The number of collisions with impact parameters between b and $b + db$ is the number of electrons $n2\pi b\, db\, \Delta x$ in a cylindrical shell of radius b, thickness db, and length Δx. Here n is the number of electrons per unit volume. Hence, employing 9.9, the total energy ΔE lost in a distance Δx is

$$\Delta E = \int_{b_{\min}}^{b_{\max}} \frac{Z^2 e^4}{4\pi\epsilon_0{}^2 m b^2 v^2}\, n\, \Delta x\, b\, db \tag{9.10}$$

and the stopping power is given by

$$\frac{dE}{dx} = \frac{\Delta E}{\Delta x} = \frac{Z^2 e^4 n}{4\pi\epsilon_0{}^2 m v^2} \int_{b_{\min}}^{b_{\max}} \frac{db}{b} = \frac{Z^2 e^4 n}{4\pi\epsilon_0{}^2 m v^2} \ln \frac{b_{\max}}{b_{\min}} \tag{9.11}$$

We observe that the value of b cannot be zero in the lower limit of 9.11 or infinite in the upper limit since either circumstance would result in an infinite stopping power.

We next compute the value of $b_{\min}$. The maximum energy transferred in any collision occurs for a head-on collision. In a head-on collision between a heavy mass in motion and a light mass initially at rest, momentum and energy considerations show that the final velocity of the light mass is nearly twice the incident velocity v of the heavy mass. Therefore the maximum energy $\Delta E_{e_{\max}}$ that the light mass m can acquire is

$$\Delta E_{e_{\max}} = \tfrac{1}{2} m (2v)^2 \tag{9.12}$$

Since there is a maximum energy transfer per collision, there is in effect a minimum value $b_{\min}$ for the impact parameter, which can be found from the energy-impact parameter relation 9.9, and 9.12

$$b_{\min} = \frac{Ze^2}{4\pi\epsilon_0 m v^2} \tag{9.13}$$

The parameter $b_{\max}$ may be estimated from the consideration that the minimum energy which a bound electron can accept is the excitation energy E_e of the atoms of the medium. Thus using 9.9 again

$$b_{\max} \approx \frac{Ze^2}{2\pi\epsilon_0 v \sqrt{2mE_e}} \tag{9.14}$$

Substitution of 9.13 and 9.14 into 9.11 gives the following approximate formula for the stopping power of a medium for a heavy particle.

$$\frac{dE}{dx} \approx \frac{\Delta E}{\Delta x} = n \frac{Z^2 e^4}{4\pi\epsilon_0{}^2 m v^2} \ln \frac{2mv}{\sqrt{2mE_e}} \tag{9.15}$$

Since the log term is a slowly varying function of v and the techniques we have used to evaluate $b_{\max}$ and $b_{\min}$ are only approximate, we may for convenience treat the log term as a constant. If we denote the *average* energy lost per ion pair formed by E_{ic}, where $E_{ic} \approx 30$ ev, dN/dx, the number of ion pairs produced per unit length of path, is

$$\frac{dN}{dx} = \frac{1}{E_{ic}} \frac{dE}{dx} \approx C \frac{nZ^2}{v^2} \tag{9.16}$$

Here the approximately constant quantity C is given by

$$C = \frac{e^4}{4\pi\epsilon_0{}^2 m E_{ic}} \ln \frac{2mv}{\sqrt{2mE_e}} \tag{9.17}$$

The classical stopping power theory predicts that the space rate of energy loss of a fast-moving heavy charged particle is smaller at higher particle velocities. The smaller stopping power at higher velocities results from the charged particle spending a shorter time in the vicinity of the individual electrons and losing less momentum and energy per collision. It is found experimentally that at sufficiently large incident particle energies the stopping power reaches a minimum value and increases at still higher energies.

For very high energies not only must relativistic effects be considered but additional energy loss mechanisms appear. The heavy charged particle may collide with a heavy nucleus and emit "bremsstrahlung," a continuous distribution of photons, as a result of the sudden deceleration of the moving charge. If the velocity of the fast-moving charge exceeds the velocity of light in the medium, another form of electromagnetic radiation known as Cerenkov radiation is emitted. The geometrical characteristics of Cerenkov radiation resemble a shock wave generated by a large-scale object moving at a speed faster than the velocity of sound through a medium. Cerenkov radiation is an interesting example of the interaction of fast-moving charged particles with slower moving electromagnetic waves. A similar interaction occurs in the traveling-wave tube (see Chapter 16).

9.4 Cross section and mean free path

We now derive a formula for the mean free path, the average distance a particle travels between collisions, in terms of the density of scattering atoms and a parameter called the collision cross section. Cross sections generally have the dimensions of area and are used to describe the probability of an event or process occuring during collisions between particles. For example, the probability of a particle being captured during a collision is described by the capture cross section, the probability of a particle being scattered per unit solid angle is described by the differential scattering cross section. In order to experience a collision with a scattering atom, the center of a particle must be aimed so that it would pass within a certain distance R of the center of the scattering atom. If one uses hard spheres to represent atoms, the critical distance R becomes the sum of the radii of

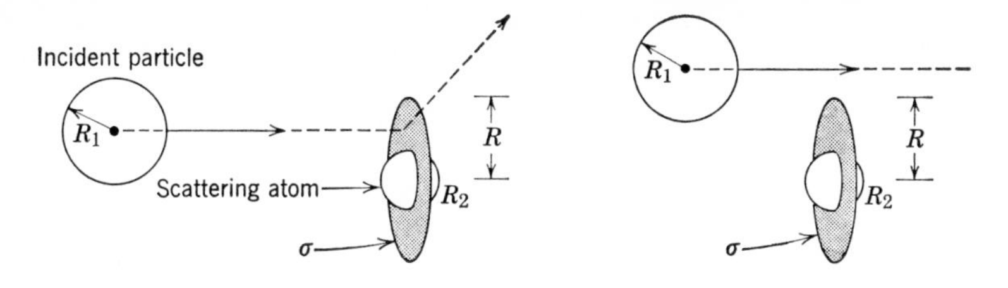

Fig. 9.3. Geometrical significance of collision cross section σ.

the colliding atoms, and the collision cross section or microscopic cross section σ is the area of a circle of radius R.

$$\sigma = \pi R^2 = \pi(R_1 + R_2)^2 \tag{9.18}$$

Here R_1 and R_2 are the radii of the colliding atoms. The conditions under which a collision will occur are shown in Fig. 9.3. If the radius of the moving particle is negligibly small compared to the radius of a scattering atom, the collision cross section becomes the "cross-sectional area" of the scattering atom.

We next show how a beam of electrons is attenuated by collisions with gas atoms. In this case, we may, as a first approximation, neglect the size of the electrons. Since electrons normally travel at much greater speeds than the average speed of the atoms of gases at normal temperatures, we may assume that the atoms are stationary. Figure 9.4 shows a beam of electrons impinging on a region containing a uniform density of atoms.

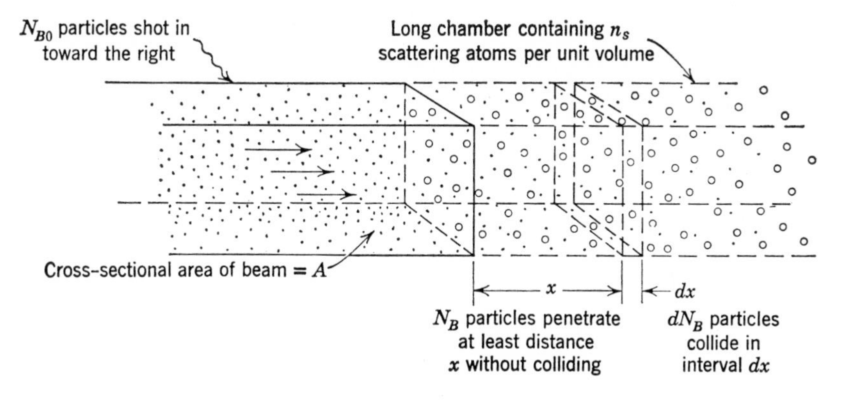

Fig. 9.4. Geometry for the derivation of a formula for mean free path.

Let A = the cross-sectional area of the beam.
n_s = number of scattering atoms per unit volume.
N_{B0} = total number of electrons shot in at $x = 0$.
N_B = number of electrons left in the beam after a distance of travel x in the scattering chamber.
dN_B = number of electrons scattered or absorbed in the element of volume $A\,dx$.

The fraction dN_B/N_B of the electrons arriving at the volume element $A\,dx$ which are scattered or absorbed in passing through the element is equal to the fraction of the area of the element which is obstructed by scattering-atom cross sections

$$\frac{dN_B}{N_B} = \frac{-(\text{number of scattering atoms})\cdot\sigma}{A} = \frac{-n_s A\,dx\,\sigma}{A}$$
$$= -n_s\sigma\,dx \qquad (9.19)$$

Integrating 9.19 subject to the condition that $N_B = N_{B0}$ at $x = 0$, we find

$$N_B = N_{B0}e^{-n_s\sigma x} \qquad (9.20)$$

which indicates that the intensity of the beam falls off exponentially with distance. The product, $n_s\sigma$, which appears in equation 9.19 and 9.20 is sometimes called the macroscopic cross section or the total attenuation coefficient.

It should be noted that our simple derivation of equation 9.20 has neglected "shadowing" of atoms further down the long chamber by atoms near the front of the chamber, and has also neglected the possibility of multiple scattering which may lead to a significant number of electrons being scattered back into the original beam.

The mean free path $\bar{l}$ is the average distance traveled by an electron before collision. Using the definition of an average given by equation 3.10, we write

$$\bar{l} = \frac{\int x\,dN_B}{\int dN_B} \qquad (9.21)$$

Substituting 9.19 and 9.20 into 9.21 and letting $n_s\sigma x = u$, we find

$$\bar{l} = \frac{\int_0^\infty x n_s\sigma N_{B0}e^{-n_s\sigma x}\,dx}{-N_{B0}} = \frac{1}{n_s\sigma}\int_0^\infty ue^{-u}\,du \qquad (9.22)$$

The definite integral can be done by parts. Its value is unity, so

$$\bar{l} = \frac{1}{n_s\sigma} \qquad (9.23)$$

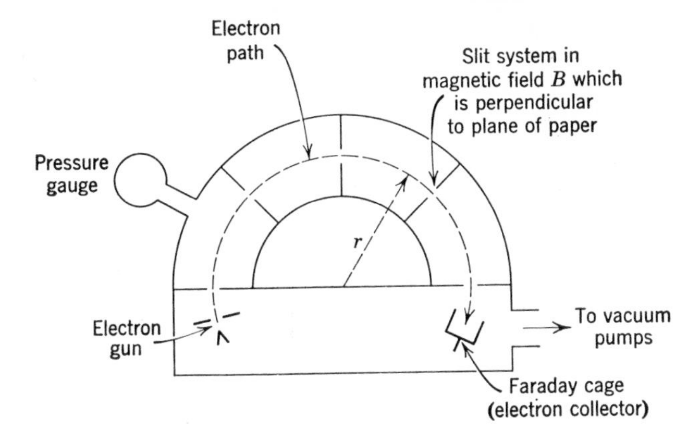

Fig. 9.5. Collision cross section apparatus.

Equation 9.23 was derived without taking into account the velocities of the scattering atoms. Some atoms move toward the electrons, some move away. $\bar{l}$ may be less than that given by equation 9.23 because an electron can be struck from the side by moving scattering atoms which it would not have struck by its own motion alone. The derivation also assumes that the zone of influence of a scattering atom is finite.

An apparatus such as that sketched in Fig. 9.5 can be used to measure the collision cross section σ (or mean free path $\bar{l}$) of electrons in a gas. In this apparatus the velocity of the electrons and the magnetic field strength are adjusted such that the electrons from the electron gun will, in the absence of gas atoms, traverse the semicircular path of radius r defined by the slit system. The current I_0 without gas present is measured. Next, gas at a pressure p and temperature T is introduced, and the smaller current I resulting from loss of electrons by scattering is measured. The numerical density of the scattering atoms n_s can be computed from the pressure and temperature data. For this experiment monoenergetic electrons are used and the beam currents are proportional to particle numbers. Equation 9.20 becomes

$$I = I_0 e^{-n_s \sigma \pi r} \tag{9.24}$$

where πr is the length of the electron path in the gas. Since all quantities in equation 9.24 except σ are measured or known, the electronic collision cross section for various gas atoms may be determined. When this experiment is performed as a function of electron velocity,

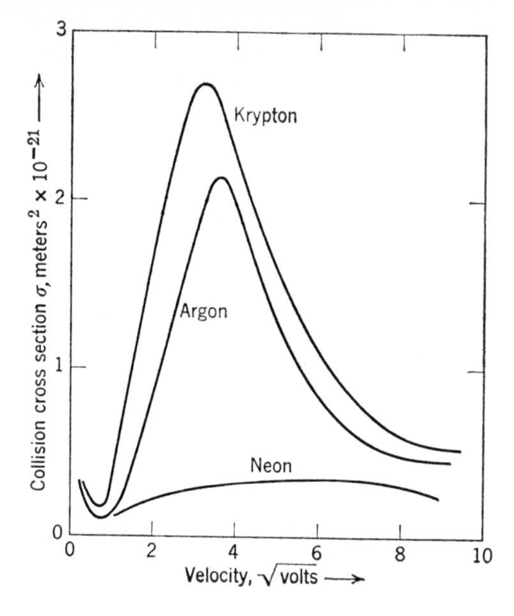

Fig. 9.6. Cross section as a function of electron velocity.

data such as those plotted in Fig. 9.6 result. Kinetic theory experiments using a different method yield values of molecular radii such as those given in Table 9.1. Examination of the data of Fig. 9.6 suggests that the cross sections of molecules for electrons are of the order of magnitude predicted by kinetic theory, but vary with electron velocity.

Table 9.1. Radii of atoms obtained from kinetic theory experiments

Molecule	Radius (angstroms)
Argon (A)	1.43
Hydrogen (H_2)	1.09
Krypton (Kr)	1.59
Mercury (Hg)	1.82
Neon (Ne)	1.17
Nitrogen (N_2)	1.58
Oxygen (O_2)	1.48

The electronic collision cross sections for heavy noble gas atoms may become exceedingly small at low electron velocities. This phenomenon, known as the Ramsauer effect, appears when the waves of the electron wavepackets reflected from the "front" and "back" sides of the potential energy wells representing the noble gas atoms interfere destructively in the back direction. The physics of the Ramsauer effect is similar to that of nonreflecting coatings on glass. The rigorous theory of electron collisions requires the use of quantum mechanics and is not treated here.

9.5 Townsend discharge

In this section we begin an elementary description of gaseous conduction through a discussion of the Townsend discharge, a low-current gaseous conduction process. In Fig. 9.7 a circuit is shown for the determination of the current-voltage characteristic of a cold-cathode gas diode. When the supply voltage E_{bb} is zero, the potential difference V between anode and cathode is zero. In this case an equilibrium exists between ionization produced by cosmic rays and traces of radioactive elements nearby, and recombination which occurs principally at the walls and electrodes of the tube. As E_{bb} is increased, the electric field draws electrons to the anode and positive ions to the cathode, thus creating a small current. Some recombination still occurs at the walls of the tube. If E_{bb} is increased sufficiently, electrons are attracted to the anode and positive ions to the cathode as fast as they are produced. In this circumstance practically all recombination occurs at the cathode. The current is now limited by the rate of ionization and is practically independent of voltage. In the current-voltage characteristic of Fig. 9.8 this "ionization-limited" or saturation region occurs when V is between V_1 and V_2. Typical

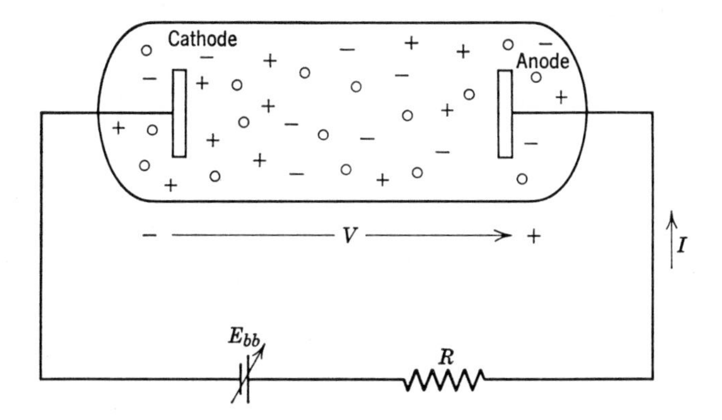

Fig. 9.7. Cold-cathode gas diode.

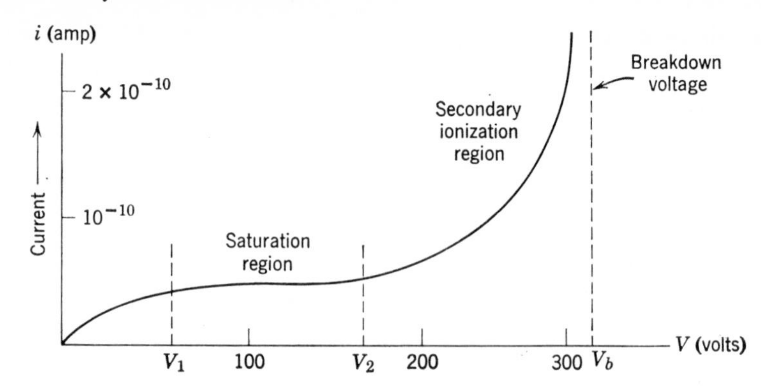

Fig. 9.8. Current-voltage relationship in a cold-cathode gas diode. (Townsend discharge region.)

saturation currents in a Townsend discharge are of the order of 10^{-10} amperes. Ionization chambers are operated in this saturation region.

At still higher voltages ($V > V_2$ in Fig. 9.8) some electrons acquire sufficient energy during their free paths to ionize some of the atoms with which they collide. This secondary ionization leads to a further increase in current as shown in Fig. 9.8. Proportional counters are operated in the region where currents are multiplied by secondary ionization. When the voltage exceeds a certain potential V_b (the sparking potential), breakdown occurs. After breakdown, currents increase enormously and glow or arc discharges begin. When breakdown occurs, the current must be limited by an external resistor or the tube or its power supply may be destroyed by overloading. A Geiger-Müller tube obtains its enormous current amplification through breakdown when triggered by initial ionization.

In a Townsend discharge the current is said to be non-self-maintaining since it depends on the number of ions formed by cosmic rays and trace amounts of natural radioactivity and fallout. After breakdown has occurred, the current becomes independent of external radiation and is said to be self-maintaining.

We now examine how the non-self-maintaining current depends on electrode separation d in a constant electric field when secondary ionization occurs. The increase dN in the number of electrons or ions due to secondary ionization as the electrons move a distance dx toward the anode is assumed to be proportional to the number of electrons N entering the interval dx and to the distance dx. That is,

$$dN = \alpha N \, dx \tag{9.25}$$

The constant of proportionality α is known as the first Townsend coefficient. α depends on the energy gained by an electron in a mean free path and the ionization energy of a gas atom. If α is independent of x and if we assume that all of the primary ionization N_0 occurs near the cathode, equation 9.25 integrates to

$$N = N_0 e^{\alpha x} \tag{9.26}$$

Here N is the number of electrons (resulting from the original number N_0) moving toward the anode at a distance x from the cathode. If the anode is at a distance d from the cathode, the number of electrons N_a reaching the anode is given by

$$N_a = N_0 e^{\alpha d} \tag{9.27}$$

If we assume that the average drift velocity of the electrons is independent of x, we may write

$$I_a = I_0 e^{\alpha d} \tag{9.28}$$

where I_a is the current of electrons reaching the anode and I_0 is the saturated electron current (produced near the cathode in the present case). It should be noted that I_a may be much greater than I_0. The discharge is non-self-maintaining since, when the primary ionization is removed ($I_0 = 0$), the measured current I_a becomes zero.

An electron avalanche is that multiplication process in which, by secondary ionization, $e^{\alpha d}$ electrons reach the anode for each electron leaving the cathode or its vicinity. Equation 9.26 implies that in a single avalanche the number of electrons in the avalanche front increases exponentially with distance toward the anode. The avalanche resulting from a single electron is sketched at successive intervals of time in Fig. 9.9.

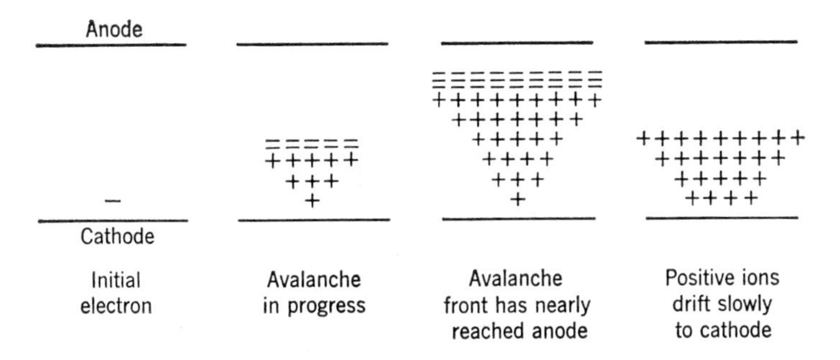

Fig. 9.9. An electron avalanche or a function of time.

We now consider the conditions under which breakdown will occur. For breakdown, some auxiliary process must emit second generation electrons from the cathode to make the discharge self-maintaining. Positive-ion secondary emission is one possible mechanism and photoelectric emission at the cathode from soft x-rays produced when the electron avalanche strikes the anode may also occur. If these are the principal mechanisms, the discharge after breakdown is called a glow discharge. If, on the average, γ electrons are emitted for each electron striking the anode, for each original or first generation electron leaving the cathode, $\gamma e^{\alpha d}$ electrons leave the cathode in the next generation. If $\gamma e^{\alpha d}$ is slightly greater than one, each original electron more than reproduces itself on the average and breakdown occurs (a population explosion). The threshold condition for breakdown may be written

$$\gamma e^{\alpha d} = 1 \tag{9.29}$$

The breakdown condition depends on (1) the nature of the cathode material (which determines γ), (2) the electrode separation d, and (3) the pressure, electrode voltage, and gas used (which jointly determine α).

Paschen's law states that the breakdown voltage is constant when the product of gas pressure and electrode separation is held constant. Since the pressure is proportional to the numerical density of gas molecules, the number of free paths between the electrodes will be constant if the product of pressure and electrode separation is constant. Under these conditions, and if the applied voltage is constant, the average energy electrons acquire between collisions will be constant, the number of secondary electrons produced in an avalanche will be constant, and the $e^{\alpha d}$ term in equation 9.29 will be constant. Thus breakdown occurs at the same voltage if the pressure and separation are changed, provided their product remains the same.

9.6 Glow discharges

In the derivation of the Langmuir-Child law in Chapter 6 we saw that the presence of space charge modifies the potential distribution between parallel plane electrodes. In that case, the space charge was negative and the potential versus distance curve which we obtained from Poisson's equation was concave upward. The positive ions which are formed in a gaseous discharge are much heavier than electrons and generally move much more slowly. In Fig. 9.9 we saw how the electron component of an avalanche was rapidly withdrawn to the

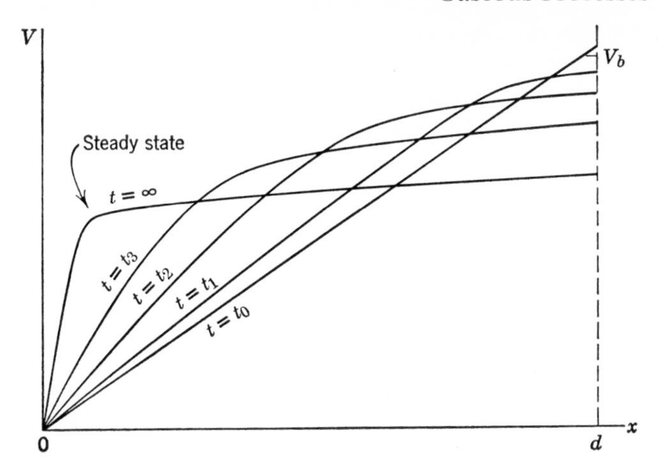

Fig. 9.10. Time variations of potential distributions during breakdown.

anode, whereas the positive ions were slowly collected by the cathode. During the breakdown process there is a predominance of positive ions present and the potential versus distance curve for the gas diode must be concave downward.

Figure 9.10 shows how the potential distribution in a parallel plane, gas-filled diode may change with time as breakdown proceeds towards an externally limited steady-state current and a glow discharge. At $t = t_0$, a voltage slightly greater than the breakdown voltage V_b is suddenly applied to the tube. At $t = t_0$ the net space charge is zero and the potential versus distance curve is linear. At $t \approx t_1$, avalanches begin and extend to the anode. The positive ion concentration is greatest near the anode, and the potential curve begins to depart from a straight line as the electrons are rapidly drawn to the anode. At $t \approx t_2$, the positive ion concentration becomes large enough to make the field near the anode small. The energy carried into the low-field region by the electrons raises the temperature in this region and thermal ionization begins. The avalanche ionization region begins to shrink toward the cathode. At $t \approx t_3$, the length of the avalanche region is greatly reduced and thermal ionization becomes of greater importance. The net charge in the low-field region approaches zero. When a steady state is achieved, the discharge has developed two distinct regions, a low-field, neutral region known as a *plasma* in which the ionization is produced thermally, and a narrow *cathode-fall region* or *sheath* in which electrons leaving the cathode are accelerated. A discharge of this type is called a glow discharge.

In the steady-state condition the current through the discharge has reached a value determined by the external resistance and potential (R and E_{bb} of Fig. 9.7). The hot plasma region is a good conductor of electricity as evidenced by the fact that the potential drop across the plasma is low. Although in the plasma the electron "temperature" is sufficiently high for ionization to occur thermally, only a very small fraction of the electron-atom collisions result in ionization, namely, those at the high-velocity end of the energy distribution. Usually only a small fraction of the total number of gas atoms are ionized. A rigorous definition of a plasma is given in Chapter 11.

In the steady-state case, the cathode-fall region has shrunk to a distance of the order of an electron mean free path. Since the major portion of the potential drop in a glow discharge occurs across the cathode-fall region, and electrons suffer few collisions in traversing this narrow region, they are accelerated to a sufficient kinetic energy to heat the plasma. The potential drop across the cathode-fall region is dependent upon the type of gas and the cathode material. The cathode-fall region is not electrically neutral. Since positive ions are much heavier than electrons, they pass through the cathode-fall region much more slowly than the electrons, and a net positive charge results. Although visual inspection of a glow discharge reveals that the cathode-fall and plasma regions have irregularities, such details are not of great importance to our understanding of glow discharges. The light emitted in a glow discharge results principally from photons emitted during the recombination of ions and electrons, and from collisionally excited neutral atoms.

In a glow discharge the electrons are released from the cathode principally by positive ion bombardment, a relatively inefficient process. The large voltage drop across the cathode-fall region provides the relatively large positive ion bombardment energies needed. In a glow discharge, the voltage across the tube must be less than the breakdown voltage because of the IR drop across the external resistor. Currents in glow discharges are generally in the milliampere range.

It is found experimentally that at low currents a glow discharge does not cover the full cross-sectional area of the cold cathode. As the current is changed in a glow discharge (via the external circuit), the cross-sectional area of the discharge adjusts to keep the current density approximately constant. As long as the cross-sectional area of the discharge is smaller than the geometrical cross section of the cathode, the potential drop across the tube remains approximately constant and the discharge is said to be a normal glow discharge. When the current is larger than that required for the discharge to fill the cross-

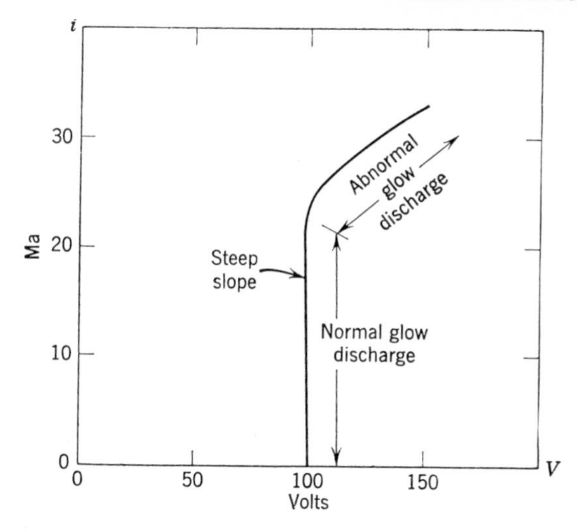

Fig. 9.11. Current-voltage characteristic of a glow discharge.

sectional area of the cathode, the potential drop increases and the discharge enters the so-called abnormal glow region. In the abnormal glow region, recombination losses increase sharply because the plasma comes in contact with the containing walls of the tube. The additional potential drop is needed to create the extra number of ions to balance the extra losses.

The current-voltage characteristic for a typical glow discharge is shown in Fig. 9.11. Currents in glow discharges must be limited by external resistances.

9.7 Arc discharges

Arc discharges occur after breakdown when an efficient mechanism is utilized for electron emission at the cathode. Electron emission in an arc discharge is usually obtained by thermionic emission, but may in some devices be the result of high-field emission. In arc discharges the total potential drop is usually of the order of the ionization potential of the gas. The much higher potential drop across the cathode-fall region in a glow discharge is needed to supply sufficient energy for secondary emission by the inefficient positive ion bombardment process.

Arc currents are normally in the ampere range. In arc discharges, higher gas pressures are usually used, higher current densities result,

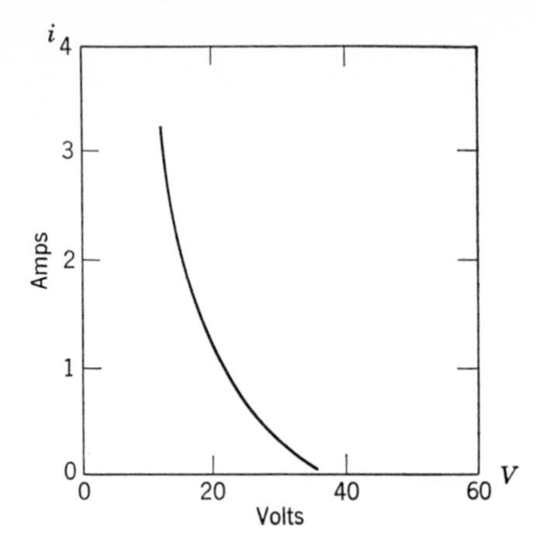

Fig. 9.12. Current-voltage characteristic of an arc discharge.

and arc plasmas are generally at a higher temperature than glow-discharge plasmas. Figure 9.12 shows a typical arc current-voltage characteristic. It will be noticed that the arc discharge has a negative resistance characteristic so that an external resistance is required to limit the current.

9.8 Sheaths

In section 9.6 we noted that the cathode-fall region of a glow discharge has a net positive charge. This cathode-fall region is a boundary region to the plasma and may be called a positive-ion sheath or a current-carrying sheath.

If one inserts a negative electrode into a plasma, it attracts a positive ion sheath by repelling the electrons of the plasma and attracting the positive ions. The thickness of the sheath is of the order of the mean free path for the gas. The positive-ion current from the plasma to the electrode becomes space-charge-limited, and for positive ions the plasma acts like a "cathode" and the negative electrode acts like an "anode." The thickness of a positive-ion sheath is frequently estimated by substitution in the Langmuir-Child law (equation 6.10). Equation 9.30 is the Langmuir-Child law rearranged for l_s, the sheath thickness.

$$l_s = \left(\frac{4}{9}\frac{\epsilon_0}{J}\right)^{1/2} (2\eta)^{1/4} V^{3/4} \tag{9.30}$$

Substitution of typical values of J and V into equation 9.30 leads to sheath thicknesses of the order of 10^{-2} cm.

If the positive ions in a sheath collide with neutral atoms or other ions while passing through the sheath, the current density becomes "mobility" limited in addition to space-charge-limited. We proceed to make an estimate of sheath thickness for this case. In Fig. 9.13 a plane electrode adjacent to a sheath is shown.

Using Maxwell's first equation (Appendix D), an alternate form of Poisson's equation, we may write

$$\frac{d\mathcal{E}}{dx} = \frac{\rho}{\epsilon_0} \tag{9.31}$$

from equation (8.14)

$$J = |\rho| \mu \mathcal{E} \tag{8.14}$$

Combining equations 8.14 and 9.31 gives

$$\mathcal{E} \frac{d\mathcal{E}}{dx} = \frac{J}{\mu \epsilon_0} \tag{9.32}$$

This equation becomes after integration

$$\mathcal{E}^2 = \frac{2Jx}{\mu \epsilon_0} + C \tag{9.33}$$

If the electric field in the plasma is negligible, the constant of integration C is zero. If V is the potential difference between the plasma and the negative electrode and l_s is the distance between them,

$$V = \int_0^{l_s} - \mathcal{E}\, dx = \int_0^{l_s} \left(\frac{2Jx}{\mu \epsilon_0}\right)^{1/2} dx \tag{9.34}$$

$$V = \sqrt{\frac{2J}{\mu \epsilon_0}} \cdot \frac{2}{3} l_s^{3/2} \tag{9.35}$$

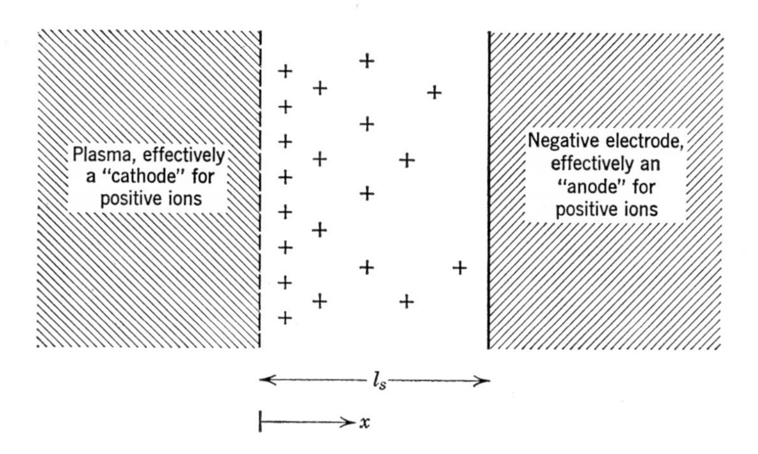

Fig. 9.13. Sheath "diode."

Hence

$$V^2 = \frac{8}{9} \frac{J l_s^3}{\mu \epsilon_0} \tag{9.36}$$

If A is the cross-sectional area of the sheath, the current i is given by

$$i = JA = \frac{9}{8} \frac{A \mu \epsilon_0}{l_s^3} V^2 \tag{9.37}$$

Note that the current here is proportional to V^2 and does not obey Ohm's law. Solving equation 9.36 for l_s, we obtain

$$l_s = \left(\frac{9}{8} \frac{\mu \epsilon_0}{J} \right)^{1/3} V^{2/3} \tag{9.38}$$

If we substitute typical values into equation 9.38, sheath thicknesses of the order of 10^{-3} cm are obtained. Thus both the Langmuir-Child model and the "mobility" model predict small sheath thicknesses.

Suggested References

L. Loeb, *Fundamental Processes of Electrical Discharge in Gases*, John Wiley and Sons, 1939. Loeb presents a somewhat loosely organized detailed discussion of gaseous processes on a slightly higher level.

S. C. Brown, *Basic Data of Plasma Physics*, Technology Press and John Wiley and Sons, 1959. This book contains useful clear discussions of many of the topics introduced in our Chapters 9 and 10.

PROBLEMS

9.1. Show that in the derivation of the Bohr stopping power formula

$$\Delta p_x = 0$$

9.2. Prove that a light body in collision with a heavy body initially at rest cannot stick to the heavy body and satisfy both momentum and energy conservation laws without losing energy or having a third body with which to share momentum.

9.3. An electron of mass m collides with a molecule of mass M at rest. Show that the fraction of the electron energy transferred to the molecule in a head-on collision is $4mM/(m + M)^2$, and evaluate this for $M = 200$ proton masses.

9.4. Experimentally it is found that a 5 Mev α-particle has a range of 5 cm in air at standard conditions.

(*a*) Estimate the range of a 5 Mev α-particle in aluminum.

(*b*) Estimate the range of a 5 Mev proton in air.

9.5. Show that the ranges of a proton, a deuteron, a triton, a He^3 particle, and an α-particle having the same initial velocity should be proportional to 1, 2, 3, $3/4$, and 1 respectively.

9.6. Carry out the steps between equations 9.3 and 9.5.

9.7. Determine how the numerical density of positive ions increases as a function of time when initially $n_+ = n_- = 0$ and ionization occurs uniformly throughout the region at a constant rate q. Let R represent the recombination coefficient.

9.8. Assume that recombination in a certain neutral region requires a three-body collision and that only ions can make collisions so that the rate of recombination becomes Rn_-^3, which is equal to Rn_+^3. Work out Problems 9.6 and 9.7 under these circumstances.

9.9. The microscopic electron cross section for argon may be obtained from Fig. 9.6. What would be the mean free path of a 16-ev electron in argon at 0.01 mm Hg pressure and 300° K?

9.10. If the "radius" of a nitrogen molecule is independent of electron velocity and is that given in Table 9.1, to what pressure must a diode containing nitrogen be evacuated if 1% of the electrons in the diode collide with nitrogen molecules in traveling 1 cm in the diode.

9.11. Calculate the "radius" of neon atoms at 0.1 mm pressure and 0° C when a beam of electrons is reduced to 20.8% of its original intensity in 10 cm.

9.12. A 1 ma electron beam is reduced by 99% by 5 cm of argon gas at 20° C and 0.0429 mm Hg pressure. Calculate the effective cross section of the argon atoms for electrons, and the mean free path of the electrons. Compare with the mean free path of argon atoms at the same T and p. The mean free path of argon atoms at STP is 8.84×10^{-6} cm.

9.13. Calculate the mean free path of a nitrogen molecule in gaseous nitrogen (radius of nitrogen molecule 1.9 Å) at atmospheric pressure, and at 10^{-6} mm Hg pressure. If a vacuum tube 0.02 meter in diameter contains nitrogen at this latter pressure, is a nitrogen molecule more likely to hit the tube wall or another molecule?

9.14. Let us assume for a derivation of the breakdown condition that

$$(1)\quad I_a = I_0 e^{\alpha d}$$

$$(2)\quad I_0 = \gamma(I_a - I_0)$$

(*a*) Explain in words the meaning of each symbol and equation.
(*b*) Eliminate all currents from these equations to determine the conditions for breakdown.

9.15. In a certain Townsend discharge the electron concentration at the cathode is zero (no photo current, no secondary emission). An external source produces a uniform volume ionization of q ions per meter³ per sec. Show that the current density at any distance x is given by

$$J = qe(e^{\alpha x} - 1)/\alpha$$

where α is the first Townsend coefficient.

9.16. Repeat the derivation leading to equation 9.38 using the assumption that the drift velocity is proportional to the cube root of the applied field (that is, $v_D = k\mathcal{E}^{1/3}$).

9.17. Determine the ratio of the sheath thicknesses predicted by equation 9.30 and 9.38. Explain your result qualitatively.

9.18. In a certain mercury arc discharge, the random ion current density is 6.0 amp/meter^2. If an electrode is at -10.0 volts with respect to the plasma, what is the approximate thickness of the positive ion sheath?

9.19. Ionized gas layers at several altitudes in the earth's atmosphere reflect radio waves. The frequency for critical reflection is proportional to the square root of the numerical density of the ionization (the plasma frequency, see Chapter 15) and to the secant of the angle of incidence. Some of the physical properties of those layers during daylight are

Name	Coefficient of recombination R	Altitude	Daytime ion density
E	1×10^{-8} cm^3 sec^{-1}	95 km	3×10^5 ions/cm^3
F_1	4×10^{-9} cm^3 sec^{-1}	150 km	4×10^5 ions/cm^3
F_2	1.5×10^{-10} cm^3 sec^{-1}	220 km	3×10^6 ions/cm^3

The ions are produced mainly by solar ultraviolet radiation.

(*a*) Determine the percent reduction of ion densities during a 12-hr night.

(*b*) Explain graphically from your result why short radio waves reflect greater distances at night.

10. gaseous devices

In this chapter we consider briefly the physics of electron devices in which the conductivity between the electrodes is in some way modified by the presence of a gas or vapor. We begin by treating gaseous devices which do not have a heated cathode and follow with a discussion of devices which utilize thermal energy for electron emission.

10.1 Ionization chambers

An ionization chamber is a cold-cathode, two-electrode gas tube in which the conductivity is dependent on the ionization from external radiation. Ionization chambers are used to measure the intensity of various types of cosmic and nuclear radiations. Ionization chambers may have electrodes of parallel plane, cylindrical, or almost any geometrical shape. The geometry of a particular chamber depends on the type of radiation to be measured.

The Bohr stopping power formula 9.16 indicates that the stopping power of a medium for fast-moving charged particles is proportional to the number of electrons per unit volume n. In addition, it may be shown that low-energy gamma and x-rays are principally absorbed by the photoelectric effect for which it is important to have a large number of electrons tightly bound to atoms. At higher energies where gamma rays and x-rays lose their energy by the Compton effect and by pair production, large numbers of loosely bound electrons and heavy nuclei are desirable for the absorbing medium of the ionization chamber. For these reasons, heavy gases such as argon and krypton are frequently used in ionization chambers. The numerical density of the gas atoms is kept large by operating the chamber at atmospheric pressure or greater. Sometimes pressures as high as 50 atmospheres are used.

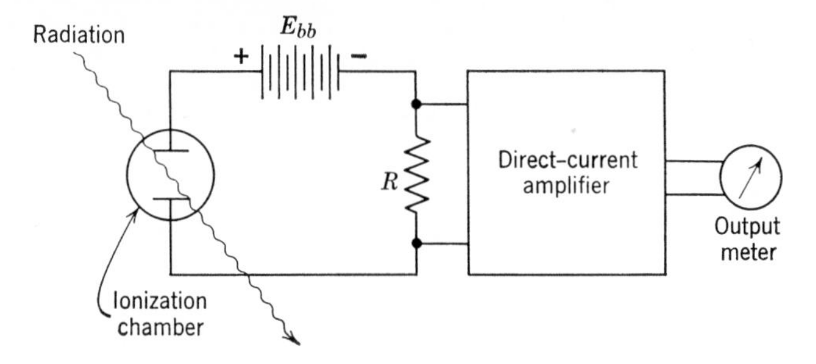

Fig. 10.1. Ionization chamber in use.

Ionization chambers are generally operated at voltages such that the Townsend current is in the saturation region (see Fig. 9.8) and secondary ionization multiplication does not occur.

Figure 10.1 shows a parallel-plate ionization chamber connected to a high-voltage source, an amplifier, and a meter for the measurement of radiation by a d-c technique. The battery E_{bb} provides the electric field within the ionization chamber to collect the ions. The resistance R is used to convert the small ionization current to a voltage which is then amplified and used to deflect a meter. It should be noted that when ionization chambers are operated under high-sensitivity conditions the time required for equilibrium currents to develop may be several seconds or larger. The time constant usually depends on RC, where C is the capacitance of the ionization chamber and R is the series resistance (generally very large).

Ionization chambers may be used to detect individual ionization trails formed by individual fast-moving heavy ions. In this pulse-detection application the amplifier must be an a-c amplifier and the output meter is frequently replaced by an oscilloscope. With the help of the Bohr stopping power theory (see equation 9.16) which indicates that the number of ions formed per unit length of path is proportional to the square of the atomic number of the fast-moving heavy ion, it is possible to distinguish types of radiation by pulse-amplitude measurements. The widths of the pulses depend on the times required for the ions formed by the radiation to reach the electrodes of the ionization chamber.

10.2 Proportional counters

Proportional counters are gas-filled, cold-cathode diodes which are similar to ionization chambers in geometry. They usually operate, however, at lower gas pressures and higher voltages in order that secondary ionization will increase the initial ionization currents by factors ranging from 10 to 500. The following is a brief discussion of this process which is sometimes called gas ion multiplication.

If we assume a parallel plane geometry and that N_0 ions are formed initially by the radiation at a location not far from the cathode, N electrons will reach the anode. N and N_0 are related by equation 9.27.

$$N = N_0 e^{\alpha d} \tag{9.27}$$

If γ is, as before, the probability of emitting a second-generation electron from the cathode per electron striking the anode, then $N\gamma$ second-generation electrons will be emitted at the cathode. The number of second-generation electrons reaching the anode will be

$$N\gamma e^{\alpha d} = \frac{N^2\gamma}{N_0} \tag{10.1}$$

Similarly, $N^2\gamma^2/N_0$ third-generation electrons are emitted at the cathode and the number of third-generation electrons reaching the anode will be

$$\frac{N^2\gamma^2 e^{\alpha d}}{N_0} = \frac{N^3\gamma^2}{N_0^2} \tag{10.2}$$

The total number of electrons reaching the anode, N_t, will then be

$$N_t = N + \frac{N^2\gamma}{N_0} + \frac{N^3\gamma^2}{N_0^2} + \frac{N^4\gamma^3}{N_0^3} + \cdots \tag{10.3}$$

By definition the gas ion multiplication ratio M is

$$M \equiv \frac{N_t}{N_0} \tag{10.4}$$

and using 10.3 we may write

$$M = \frac{N}{N_0} + \frac{N^2\gamma}{N_0^2} + \frac{N^3}{N_0^3}\gamma^2 + \frac{N^4}{N_0^4}\gamma^3 + \cdots \tag{10.5}$$

The gas ion multiplication ratio r per generation is

$$r = \frac{N}{N_0} = e^{\alpha d} \tag{10.6}$$

The total gas ion multiplication ratio M can be written

$$M = r + r^2\gamma + r^3\gamma^2 + \cdots = \frac{r}{1 - r\gamma} \tag{10.7}$$

Equation 10.7 indicates that M becomes large when $r\gamma$ approaches one.

When $r\gamma$ equals one, breakdown occurs. Note that here we have derived the breakdown condition from a build-up viewpoint, whereas in section 9.5 the breakdown condition was obtained from a steady-state viewpoint.

It should be noted that equation 10.7 requires the initial ionization to be close to the cathode and space-charge effects from the positive ions to be negligible. Proportional counters, as their name suggests, provide an output current proportional to the initial ionization and thus may be used to identify types of radiation.

10.3 Geiger-Müller tubes

Geiger-Müller tubes utilize breakdown to achieve enormous current amplification. In a Geiger-Müller tube (GMT) nonuniform electric fields enable the ionization to be shut off in such a way that the same amount of charge is collected during each discharge. Figure 10.2 shows the typical cylindrical geometry of a GMT during a discharge wherein a positive ion sheath develops around the anode. From Gauss' law the electric field $\mathcal{E}$ between the cylindrical anode of radius r_a and the concentric cylindrical cathode of radius r_c is found to be

$$\mathcal{E} = \frac{V}{r \ln \frac{r_c}{r_a}} \tag{10.8}$$

where V is the applied potential and r the distance from the axis of the cylinder. Notice that the field intensity is largest when $r \to r_a$ and when r_a is small. In GMTs fine tungsten wire anodes are often used.

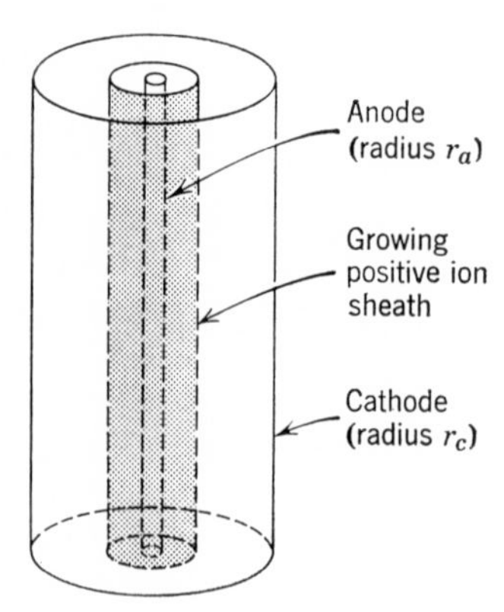

Fig. 10.2. Cylindrical Geiger-Müller tube during discharge.

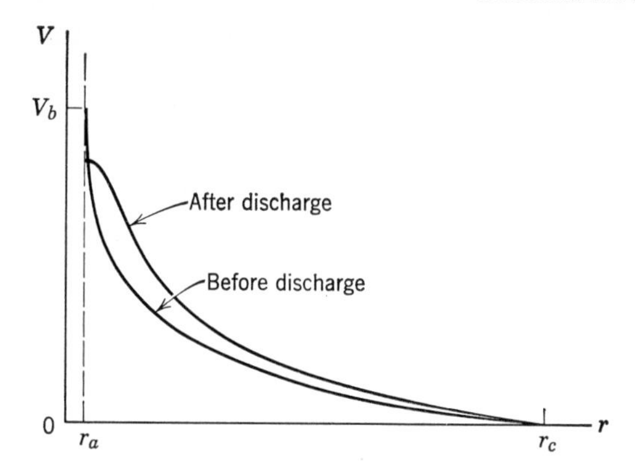

Fig. 10.3. Potential versus radius for cylindrical GMT.

When an ionizing particle or photon passes through the Geiger-Müller tube and the applied potential V is above the breakdown voltage V_b, avalanche ionization begins near the anode where the electric field is sufficient for some electrons to acquire enough energy for ionization in a free path. Electrons are rapidly drawn to the anode and a relatively slowly moving positive ion sheath develops around the anode. As this somewhat fuzzy positive ion sheath grows, the potential distribution within the tube changes as suggested by Fig. 10.3. The positive ion sheath will grow until the electric field intensity (the gradient of the potential) within the tube is insufficient to maintain the discharge. After the discharge stops, the positive ions drift to the cathode and in so doing induce a negative voltage pulse in the external circuitry. The "dead time" of a GMT is determined by the time required for the positive ions to be swept out of the tube, a time generally of the order of a fraction of a millisecond. During the "dead time" the tube cannot be triggered by external ionization.

Since the final number of positive ions in the sheath is determined by the point at which the discharge stops and is independent of the number of initial ions, GMT's provide a constant voltage pulse per discharge and are unable to distinguish different kinds of radiation.

Unless precautions are taken, photoelectric emission at the cathode of the Geiger-Müller tube will cause retriggering of the discharge after most of the positive ions have been swept out. The photons responsible for this photoelectric emission arise primarily during the recombination of the positive ions at the cathode. Retriggering of the discharge can be prevented either by shutting off the tube voltage momentarily and allowing the positive ions to be swept out by diffusion or by adding a quenching gas.

A suitable quenching gas, such as ethyl alcohol at 10% partial pressure, absorbs ultraviolet light and dissociates on neutralization. If the ionization potential of the quenching gas molecules is less than that of argon (a typical main gas constituent), the positive argon ions will collisionally remove electrons from the quenching gas molecules during the avalanche ionization and the positive ion collection periods. The ultraviolet photons which are released as a result of this charge transfer process are absorbed by the quenching gas and excite rotational or vibrational energy states. The positive ions reaching the cathode will consist entirely of alcohol-molecule ions if the mean free path of the gas is very small compared to the dimensions of the tube. When the alcohol ions reach the cathode and are neutralized, they dissociate (the molecules break up) and no photons result. Since no photons illuminate the cathode, retriggering cannot occur and quenching has been achieved. Since in the quenching process alcohol molecules are used up, such tubes have a finite life, of the order of 10^{10} counts. Geiger-Müller tubes using halogen gases for quenching have been developed. Such tubes have indefinite lives since halogen quenching molecules can reform after dissociation.

10.4 Voltage-regulator tubes

A voltage-regulator tube (VR tube) is a cold-cathode diode which, if operated in the normal glow discharge region with an appropriate series resistance, will provide an approximately constant voltage output over a moderate range of load resistances and/or supply voltages. Figure 10.4 shows a VR tube in such a circuit.

In Fig. 10.4, a change in the load resistance R_L will modify the distribution of current between the load resistance and VR tube in such a way that the voltage drop across the load is kept nearly constant. A change in the supply voltage E_{bb} results in a change in the potential drop across the series resistor R and a change in the current through the VR tube, but again the voltage across the load resistance is nearly constant provided the VR tube is operated in the normal glow range.

Voltage-regulator tubes generally have large cylindrical cathodes and concentric wire anodes. Their cathodes are generally coated with materials which have been found to increase γ, the probability of positive ion secondary emission. A larger value of γ results in a lower breakdown voltage and leads to a reduced cathode-fall potential drop (which approximately equals the total potential drop across the VR

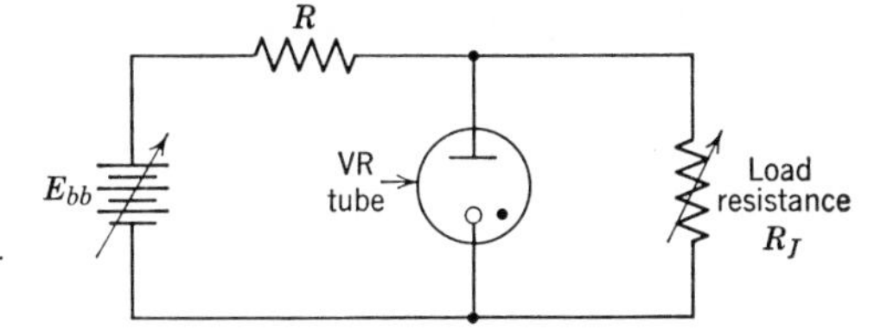

Fig. 10.4. Simple voltage regulator circuit.

tube). The potential drop across a VR tube also depends on the gas used (neon, helium, or argon). Voltage regulator tubes are made commercially for output voltages of 75, 90, 105, and 150 volts and currents ranging from 5 to 40 ma.

10.5 Gas-filled rectifier tubes

When gas-filled diodes are used for rectification of a-c current, arc discharges are utilized. The electron emission necessary to form the arc may result from a thermionically heated cathode, from high-field emission as in a mercury pool cathode tube, or from a smaller triggering arc as in an ignitron. Arc tubes may use mercury vapor as their conducting gas. Other arc tubes use hydrogen or a noble gas such as argon. If thermionic emission is used in a mercury-vapor tube, provision must be made for turning on the filament for a few minutes before plate voltage is applied to allow the mercury droplets present to evaporate and the mercury-vapor pressure to reach the operating pressure. If this is not done, the arc will not completely form, the potential drop will be high, and positive ions will strike the cathode with excessive energy. Cathodes can be destroyed by positive ion bombardment—a process called sputtering.

Arc rectifier tubes are used where high currents (amperes to thousands of amperes) are to be handled. The current-voltage curves are such that no current flows until a certain critical voltage is present (of the order of the ionization potential) and then the arc current-voltage curve rises nearly vertically with a negative-resistance characteristic. Arc tubes must have current-limiting resistances in series with all current carrying electrodes.

10.6 Thyratrons

A thyratron is a gas-filled triode with a thermionically heated cathode. It operates under arc discharge conditions. Figure 10.5 shows a sketch of a thyratron.

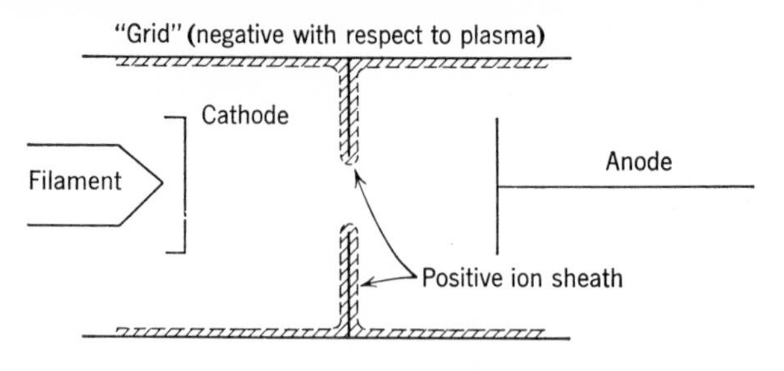

Fig. 10.5. A thyratron.

It is found experimentally that the anode voltage required for breakdown depends on the grid-cathode potential, and that for a fixed anode voltage the arc can be started by an appropriate adjustment of grid voltage. Figure 10.6 shows a curve known as the critical grid characteristic for a typical negative-control thyratron. In Fig. 10.6 the arc will be established if the point defined by the grid and anode voltages is anywhere on or above the characteristic curve (in the shaded region). Positive-control thyratrons also exist. These require positive grid voltages for breakdown.

Once established, the arc discharge in a thyratron cannot be turned off by making the grid more negative. The positive ion sheath surrounding the grid is much too small and does not grow enough with increased potential drops to modify significantly the cross-sectional area of the plasma passing through the grid. Currents in thyratrons are normally turned off by reducing the anode voltage to zero. Thyratrons must be brought to their full operating temperature before arc currents are passed through them to avoid destruction of their cathodes by high-energy positive-ion bombardment.

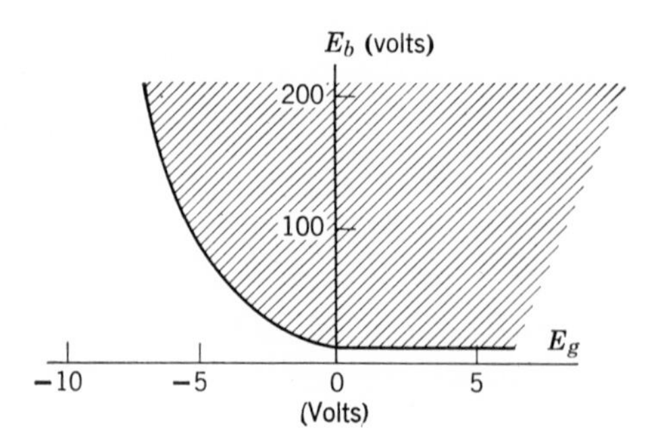

Fig. 10.6. Critical grid characteristic for a typical negative control thyratron.

Suggested References

A. E. S. Green, *Nuclear Physics*, McGraw-Hill Book Company, 1955. Chapter 5 contains readable descriptions of particle detectors and also of stopping power.

S. C. Brown, *Nucleonics* **2,** 19 (1948); **3,** 50 (1948); **3,** 46 (1948). These articles present a detailed but easily understood treatment of the physics of Geiger-Müller tubes.

J. Millman and S. Seely, *Electronics*, second edition, McGraw-Hill Book Company, 1951. Chapter 11 contains a helpful description of commercial gas tubes.

PROBLEMS

10.1. Let the mobility of argon ions in a parallel plane gas rectifier be 1.4 cm^2/volt-sec. If the anode-cathode distance is 1 cm, estimate the maximum frequency square wave of 1000-volt amplitude which this tube will rectify.

10.2. The figure below shows a parallel-plane ionization chamber connected to an amplifier and the output of the amplifier connected to an oscilloscope. Show pictorally how the pulse shape and amplitude on the oscilloscope, resulting from a cosmic ray particle, depend on (*a*) the angle θ; (*b*) the particle charge; and (*c*) the pressure of the gas in the ionization chamber.

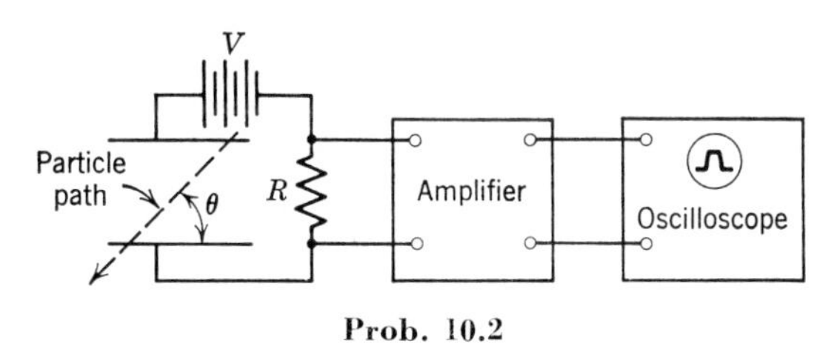

Prob. 10.2

10.3. If a Geiger-Müller tube of volume 50 cm^3 which contains argon and alcohol at partial pressures of 90 and 10 mm of Hg respectively has a lifetime of 10^{10} counts, calculate the number of alcohol molecules dissociated in each discharge, assuming the tube life ends when all the alcohol molecules have been dissociated.

10.4. (*a*) Prove that for a Geiger-Müller counter with dead time τ the relation between true and observed counting rates, n_t and n, is $n_t = \dfrac{n}{1 - n\tau}$.

(*b*) A Geiger-Müller tube with a dead time of 250 μsec indicates a counting rate of 15,100 counts/min. What is the true counting rate?

10.5. A Geiger-Müller tube with a 200 μsec dead time is used for 2-min counts on a source giving about 20,000 counts/min. Would the dead time loss be significant compared with the other errors present? (Root-mean-square fluctuation of total number N of counts $\approx \sqrt{N}$.)

10.6. Two radioactive sources give observed counting rates n_1 and n_2 separately, and n_{12} simultaneously, with a certain Geiger-Müller tube.

Prove that the counter dead time τ is approximately $\tau \approx \dfrac{n_1 + n_2 - n_{12}}{2n_1n_2}$, provided the counting rates are not too large.

10.7. Two cylindrical glow-discharge tubes have cathodes 5 and 10 cm long with diameters 2 and 4 cm respectively, made of the same material. The smaller tube has a current range of 5 to 50 ma. If the tubes are filled with the same gas to the same pressure, what is the maximum current rating of the larger tube?

10.8. Assume that the VR tube in Fig. 10.4 has the current-voltage characteristic given in Fig. 9.11. Let $E_{bb} = 200$ volts.

(*a*) For what value of R_L will the current in R_L be 5 ma?

(*b*) Choose an appropriate value of R.

(*c*) Using your value of R, compute the largest value E_{bb} can have and keep the current through R_L constant at 5 ma.

(*d*) If E_{bb} is constant at 200 volts, how small can R_L become and still have a constant voltage drop?

10.9. (*a*) An OC3 voltage-regulator tube is used in the circuit of Fig. 10.4, with load currents varying between 40 and 60 ma, and a fixed supply voltage of 245 volts. If the normal operating range of the tube is 5 to 40 ma, find the value of R to maintain the load voltage at 105 volts. (*b*) With R set as in part (*a*) find the range of supply voltage variation possible without affecting the output voltage.

10.10. The circuit of Fig. 10.4 can be changed into a simple relaxation oscillator by replacing the load resistor R_L by a capacitor C, which is continually charged by E_{bb} and intermittently discharged through the VR tube when the latter strikes. (*a*) Show that the period of oscillation is

$$T = RC \ln \left(\frac{E_{bb} - E_e}{E_{bb} - E_f} \right)$$

where E_f and E_e are the firing and extinguishing voltages of the gas tube. (*b*) Plot the voltage across the capacitor C as a function of time.

10.11. A thyratron is used as the discharging switch in a simple relaxation oscillator circuit in which a 0.01 μf capacitor is charged through a 50 K resistor from a 500-volt supply. The thyratron strikes at 260 volts and extinguishes at 10 volts. What is the frequency of the oscillation?

11. the liquid state and plasmas

One of the major gaps in physics lies in current knowledge concerning the liquid state. In this chapter we consider models of the liquid state, the phenomenon of superfluidity, and conduction processes in liquids. Plasmas are defined using the Debye-length concept originally developed for the theory of electrolytic conduction in liquids. A few effects peculiar to plasmas are described. The understanding of plasma characteristics is important, not only in gas-discharges previously considered but also in the following: thermonuclear fusion reactors, astrophysics, some electron-tube and solid-state devices, and the direct conversion of heat energy into electricity (thermionic converters).

11.1 Liquid-state models

In the study of gases the ideal gas law may be derived by considering the limiting case of low density. In solid-state physics one often considers another limiting case, that of a perfect crystal at absolute zero. The liquid state is, from a theoretical viewpoint, a somewhat awkward in-between state. Theoretical attempts at understanding the liquid state have generally regarded a liquid either as a limiting case of a very dense gas, or as a limiting case of a solid with numerous vacancies in its crystal structure.

Van der Waals presented a modification of the ideal gas law which more accurately described the behavior of real gases. His theory took into account molecular sizes and intermolecular forces. Van der Waals' law, in the high-density limit (molecules close together), has been used to describe the behavior of liquids. For example, his theory suggests that the compressibility of liquids should be small which is in agreement with experiment.

We begin a comparison between solids and liquids by listing in Table 11.1 the ratios of some characteristic constants for the same materials in solid and liquid forms. Examination of the ratios of the latent heats of fusion to the latent heats of vaporization for the substances listed in Table 11.1 suggests that the internal-energy change in the solid-liquid transition is small compared with the internal-energy change in the liquid-vapor transition. This implies that the work done against the short-range intermolecular forces in changing a sample from a solid to a liquid is small compared to the work done in vaporizing a liquid.

Table 11.1. Comparison of some characteristics of solids and liquids

	Latent Heat of Fusion Divided by Latent Heat of Vaporization	Specific Heat of Solid Divided by Specific Heat of Liquid	Density of Solid Divided by Density of Liquid
Na	0.024	0.94	1.02
Al	0.038	1.08	1.04
Hg	0.037	1.00	1.03
O_2	0.05	0.85	—
H_2O	0.127	1.00	0.92
NaCl	0.037	—	1.27
KBr	0.018	—	1.24

The specific heats of liquids are generally not greatly different from the specific heats of solids, which suggests that the internal energy-storage mechanism must be similar in liquids and solids. Also the densities of liquids are usually only a little less than the equivalent solids, which suggests that the average distances between atoms or molecules are only slightly greater in liquids than in solids. Thus far our evidence has suggested that in liquids, the atoms and molecules are in close contact, being held together by strong interatomic and intermolecular forces. We next consider how the atoms of a liquid are arranged with respect to one another. For help, we turn to x-ray diffraction.

In Chapter 1 we used the diffraction of electrons by the regular arrays of atoms in crystals as evidence for the wave characteristics of electrons. For many years solid-state physicists have used short

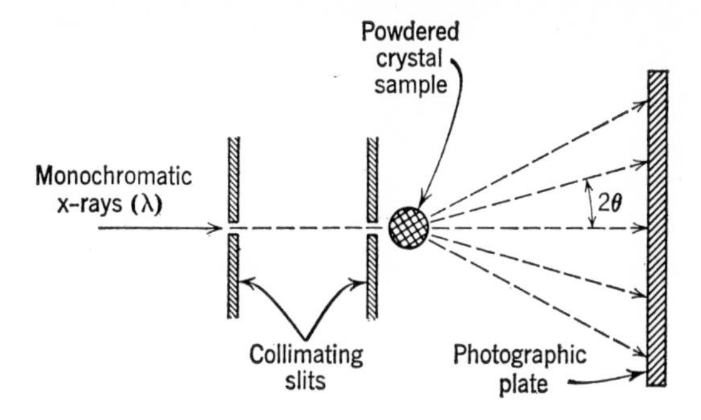

Fig. 11.1. X-ray diffraction experiment.

wavelength electromagnetic waves (x-rays) to study crystal structures. The Bragg relation, the basic equation for diffraction studies, is

$$n\lambda = 2a \sin \theta \tag{11.1}$$

where n is an integer, λ the wavelength, a the interatomic spacing, and θ is half the diffraction angle. A typical arrangement for taking x-ray diffraction pictures is shown in Fig. 11.1.

From a measurement of the diameters of the diffraction rings on the photographic plate, one may determine sin θ's and knowing λ one may compute interatomic separations in crystals and crystal structures. Figure 11.2 presents sketches of two diffraction patterns, one for a typical powdered crystalline solid and the other for a typical liquid.

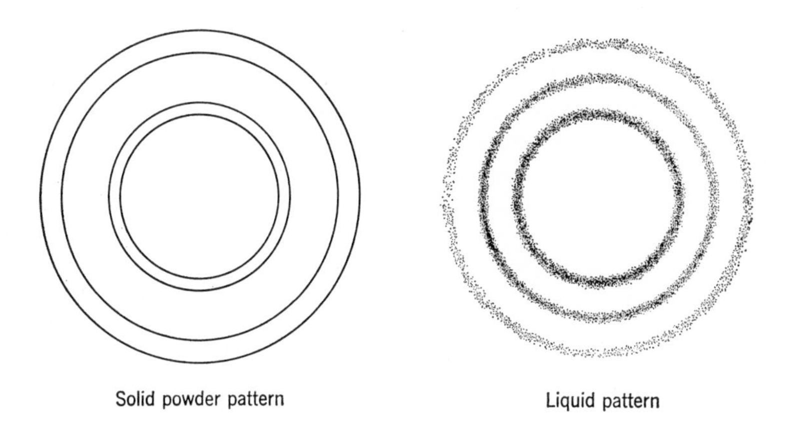

Fig. 11.2. X-ray diffraction patterns.

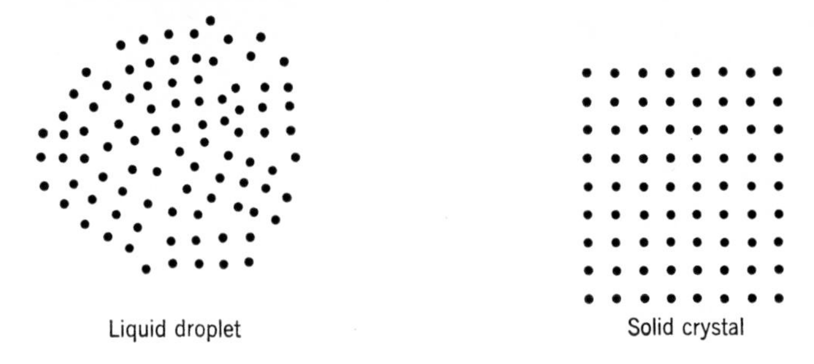

Fig. 11.3. Micro-microscopic views of liquids and solids.

This figure suggests that the patterns are similar, except that the powder pattern gives sharp lines and the liquid pattern gives lines that are fuzzy and faint. We may regard the powered crystal sample as a collection of randomly arranged diffraction gratings. We recall from optics that the resolving power of a grating is proportional to the number of lines in the grating or the width of the grating in wavelength units. In powdered crystal samples the widths of the individual particles are large (many thousands of x-ray wavelengths) and therefore the diffraction lines are well defined and sharp.

The fact that x-rays are diffracted by liquids reveals that liquids have some crystal structure. That the rings are fuzzy and weak shows that the sizes of the crystal elements (diffraction gratings) in liquids are small. In other words, the crystal structure in liquids has short range order. We may think of a liquid as equivalent to an extremely fine powder wherein each particle is cohesively held to its neighbors. Such a model has the flow characteristics and the constant volume characteristics which we associate with liquids. An equivalent way of describing the distinction between a solid and a liquid is to say that the liquid form has many more dislocations or vacancies per unit volume than the same material in solid form. Figure 11.3 suggests the difference between the internal structures of liquids and solids.

The number of atoms per liquid "crystallite" varies from one material to another. The lack of sharpness of the diffraction patterns suggests that the ordering in liquids extends for distances of two to five atomic layers. One may also make an estimate of the sizes of the "crystallites" by noting that the density of a liquid is usually about 3 or 4% less than that of the equivalent solid.

Since man has not yet been able to solve analytically the three-body problem (in which significant forces act between three bodies), we should not be surprised that he has not yet been able to treat adequately liquids, which are many-body problems. These problems become even more difficult when quantum-mechanical solutions are attempted. Thus far little progress has been made toward a fundamental understanding of the liquid state.

11.2 Superfluidity

A particular problem concerning liquids for which the techniques of quantum mechanics (and statistical mechanics) do provide an understanding is that of superfluidity, a startling phenomenon that occurs in liquid helium below 2.18° K. Helium atoms are bosons, that is, they obey Bose-Einstein statistics. Our understanding of superfluidity is approached by calculating the numerical density N/V of bosons in a three-dimensional "box" as a function of temperature.

The average number P_{BE} of particles per state under the assumptions of Bose-Einstein statistics is given in Chapter 3 as

$$P_{\text{BE}} = \frac{1}{e^{\alpha_1+\beta_1 E} - 1} \tag{3.31}$$

Since from 3.41 $\beta_1 = 1/kT$, we write

$$P_{\text{BE}} = \frac{1}{e^{E/kT+\alpha_1} - 1} \tag{11.2}$$

The energy density of states dS/dE is half of that given by equation 2.46

$$\frac{dS}{dE} = \frac{4\pi V \sqrt{2} m^{3/2} E^{1/2}}{h^3} \tag{11.3}$$

The factor of one-half appears because helium atoms have zero spin and there is only one, and not two, spin state for each spatial wavefunction. Following the technique of section 3.5,

$$N = \int_0^\infty P_{\text{BE}} \frac{dS}{dE}\, dE = \frac{4\pi V \sqrt{2}\, m^{3/2}}{h^3} \int_0^\infty \frac{E^{1/2}\, dE}{e^{E/kT+\alpha_1} - 1} \tag{11.4}$$

The result after integration may be expressed as

$$N = V \left(\frac{2\pi mkT}{h^2}\right)^{3/2} F(\alpha_1) \tag{11.5}$$

where $F(\alpha_1)$ is a function of the parameter α_1. Some of the values of $F(\alpha_1)$ are given in Table 11.2.

Only positive values of the normalization constant α_1 are permissible since a negative α_1 would imply in equation 11.2 negative probabilities for very low E's. Since the maximum value of $F(\alpha_1)$ is 2.612, we may write

$$\frac{N}{V} \leq 2.612 \left(\frac{2\pi mkT}{h^2}\right)^{3/2} \tag{11.6}$$

Table 11.2. Values of the function $F(\alpha_1)$

α_1	$F(\alpha_1)$
0.000	2.612
0.001	2.501
0.010	2.271
0.100	1.635
0.200	1.318
0.500	0.815
1.000	0.426
2.000	0.142

For a liquid, N/V is essentially constant, so that this equation cannot be satisfied using our simple model if the temperature is lower than a critical temperature T_c given by

$$T_c = \frac{h^2}{2\pi mk}\left(\frac{N}{2.612V}\right)^{2/3} \tag{11.7}$$

Equation 11.6 suggests that something peculiar may happen to a Bose-Einstein fluid if the temperature is sufficiently reduced.

Equation 11.6 taken at face value indicates that at temperatures below T_c some atoms must "disappear." In effect, at temperatures below T_c helium atoms begin to drop into a "zero-momentum" state which our theory has not taken into account. In view of the uncertainty principle, this "zero-momentum" state means that the helium atom wavepackets have macroscopic sizes, that is, wavelengths of the order of the size of the containing vessel. Particles which obey the Bose-Einstein statistics are not subject to the exclusion principle and thus a large number of bosons may occupy this "zero momentum" state. As the temperature of the liquid helium is reduced below T_c, a larger and larger fraction of the helium atoms drop into this lowest energy or superfluid state. It is customary to speak of helium at temperatures above 2.18° K as helium I, and helium at temperatures below 2.18° K as helium II. Helium

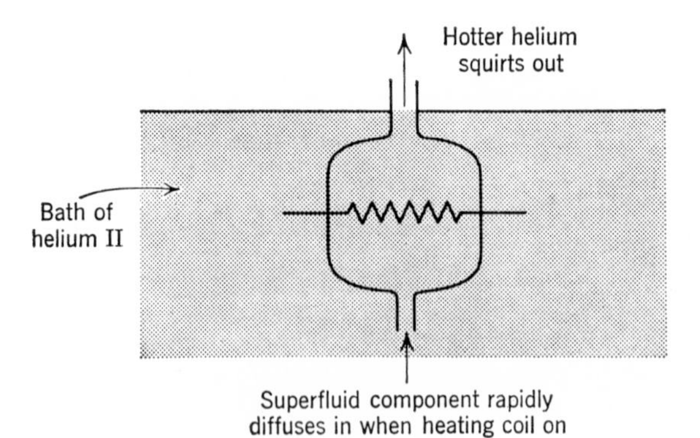

Fig. 11.4. Fountain effect.

II may be thought of as a noninteracting mixture of normal helium atoms and superfluid helium atoms.

The property of helium II from which the name superfluidity is derived is that its viscosity becomes exceedingly small and it can easily pass through holes as small as 10^{-5} in. in diameter. In fact, Pyrex glass is too porous to contain helium II. Another "super" characteristic of helium II is its enormous thermal conductivity which is so large that helium II boils without bubbling.

Figure 11.4 shows a diagram for an experiment which demonstrates the "fountain" effect in helium II. Heating helium II reduces the fraction of the superfluid component inside the chamber and additional superfluid molecules rapidly diffuse into the heated chamber because of a concentration gradient. Since the normal component of helium II cannot diffuse out of the chamber as rapidly as the superfluid component can diffuse in, the pressure in the chamber rises and helium II squirts out the top of the chamber.

11.3 Conduction in liquids

Liquid metals conduct electricity by the same mechanism as solid metals, with conductivity values on the order of one-half of those of the same materials in solid form. Since metallic conductors are discussed from the band theory viewpoint in Chapter 12, we make no further comment concerning them here.

Electrolytic conduction in liquids is of considerable importance. When salts such as NaCl or $CuSO_4$ dissolve in water, the Coulomb forces holding the atomic constituents of the molecules together are weakened by the high dielectric constant of water ($\kappa = 80$). In fact, it is generally true that good solvents for ionic crystals have large dielectric constants. The thermal energy of the atoms of molecules in solutions is normally sufficient to dissociate the molecules resulting in the formation of ions as suggested by Arrhenius. The conduction of current in electrolytic solution in the presence of an electric field is the result of the motion of ions impeded by collisions with other ions and molecules. The conductivity σ of *dilute* solutions is given by

$$\sigma = \rho_a \mu_a + \rho_k \mu_k \tag{11.8}$$

where ρ_a is the charge density due to positive ions (anions), ρ_k is the charge density due to negative ions (cations), and μ_a and μ_k are the mobilities of these ions. Since ions have relatively large masses and since the molecules of a liquid are close together, the mobilities of electrolytic ions are small (see equation 8.19). The conductivity of solutions depends on ion concentration, and conductivity measurements may be used to measure the concentrations of solutions. For example, the purity of water is often specified by its conductivity.

At high concentrations the conductivities of electrolytes are no longer proportional to concentration and are much less than one would expect if the ions in a liquid were completely dissociated. Debye and Hückel first explained this and other phenomena by calling attention to the fact that a charge in an electrolyte will tend to attract an oppositely charged cloud of ions around it. The size of the individual ion clouds or "atmospheres" is specified by the Debye length λ_D and depends on the temperature and concentration of the ions. The conductivity of electrolytes at high concentrations depends partly on the size of these localized ion "atmospheres." We will see in the next section that the Debye length is an important parameter in plasma physics.

In electrolytic conduction, ions are drawn to both electrodes. In some cases when these ions are neutralized at the electrodes they appear in gaseous form. When metal ions are neutralized, they often electroplate the electrodes. In some other cases nonconducting metal oxides are deposited on the electrodes. The electrolytic capacitor, for example, utilizes a thin aluminum-oxide film electrolytically deposited to insulate the plates. If the polarity of an electrolytic capacitor is reversed, the oxide coating dissolves and the capacitor may destroy itself. However, at low currents electrolytic capacitors may be used for rectification.

Electrolytic conductivities increase nonlinearly with temperature by amounts of the order of 2% per degree centigrade in aqueous solutions. Water solutions of electrolytes show an interesting shrinkage in volume ("electrostriction") as the ionization of an electrolyte is increased. Using the inverse of this effect, it is possible to make devices whose conductivity is pressure sensitive.

11.4 Plasmas

Although it is fashionable to speak of plasmas as the fourth state of matter, plasmas are not really a separate state, but rather an environmental phenomenon which the gaseous, liquid, and solid states can experience in the presence of sufficient ionization. We have already considered some aspects of plasmas in Chapter 9 in our discussion of glow and arc discharges and sheath thickness. In Chapter 9 we identified a conducting region in which mobile positive and negative charges appear in nearly equal amounts as a plasma. We now add a further restriction to the definition of a plasma using the Debye length mentioned in the previous section. Let us consider a gaseous plasma in which the positive particles are ions and the negative particles are electrons.

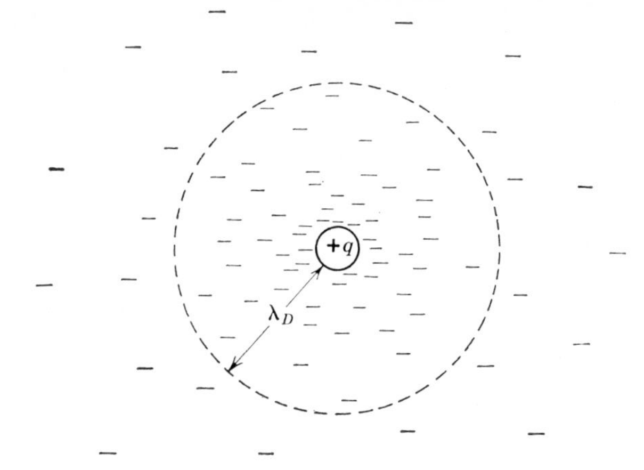

Fig. 11.5. Net charge density in vicinity of a charge irregularity $(+q)$ within a plasma.

If we add a perturbing positive charge of small dimension to a plasma, a cloud of negative electrons will gather in the vicinity of this positive charge and will effectively shield it from its surroundings. The Debye length is a measure of the size of such a space-charge cloud surrounding a charge in an ionized, but neutral, environment. An ionized environment is correctly called a plasma only when the Debye length is small compared with the dimensions of the environment. In such a case there is room in the medium for this shielding or screening action to occur, and the tendency for charge neutrality to be maintained may be asserted.

The following is a simple discussion of the Debye length λ_D. In Fig. 11.5 a positive charge q is shown along with the net negative charge cloud which surrounds it in a plasma. We let n_0 be the average numerical density of positive ions and $n_e(r)$ be the numerical density of the electrons. In the vicinity of the positive charge q, $n_e(r)$ is greater than n_0. If we assume that the electrons are in thermodynamic equilibrium, we may write from the Boltzmann relation 8.31 the following expression involving the potential $V(r)$ near q.

$$n_e(r) = n_0 e^{eV/kT} \tag{11.9}$$

If eV is small in comparison with kT,

$$n_e(r) = n_0 \left(1 + \frac{eV}{kT}\right) \tag{11.10}$$

The perturbing potential V must also satisfy Poisson's equation; hence

$$\nabla^2 V = -\frac{\rho}{\epsilon_0} = -\frac{n_0 - n_e}{\epsilon_0} e \tag{11.11}$$

Combining 11.11 and 11.10

$$\nabla^2 V = \frac{n_0 e^2 V}{\epsilon_0 kT} \tag{11.12}$$

If, for convenience, we define the parameter λ_D, the Debye length, to be

$$\lambda_D \equiv \sqrt{\frac{\epsilon_0 kT}{n_0 e^2}} \tag{11.13}$$

we may rewrite 11.12 as

$$\nabla^2 V = \frac{1}{\lambda_D{}^2} V \tag{11.14}$$

Using the spherical symmetry of the electron cloud around the perturbing positive charge q, we write

$$\frac{1}{r^2}\frac{d}{dr}\left(r^2 \frac{dV}{dr}\right) = \frac{V}{\lambda_D{}^2} \tag{11.15}$$

The potential V must satisfy two boundary conditions:

$$r \to \infty, \qquad V \to 0$$

$$r \to 0, \qquad V \to \frac{q}{4\pi\epsilon_0 r} \tag{11.16}$$

The second boundary condition represents the Coulomb potential close to the perturbing charge where the effects of the electron atmosphere are negligible. The solution of 11.15 which satisfies 11.16 is

$$V = \frac{q}{4\pi\epsilon_0 r} e^{-r/\lambda_D} \tag{11.17}$$

From 11.17 we see that the Debye length is the distance at which the potential falls to $1/e$ ($= 0.36$) of the value it would have at that distance in the absence of the neutralizing electron cloud. Note that at distances greater than several Debye lengths from the perturbing charge its effect is essentially completely screened. From equation 11.13 we note that the Debye length is dependent on the concentration of the ions and their temperature. The Debye length increases with increasing temperature since the electrons in the shielding cloud then have a higher average kinetic energy and tend to wander further from the perturbing charge. The Debye length decreases with increasing density of ions.

Since a formal definition of a plasma has now been presented, we call attention to the fact that material on plasma physics appears in several different places in this textbook in order to emphasize the generality of the plasma concept. Plasmas were first encountered in the chapter on gaseous processes (Chapter 9). This chapter, which is associated with the liquid state, defines and extends the understanding of plasmas. In Chapter 15 some resonant characteristics of and wave propagation in plasmas are introduced in connection with the physics of electron beams. Although not explicitly described in Chapters 12 to 14, solid-state plasma effects are important if the concentrations of charge carriers are sufficiently large. The development of solid-state plasmas into useful devices holds great promise.

Plasmas play a fundamental role in thermionic energy converters (conversion of heat directly to electricity with significant efficiency). Space ships probably will utilize plasma propulsion and guidance techniques after launching. The sun's corona and the earth's ionosphere are plasmas. Fusion reactor research utilizes techniques of plasma heating and compression. It is important in fusion reactors and in most other plasma devices to keep the plasma away from the walls of its container. In the next section we briefly describe some plasma measurement techniques, plasma confinement, the pinch effect, and some instabilities associated with the pinch effect.

11.5 Some plasma effects

The physical quantities of interest in a gaseous plasma are the temperature, random current densities, and the numerical densities of the electrons and positive ions in the plasma. Langmuir and Mott-Smith have shown how the current-voltage characteristic of a small electrode or probe inserted into a plasma can be interpreted to obtain these quantities. As the probe potential is made more and more negative with respect to the plasma, fewer and fewer electrons are energetically able to reach the probe, and at sufficiently large negative potentials only a small current due to random positive ion bombardment will reach the probe. From this random positive ion current and the probe area the random positive ion current density may be obtained. When the probe is at zero potential with respect to the

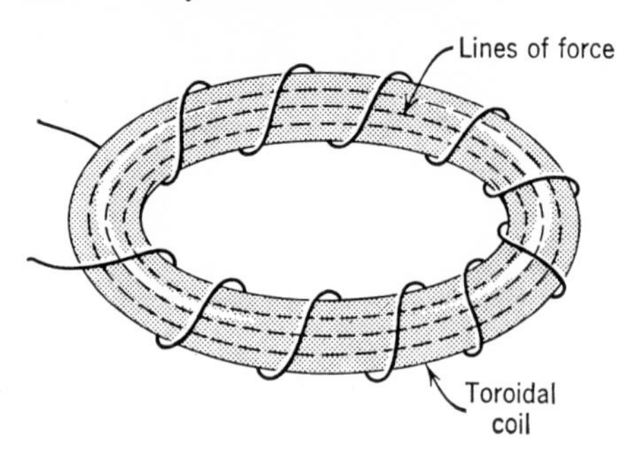

Fig. 11.6. Toroidal coil and magnetic field for plasma confinement.

plasma, the total random electron current and positive ion currents are intercepted and collected. By subtraction the random electron current density may be obtained. From the decrease in the electron current as a function of the increasingly negative potential of the probe, and the Boltzmann relation 8.31, the electron temperature may be obtained. Electron temperatures in arc-type plasmas may run as high as 50,000° K. If the plasma persists for a sufficiently long time, the electron temperature will decrease and become equal to the positive ion temperature. The numerical density of the electrons may be calculated by kinetic theory techniques from the random electron current density once the electron temperature is known. Since plasmas are electrically neutral, the average numerical density of the positive ions equals the average numerical density of the electrons. Generally, in gaseous plasmas only a small fraction of the total number of atoms is ionized. However, cesium ion plasmas can be produced in which nearly complete ionization is achieved.

If a plasma is produced in a small container, the equilibrium electron and ion densities are determined by the rates at which ions are formed and diffuse to the containing walls where recombination readily occurs. To achieve high-density plasmas, means must be found to minimize the rate at which ions reach the walls of the container. If we place the plasma in a magnetic field, the motions of the ions will be helical, and their transport perpendicular to the magnetic field will be limited to the discontinuities in their helical paths produced by collisions. The ions can still move relatively freely parallel to the magnetic field. If a toroidal field geometry is used (see Fig. 11.6), magnetic lines of force are not intercepted by the containing walls and ion transport to the walls is reduced. Such a container is called a magnetic bottle.

Another form of a magnetic bottle is shown in Fig. 11.7. In this

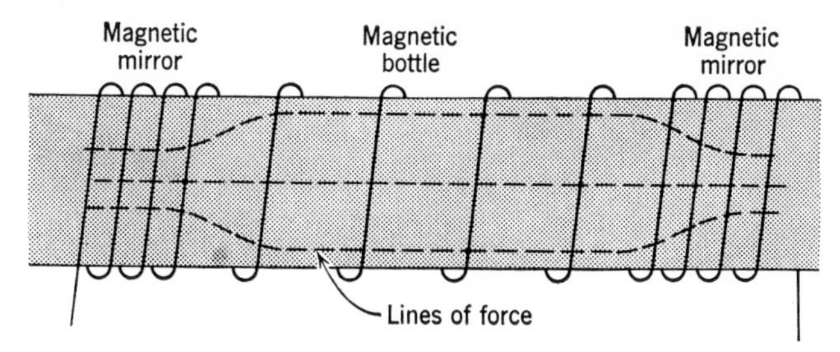

Fig. 11.7. Cylindrical field with magnetic mirrors.

type of bottle magnetic mirrors are placed at each end of a cylindrical field. A spiraling ion acts like a magnetic dipole. Whenever such a magnetic dipole reaches a region of increasing magnetic field such as exists at each magnetic mirror, the dipole experiences a reflecting force. The Van Allen radiation belts surrounding the earth and other planets are an interesting example of particle confinement by a magnetic bottle.

In fusion reactor research an interesting effect known as the pinch effect is utilized to compress a plasma in order to reach the high temperatures required for the release of significant energy. Let us consider a cylindrical plasma through which a strong cylindrically symmetric current is passing. The magnetic field lines outside the cylindrical current are concentric circles as shown in Fig. 11.8. The magnetic field within the plasma has a similar geometry except that it is weaker and decreases to zero at the axis of the cylinder. The

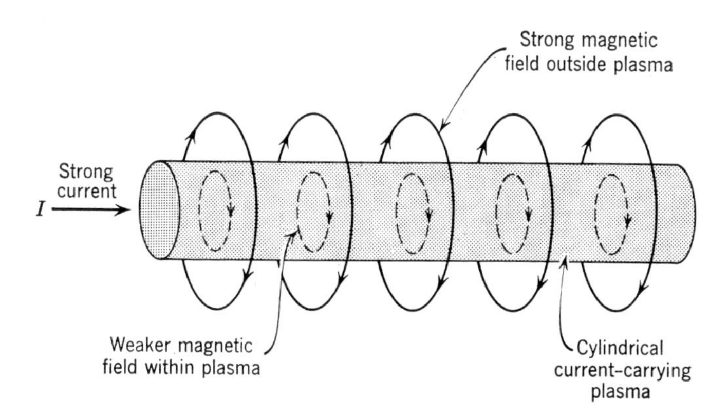

Fig. 11.8. Pinch effect geometry for cylindrical current.

direction of the self-created field causes the deflection of outer ions and electrons inward toward the axis, and decreases the cross-sectional area of the current-carrying plasma. Such a reduction of the cross-sectional area and the volume of the plasma is an example of the pinch effect. The pinch effect may be demonstrated in any good conductor. When the pinch is the result of the internal current in the conductor, it is known as a self-pinch. A pinch may also be the result of an increasing externally applied magnetic field. We may think of a pinch as the result of a sort of magnetic pressure difference between a strong field region and a weak field region acting on the current carriers in a conductor.

Experimentally it is found that the self-pinch discussed for cylindrical geometry in the previous paragraph will not in general reduce the cross-sectional area of the plasma uniformly along its length. Many types of irregularities or instabilities may appear and grow as a pinch progresses. We confine ourselves to brief qualitative comments concerning sausage- and kink-type instabilities.

Figure 11.9 shows the circular magnetic lines of force around a plasma at a constriction of a sausage-type instability. Since the self-generated magnetic field at the surface of the plasma is strongest where the cross-sectional area is the smallest, any variations in cross-sectional area tend to be magnified as a pinch proceeds.

In Fig. 11.10 a current-carrying plasma with a constant cross-sectional area and a kink instability is shown. Since the pinch forces are stronger on the "concave" side of the kink than they are on the "convex" side, the kink instability will grow and the plasma will be deflected to the left at the vicinity of the kink. The motion of such a kink instability may continue until the plasma touches the containing

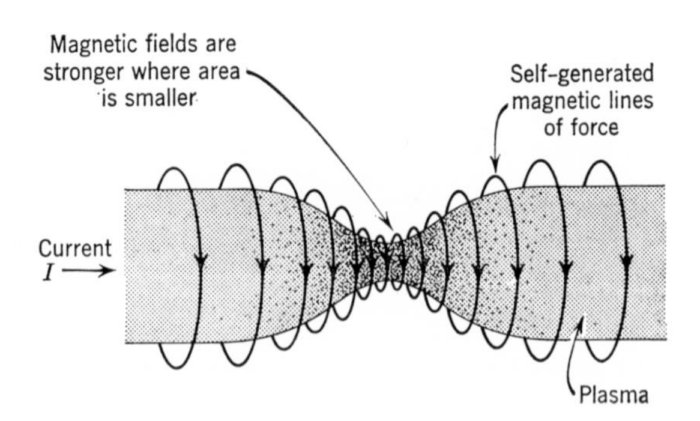

Fig. 11.9. Sausage instability

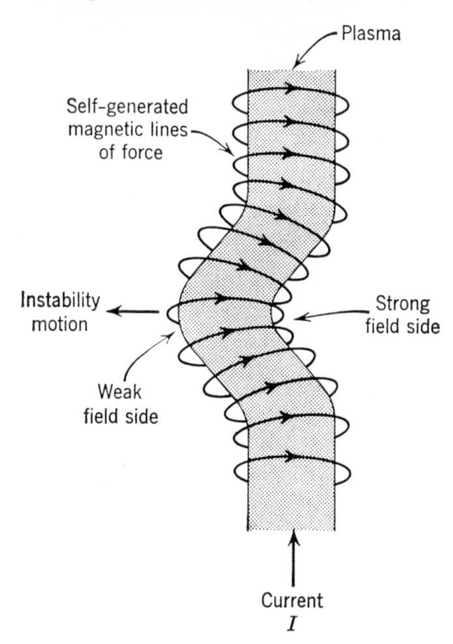

Fig. 11.10. Kink instability.

wall and either recombination extinguishes the plasma or the plasma melts the containing wall.

We will see in Chapter 15 that plasmas have inherent resonant frequencies of oscillation and are capable of transmitting a variety of unusual waves. Although these waves may be generated by the instabilities previously referred to, they can also be generated in controlled fashion and used for amplification at high frequencies.

Suggested References

S. C. Brown, *Basic Data of Plasma Physics*, Technology Press and John Wiley and Sons, 1959. This book is a useful readable basic reference for descriptions of plasma phenomena as well as for data.

F. London, *Superfluids*, John Wiley and Sons, 1950. London presents a somewhat advanced treatment of the many fascinating aspects of superfluid helium. However, much of the book should be understandable to an advanced undergraduate.

L. Spitzer, *Physics of Fully Ionized Gases*, Interscience, 1956. This monograph is another basic reference in the field of plasmas.

S. Glasstone, *Textbook of Physical Chemistry*, D. Van Nostrand Co., 1941. The Debye-Hückel theory, leading to the change of activity and conductivity with ion concentration and the concept of Debye length in electrolytes, is discussed in some detail on pages 956–959.

PROBLEMS

11.1. (*a*) How would you expect the velocity of sound in liquids to compare with that for the same material in solid form?

(*b*) What does handbook data reveal concerning this point?

11.2. Attempt to predict the lambda point for liquid helium from equation 11.7. The density of liquid helium is approximately 0.23 gram/cm^3.

11.3. Peter Kapitza, a Russian physicist, demonstrated the fountain effect with a rocket, such as that sketched below, immersed in a bath of helium II. Explain how the rocket works.

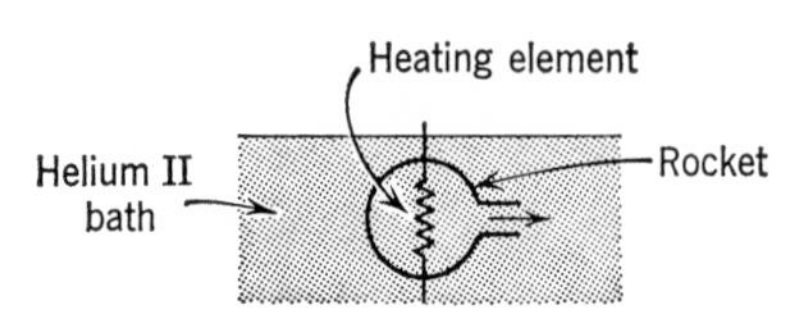

Prob. 11.3

11.4. Show that equation 11.17 is a solution of equation 11.15 which satisfies the boundary conditions of equation 11.16.

11.5. Repeat and interpret the derivation of the Debye length for a uniform parallel-plane charge in a plasma.

11.6. (*a*) Compute the Debye length for a partially ionized gas with electron and positive ion concentrations of 10^{12}/cm^3 at room temperature.

(*b*) How small can the container be and still have the gas retain the properties of a plasma?

11.7. A certain vacuum tube of volume 50 cm^3 contains a gas at a pressure of 1 mm of mercury and a temperature of 500° K. If 0.1% of the gas is ionized and the electron temperature is the same as the gas temperature, determine whether the contents behave as a plasma.

11.8. From the discussion in the first paragraph of section 11.5, sketch the shape of the current-voltage relation for a probe inserted in a plasma.

12. the band theory of solids

We now begin a discussion of solid-state physical electronics. The most successful approach to the electrical behavior of crystalline solids has been the band theory. In Chapter 2 we touched briefly upon the concept of energy bands from the standpoint of the splitting of atomic energy levels when atoms are brought together in molecules or crystals. In Chapter 12, we develop and utilize the main features of the band theory. It is hoped that the student will learn a "language" for the discussion of semiconductors and semiconductor devices in Chapters 13 and 14 and that he will acquire a physical insight into the behavior of electrons in crystals.

12.1 The potential energy of electrons in a crystal

The first consideration is to reinforce the concept that the allowed energy levels of electrons in crystals are grouped into bands which are separated by gaps of energy in which there are no allowed states. This is done by examining the solutions of Schroedinger's equation and the values of total energy E for which admissible solutions occur.

There are two important aspects of any problem to which the Schroedinger equation is applied. One is the dependence of the potential energy on the spatial coordinates; the second is the boundary conditions of the problem. For a *perfect* crystal the potential energy is periodic in space; that is, in any given direction the potential energy repeats over and over again after a distance equal to the separation of the lattice ions in that direction. Perfect crystals exist only in our

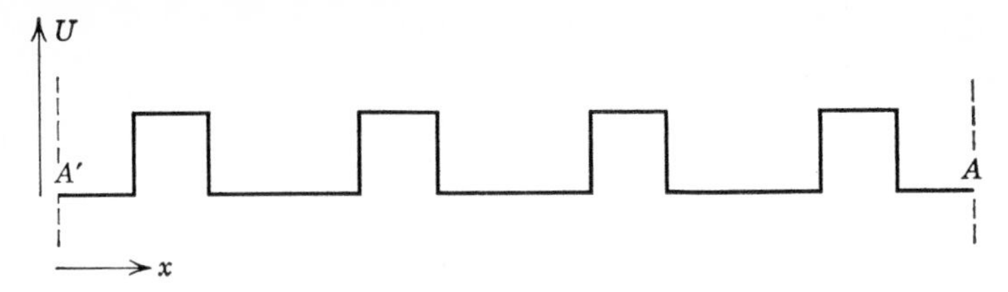

Fig. 12.1. The one-dimensional Kronig-Penney approximation to the potential energy of an electron in a crystal.

minds. In a real crystal there are always impurities and crystal defects, but more important, the atomic nuclei oscillate about their equilibrium positions. For the purposes of our discussion here we shall treat a perfect crystal and, to simplify matters even further, a one-dimensional one. The particular form of the potential energy we shall use is the so-called Kronig-Penney potential energy. In principle our method of treatment is no more difficult for any other periodic potential energy. The Kronig-Penney potential energy is a series of square wells as shown in Fig. 12.1.

The careful reader may wonder why we have not included the potential energy due to the repulsion between the electron in question and all the other electrons in the crystal. This deficiency of the "single-particle" theory may be partially overcome by including any periodic or constant parts of the electron-electron potential energy in the periodic potential energy already mentioned. The rest of the electron-electron potential energy can then be handled by Hartree's method of self-consistent fields which we will not consider here.

12.2 The boundary conditions

Two simple boundary conditions are available for the one-dimensional crystal. One boundary condition, which applies to an isolated crystal, is that the potential energy goes to infinity at the boundaries of the crystal as in the "box" model introduced in Chapter 2. This boundary condition gives rise to nonsinusoidal standing-wave solutions for ψ, which must vanish at the crystal boundaries.

The other boundary condition is called a periodic boundary condition and corresponds physically to the one-dimensional crystal being bent around in the form of a continuous ring. With this boundary condition the solutions for ψ are nonsinusoidal traveling waves or, as special cases, standing waves. We will use only the periodic boundary condition. As an example we discuss a ring of only four atoms or wells. Thus, in the periodic potential-energy curve of Fig. 12.1, the points A and A' are considered to be at the same position in space.

12.3 Wavefunctions for the Kronig-Penney model

The time-independent Schroedinger equation in one-dimension is

$$\frac{d^2\psi}{dx^2} + \frac{2m}{\hbar^2}(E - U)\psi = 0 \tag{1.22}$$

In this problem U is the periodic Kronig-Penney potential energy of Fig. 12.1. As noted earlier, when boundary conditions must be satisfied, Schroedinger's equation is an eigenvalue equation; that is, only certain values of E will permit well-behaved solutions.

It is not our purpose here to carry out an analytical solution of Schroedinger's equation, even for our oversimplified model of a crystal.[1] It is possible, however, to produce the important features of an analytical solution by making rough sketches of the wavefunctions. The two important results we will obtain from these sketches are:

(1) There exist both traveling wave and standing wave solutions of Schroedinger's equation for the crystal. Standing waves occur only for certain critical values of wavelength, which are the values for which Bragg reflections occur.

$$n\lambda = 2a \tag{12.1}$$

Here a is the "repeat length" of the periodic potential energy and n is an integer.

(2) The allowed values of energy which permit well-behaved solutions of Schroedinger's equation are grouped into bands. Between each band of energy levels is a forbidden region or gap in energy. (This is the conclusion which we reached in our discussion of the splitting of atomic energy levels in Chapter 2.)

The principle underlying the sketching of the wave functions is as follows. For values of x for which $U = 0$ (that is, in the wells), Schroedinger's equation becomes the familiar "simple harmonic oscillator" equation

$$\frac{d^2\psi}{dx^2} = -\frac{2mE}{\hbar^2}\psi \tag{12.2}$$

[1] Analytical solutions for the Kronig-Penney and other forms of periodic potential energy may be found in the books by Mott and Jones, Kittel, and Dekker, listed at the end of the chapter.

Therefore ψ is a sinusoidal function in the well regions. The wavelength of this sinusoidal variation depends on E. For the regions between wells U is positive, and for states with $E < U$ the solution is a linear combination of positive and negative exponentials. We may conclude that when $U = 0$, ψ always has a curvature toward the x-axis and when $U > E$, ψ always curves away from the x-axis. The solutions in the wells and in the barriers must join in such a way that both ψ and its first derivative are continuous.

Figure 12.2 shows the first twelve of the possible wavefunctions plotted in order of increasing energy E. The potential-energy curve of Fig. 12.1 is redrawn in part (a) for convenience. The wavelength of each entire wavefunction, which is not to be confused with the wavelength of the local sinusoidal variations in each well, is listed to the right of the wave along with the corresponding value of propagation constant k defined by

$$k = \frac{2\pi}{\lambda} \tag{12.3}$$

Each wavefunction ψ drawn in Fig. 12.2 is the spatial part of the total wavefunction. In Chapter 1 we saw that the spatial part must be multiplied by $e^{-j(E/\hbar)t}$ in order to obtain a solution of the time-dependent Schroedinger equation. If we multiply each wavefunction of Fig. 12.2 by $e^{-j(E/\hbar)t}$, each wavefunction becomes a standing wave. For example, ψ_1 simply oscillates up and down as a standing wave with frequency E_1/h, where E_1 is the particular value of E in Schroedinger's equation for which $\psi = \psi_1$. E_1 is the lowest energy for which a well-behaved solution occurs.

Part (c) of Fig. 12.2 shows a wavefunction for the next possible value of E. However, this is not the only wavefunction that can be drawn for this value of E. It should be apparent from symmetry that if the curve drawn in (c) is a solution, then so is a curve which has the same shape but which is displaced a distance a to the right. Furthermore, because Schroedinger's equation is a linear differential equation, any linear combination of the curve in (c) and the displaced curve is also a solution. It is possible to form two independent linear combinations of these two curves, one representing a wave traveling to the right, the other representing a wave traveling to the left. These two independent solutions we call ψ_2 and ψ_3. The values of E in Schroedinger's equation corresponding to these two solutions are equal ($E_2 = E_3$).

The way two traveling-wave solutions can be constructed from curves of the shape shown in Fig. 12.2c is illustrated in Fig. 12.3. We construct each of the traveling waves ψ_2 and ψ_3 from a pair of waves of the shape of that in Fig. 12.2c which differ in phase in time

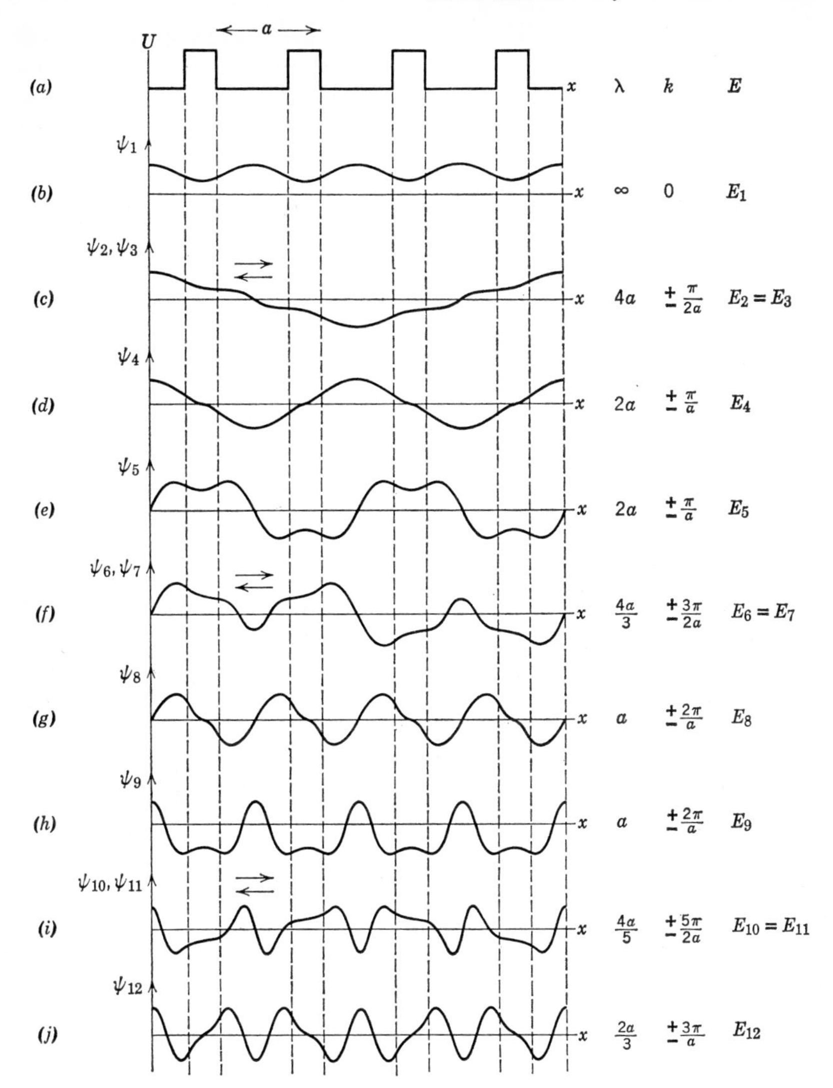

Fig. 12.2. Wavefunctions satisfying periodic boundary conditions for a four-well Kronig-Penney potential energy.

by 90°. It is convenient to represent each wave in a complex diagram, where the real and imaginary parts are simultaneously plotted against x. Parts (a) and (b) of Fig. 12.3 are each drawn at an instant of time such that one of the component waves is entirely real and the other is entirely imaginary. Since the sum of the component waves is multi-

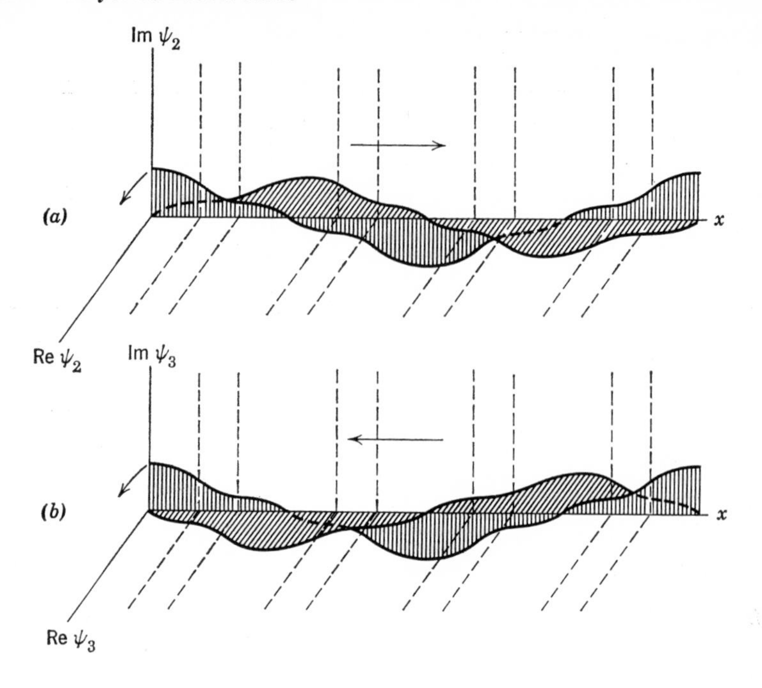

Fig. 12.3. Superpositions of two standing waves to form two traveling waves.

plied by $e^{-j(E/\hbar)t}$, each diagram is to be thought of as rotating in time about the x-axis in a counterclockwise sense to a viewer looking in the negative x-direction. The reader can verify from a study of Fig. 12.3 that the real and imaginary parts of ψ_2 progress in the $+x$-direction and that the real and imaginary parts of ψ_3 progress in the $-x$-direction. Therefore the linear combinations illustrated in this diagram do indeed behave as traveling waves.

Returning to Fig. 12.2, we see in part (d) that ψ_4 is, like ψ_1, a standing-wave solution. For energies such as E_1 or E_4 there is no second independent solution with the same energy with which we can form linear combinations to produce traveling waves.

An important feature of solutions ψ_1, ψ_2, ψ_3, ψ_4 in Fig. 12.2 is that they all have very nearly the same wavelength for their local sinusoidal variations within a well, and therefore have very nearly the same energy. We emphasize again that these sinusoidal wavelengths are not to be confused with the wavelengths λ of the entire waves. Because ψ_2 and ψ_3 have slightly shorter sinusoidal wavelengths in the wells than ψ_1, E_2 and E_3 are slightly greater than E_1 and, similarly, E_4 is slightly greater than E_2 and E_3. The values of E_1, E_2, E_3, E_4 are indicated on an energy-level diagram in Fig. 12.4 along with the energies corresponding to the other wavefunctions, ψ_5 through ψ_{12}.

ψ_5 in Fig. 12.2*e* is another standing wave. It is important to notice that, although ψ_5 has the same over-all *wavelength* as ψ_4, these two wavefunctions have significantly different *energies*. (ψ_5 has a greater curvature than ψ_4 and each well contains over half a wavelength of sinusoidal variation for ψ_5 as compared to less than half a wavelength for ψ_4.) ψ_6 and ψ_7 are wavefunctions of equal energy ($E_6 = E_7$) and only slightly higher energy than E_5. Again, as with ψ_2 and ψ_3, we can form linear combinations of the curve shown in part (*f*) and a displaced curve. These linear combinations can represent waves traveling to the left and to the right. ψ_8 is another standing wave, with only slightly higher energy than ψ_6 or ψ_7. ψ_9 is a standing wave with the same wavelength as ψ_8 but with significantly different energy. ψ_{10}, ψ_{11}, and ψ_{12} round out this group of states with nearly equal energies.

In the energy-level diagram of Fig. 12.4, the grouping of levels into bands is apparent. If we had chosen a one-dimensional crystal with N wells instead of four, there would have been N states in each band, but the widths of the bands and the widths of the gaps between the bands would have been approximately the same.

It is instructive to plot the possible energy values as a function of the propagation constant k. Figure 12.5 shows this extension of Fig. 12.4. The wavefunction to which each dot corresponds is also indicated on the diagram. Notice that, except for ψ_1, the wavefunctions which represent standing waves (ψ_4, ψ_5, ψ_8, ψ_9, and ψ_{12}) are each

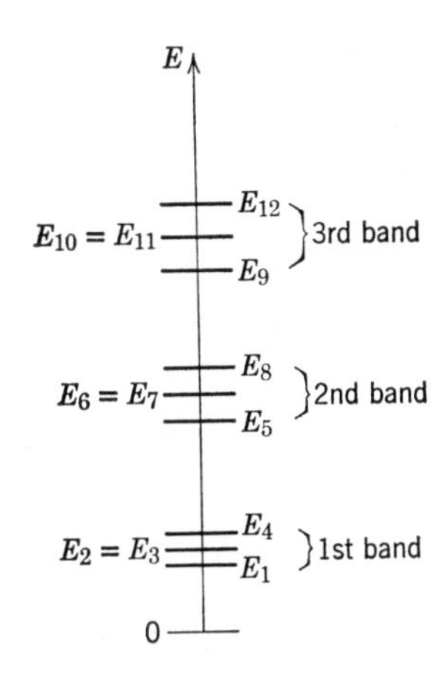

Fig. 12.4. Energy-level diagram for one-dimensional crystal with four square wells and periodic boundary conditions.

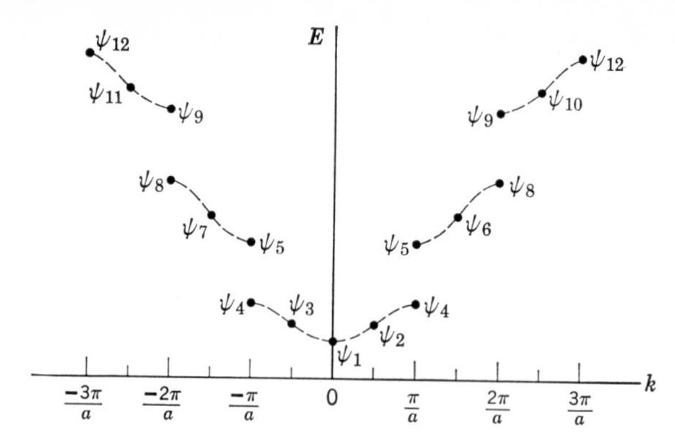

Fig. 12.5. The values of k corresponding to wavefunctions for the four-well crystal versus allowed energies.

represented by either a positive or a negative value of k. When Fig. 12.5 is extended to a large number of states per band (many atoms in the crystal), the points become extremely close together and are conveniently replaced by continuous lines for each band as drawn in Fig. 12.6. The dotted line parabola in Fig. 12.6 represents the E versus k relationship obtained in Chapter 1 for a free particle in one dimension with zero potential energy

$$E = \frac{\hbar^2 k^2}{2m} \tag{1.20}$$

The solid curve must reduce to this parabola in the limit as the barriers between the wells are made small. In the next section we will show that the slope of the curve must become zero at the top and bottom of a band. It is clear from the sketches of wavefunctions in Fig. 12.2 and the E versus k diagrams of Fig. 12.5 and 12.6 that any wavefunction which has a propagation constant given by

$$k = \frac{n\pi}{a} \tag{12.4}$$

is a standing wave. Here n is a positive or negative integer or zero. Note that 12.4 is another way of writing 12.1.

Although the foregoing discussion has applied to the special case of the Kronig-Penney potential energy, Bloch has shown that the solutions of Schroedinger's equation, when $U(x)$ has periodicity a and when the solutions ψ are periodic with period Na (N a positive integer representing the number of atoms), can always be written in the form

$$\psi(x) = e^{jkx}u_k(x) \tag{12.5}$$

Here k, the propagation constant of the wave, takes on the values

$$k = \frac{2\pi n}{Na} \tag{12.6}$$

where n is a positive or negative integer or zero. The functions $u_k(x)$ which are in general complex and are different for different values of k are periodic with the period a and are called Bloch functions.

When the space part of the wavefunction 12.5 is multiplied by $e^{-j(E/\hbar)t}$ to obtain a solution of the time-dependent equation, the general traveling-wave character of the solutions becomes evident.

$$\Psi(x,t) = e^{j(kx-\omega t)}u_k(x) \tag{12.7}$$

The solutions are traveling sinusoidal waves which are modulated periodically in space by the function $u_k(x)$. Waves with positive and negative k's move in the positive and negative directions respectively.

As is evident from an inspection of equation 12.5 or 12.7, when k has a value which is an even or odd multiple of π/a, then $\psi(x)$ is periodic either with period a or with period $2a$. If the period is a, then $\psi(x) = \psi(x + a)$ and if the period is $2a$, then $\psi(x) = -\psi(x + a)$. Either situation suggests that the solutions should be interpreted as

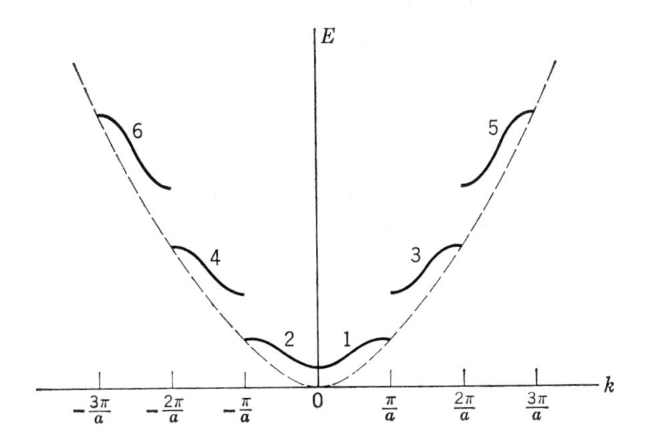

Fig. 12.6. Energy versus wavenumber for a one-dimensional crystal with a large number of potential wells.

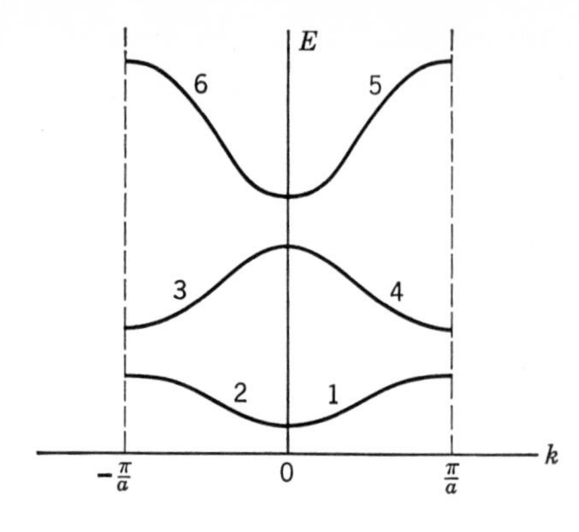

Fig. 12.7. "Reduced" E versus k diagram. The numbers on the branches correspond to those of Fig. 12.6.

standing waves for these particular values of k. This is completely in agreement with the sketches in Fig. 12.2 and is equivalent to the Bragg criterion for reflection of x-rays from a crystal

$$n\lambda = 2a \quad \text{or} \quad k = \frac{n\pi}{a} \tag{12.1), (12.4}$$

(For the Bragg relation a is to be interpreted as the internuclear distance in the direction of travel of the wave.) Physically, Bragg reflection means that the partial reflections of a traveling wave from successive obstacles all add constructively for the critical wavelength and build up to form an oppositely directed wave of amplitude equal to that of the incident wave.

An E versus k diagram such as that in Fig. 12.6 is often modified by performing a simple operation on equation 12.5.

$$\psi(x) = e^{jkx}u_k(x) \tag{12.5}$$

No matter what the value of k in equation 12.5, it is possible to multiply and divide the right side of 12.5 by $e^{jm(2\pi/a)x}$, where m is an appropriate positive or negative integer so that $k - m2\pi/a$ lies in the range from $-\pi/a$ to $+\pi/a$ inclusively. Thus 12.5 may be rewritten

$$\psi = e^{j(k-m2\pi/a)x}e^{jm(2\pi/a)x}u_k(x) \tag{12.8}$$

or

$$\psi = e^{jk'x}u'_{k'}(x) \tag{12.9}$$

Here we have defined

$$k' = k - \frac{m2\pi}{a}, \quad \left(-\frac{\pi}{a} \leq k' \leq \frac{\pi}{a}\right) \tag{12.10}$$

and

$$u'_{k'}(x) = e^{jm(2\pi/a)x}u_k(x) \tag{12.11}$$

Note that $u'_{k'}(x)$ is still periodic with period a. Using this method of reducing the wavenumber leads to the "reduced" E versus k' diagram of Fig. 12.7. The number next to each branch of the curve shows to what branch of Fig. 12.6 it corresponds. The prime symbol is left off the k for future simplicity of notation.

12.4 Wavepackets and the velocities of electrons

Until now in this chapter we have been talking about electronic wavefunctions rather than the electrons themselves. In a macroscopic crystal which contains on the order of 10^{20} atoms, the many electronic wavefunctions which exist inside the crystal interfere with one another and produce wavepackets which move in different directions with different speeds. Because of the extremely large number of wavefunctions involved it is useful to consider narrow ranges of k, and imagine that the many wavefunctions within each range interfere to produce wavepackets. Such a wavepacket moves with a velocity called the group velocity which we found in Chapter 1 to be given by

$$v_g = \frac{d\omega}{dk} = \frac{1}{\hbar}\frac{dE}{dk} \tag{1.11}$$

Thus the velocity of a wavepacket (or electron), made up of the waves near a particular value of k, is proportional to the slope of the E versus k curve at that value of k. Consider Fig. 12.8. An electron which is constructed of wavefunctions near A, C, F, or H in Fig. 12.8 has a negative velocity; an electron constructed of wavefunctions near B,

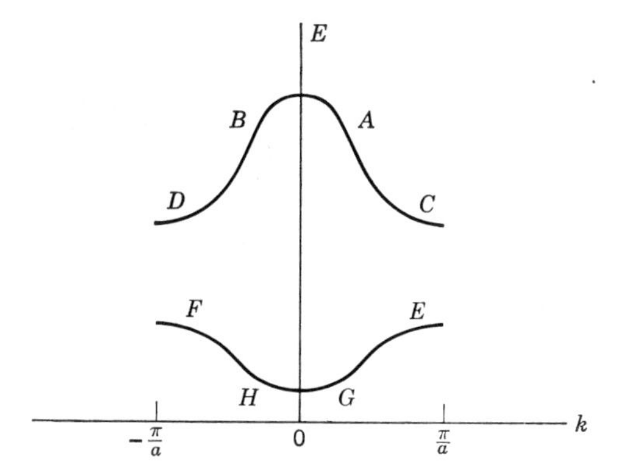

Fig. 12.8. Wavepackets are formed from states within small ranges of k.

D, E, or G has a positive velocity. We have seen that a wavefunction at the exact top or bottom of a band is a standing wave. We expect from symmetry principles that the interference pattern of the waves in a range dk located symmetrically around a value of k for which a standing wave occurs will have zero velocity. Hence from 1.11 the slope of the E versus k curve must be zero wherever a standing wave occurs.

12.5 The effect of an applied electric field and effective mass

A study of the effect on a wavepacket of an externally applied electric field leads to the unusual but important result that sometimes electrons behave as if they had negative mass! That is, when an external force is applied to them they sometimes accelerate in the direction opposite to that of the force.

Consider an electron wavepacket acted upon by a uniform, externally applied electric field. In moving a distance Δs in the direction of the force, the electron acquires an amount of energy ΔE equal to the work done. Thus, using 1.11

$$\Delta E = F\,\Delta s = -e\mathcal{E}v\,\Delta t = -\frac{e\mathcal{E}}{\hbar}\frac{\Delta E}{\Delta k}\,\Delta t \tag{12.12}$$

Rearranging and passing to the limit we have

$$\frac{dk}{dt} = -\frac{e\mathcal{E}}{\hbar} \tag{12.13}$$

If we define $p = \hbar k$, then 12.13 is seen to be a form of Newton's second law. However, the momentum defined in this manner does not satisfy the equation, $E - U = K = p^2/2m$. So that the reader does not think that we have overthrown Newtonian mechanics, we hasten to point out that the force due to the externally applied field is not the only force acting on the electron. Forces associated with the periodic potential energy of the lattice are also present. These are taken care of in the precise form of the E versus k relation.

The acceleration a of a wavepacket is the time rate of change of the group velocity. Using 1.11 and 12.13 we write

$$a = \frac{dv_g}{dt} = \frac{d}{dt}\left(\frac{1}{\hbar}\frac{dE}{dk}\right) = \frac{1}{\hbar}\left(\frac{dk}{dt}\frac{d^2E}{dk^2}\right) = -\frac{e\mathcal{E}}{\hbar^2}\frac{d^2E}{dk^2} \tag{12.14}$$

Comparing this with Newton's second law in the form $-e\mathcal{E} = ma$, we see that the quantity $\hbar^2/(d^2E/dk^2)$ plays the role of a mass. It is called the effective mass of the wavepacket and is designated by the symbol m^*.

$$m^* \equiv \frac{\hbar^2}{d^2E/dk^2} \tag{12.15}$$

Referring again to Fig. 12.8, we see that wavepackets constructed of states near C, D, G, or H have positive effective masses, but those near A, B, E, or F have negative effective masses. In other words, electrons near the top of a band have negative effective masses. We will see in section 12.9 that the concept of negative effective mass is in agreement with experimental evidence.

Let us examine the effective mass concept from somewhat more physical grounds. Suppose that an electric field is applied to our one-dimensional crystal in the negative direction so that the force $-e\mathcal{E}$ on an electron is in the positive direction. Then in view of equation 12.13 each wavefunction is modified in time by a uniform progression to higher values of k. Thus, a wavefunction at F in Fig. 12.8 moves progressively along the lower curve to H, G, and E. When it reaches the value $k = \pi/a$, it is "reflected" and reappears at $k = -\pi/a$ on the lower curve.[1] This progression to higher values of k and reflection occurs for *every* wavefunction, and we may therefore think of each wavepacket or electron doing the same. For example, a wavepacket existing near F has a small negative group velocity (proportional to the slope of the curve), and as it progresses to the right *in k-space* (to the left in the crystal) the magnitude of the negative velocity increases, despite the fact that the externally applied force is to the right! This is negative-mass behavior.

A wavepacket at H has negative velocity but, in moving to the right in k-space, the magnitude of the negative velocity decreases. This is positive-mass behavior; the electron is moving to the left but slowing down under the influence of a rightward-directed force. At G the electron is moving to the right and speeding up (positive mass), and at E the electron is moving to the right and slowing down (negative mass). Similar arguments may be made for electrons composed of wavefunctions represented on the upper curve to show that the effective mass is always negative when the E versus k curvature is concave downward and positive when the E versus k curvature is concave upward. This is, of course, in agreement with equation 12.15.

[1] If the energy gained by an electron in a mean free path is comparable to the width of the energy gap between the bands, there is a possibility that the electron will jump into the next higher band.

12.6 Holes

In many crystals at least one energy band is partially filled with electrons, that is, not completely filled or completely empty. This is analogous to a partially filled electron shell in an atom. If the nature of the band is such that almost all the states are full, it is far more convenient to talk in terms of the relatively few unfilled states rather than the many filled states. If several states adjacent in k-space are unoccupied, we may speak of unfilled wavepackets. An unfilled wavepacket is called a *hole*. Consider the E versus k diagram in Fig. 12.9.

If, as in our previous example, the electric field is directed to the left, the wavepackets all move to the right in k-space and the hole moves in the same direction *in k-space*. When the hole reaches $k = \pi/a$, it is "reflected" and reappears at $k = -\pi/a$.

As far as the flow of charge is concerned, a hole moving in one direction is equivalent to an electron moving in the opposite direction. One way to see this is by a cancellation argument. Every wavepacket in Fig. 12.9 with negative k is matched by a wavepacket with positive k except for the packet at A'. The wavepacket at A' is matched by a hole at A which has a positive velocity (from equation 1.11). The unmatched wavepacket at A' has negative velocity. Hence, the hole moves in the opposite direction to the unmatched electron and we endow the hole with positive charge.

Holes also have effective masses, which may be positive or negative depending upon what part of the band the hole is in. The sign of the effective mass of a hole is easily determined by the same sort of argument we used in section 12.5 to find the effective mass of an electron wavepacket.

Refer again to Fig. 12.8. Again we let the electric field be in the negative direction. Since the hole has a positive charge, the force on a hole is in the negative direction. Consider a hole at F. Since all the wavefunctions progress to higher values of k, the hole moves from

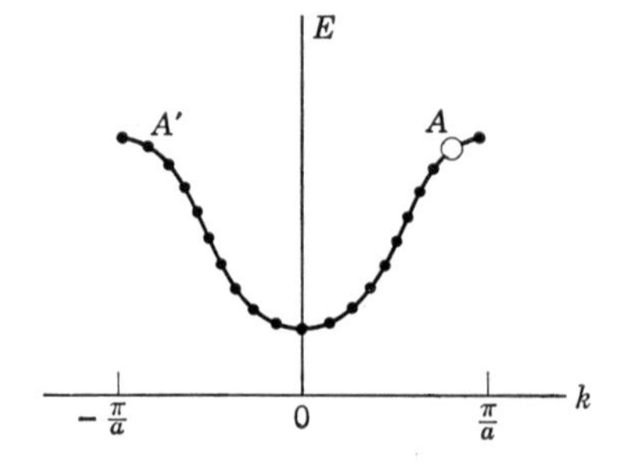

Fig. 12.9. A single hole in an otherwise filled band.

F to H to G to E and then is reflected. When at F the hole has negative velocity which is increasing in magnitude—a negative acceleration. The force is also in the negative direction, so the effective mass of a hole at F is *positive.*

At H the velocity is still negative and is decreasing in magnitude. This represents a positive acceleration and therefore a negative effective mass. In general, the effective mass of a hole is *positive* where the E versus k curve is concave *downward* (near the top of any band) and is *negative* where the E versus k curve is concave *upward* (near the bottom of any band). We will find the concept of a hole to be extremely useful in explaining the Hall effect (section 12.9) and in discussing semiconductors and semiconductor devices (Chapters 13 and 14).

12.7 The band structure of real crystals

Until now we have dealt only with one-dimensional perfect crystals. In this section we extend the band theory to three-dimensional crystals and in section 12.8 discuss the effect of imperfections in crystals.

In a two- or three-dimensional crystal the wavenumber must be regarded as a two- or three-dimensional vector **k**. In any one direction in k-space the gross features of the one-dimensional crystal are maintained. That is, as **k** increases from zero the allowed states have a virtually continuous range of energies (a band). When the magnitude of **k** reaches a critical value, there is a discontinuity in the values of energy associated with the allowed wavefunctions and a new energy band is started.

In two or three dimensions the velocity of a wavepacket is proportional to the gradient of the energy with respect to the components of **k**. The effective mass becomes a tensor with nine components in three dimensions (four in two dimensions):

$$\frac{\hbar^2}{\partial^2 E/\partial k_x^{\,2}},\ \frac{\hbar^2}{\partial^2 E/\partial k_x \partial k_y},\ \frac{\hbar^2}{\partial^2 E/\partial k_y^{\,2}},\ \text{etc.}$$

There is one important complication that occurs for two- or three-dimensional crystals that does not occur in one-dimensional crystals; namely, the gap in energy may occur at different values of energy for different directions in k-space. This creates the possibility of "overlap"; that is, the lowest energy of one band may be lower than the highest energy of the next lower band. Overlap is illustrated in Fig. 12.10 for a two-dimensional crystal. When overlap occurs, the crystal behaves as if there were no gap; that is, the allowed energy values are

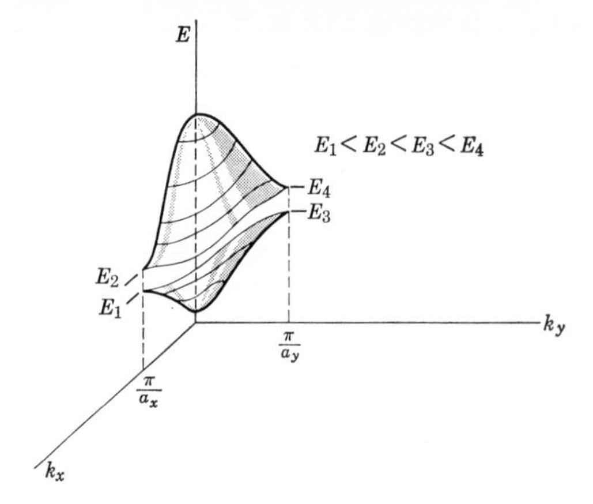

Fig. 12.10. E versus k surfaces for a two-dimensional crystal in which the two bands overlap in energy.

practically continuous. Overlap always occurs among the higher lying bands of real crystals.

In 1934 Slater calculated the positions of the energy bands in sodium as a function of the internuclear spacing R. His results are summarized in Fig. 12.11. The narrowing of the bands at larger values of R is expected because the allowed levels must become the atomic energy levels as the atoms exert less and less influence on one another. The observed value of R from x-ray diffraction experiments on sodium

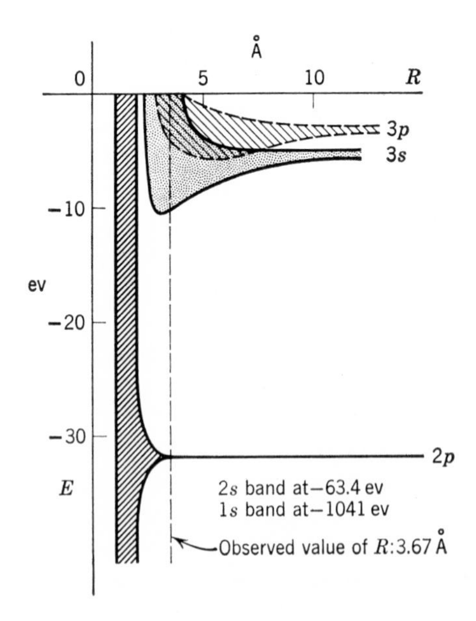

Fig. 12.11. Band structure of sodium. [From J. C. Slater *Phys. Rev.* **45**; 794 (1934).]

is 3.67 Å. At the observed spacing the bands derived from the $2p$ and the lower lying $2s$ and $1s$ atomic levels (not shown in Fig. 12.11) are very narrow, but the $3s$ and $3p$ bands are wide and overlap. The $1s$ and $2s$ bands each contain enough states for two electrons per atom. The $2p$ band contains enough states for six electrons per atom. The remaining electrons (one from each atom) occupy states in the $3s$ band, which contains enough states for two electrons per atom. Thus the $3s$ band is a partially filled band which accounts, as we shall see in the next section, for the electrical conductivity of sodium.

12.8 Conductivity and mobility in crystals

In section 12.5 we showed that, in the presence of an external electric field in the negative direction, each wavepacket progresses uniformly to higher values of k and then is "reflected" from $k = \pi/a$ to $k = -\pi/a$. Such a progression would occur only in a perfect crystal. As we stated earlier all real crystals contain imperfections of one sort or another. Also, at any one instant of time, the potential energy will not be exactly periodic because of the thermal vibrations of the nuclei (lattice vibrations) around their equilibrium positions.

Any nonperiodicity in the potential energy seen by a traveling wave can cause a reflection of the wave. Reflections of traveling waves are associated with the scattering of wavepackets. Scattering tends to "randomize" the velocities of electrons; thus when an electric field is applied, there is competition between the "ordering" effect of the field in urging the electrons in one direction and the "randomizing" effect of the crystal imperfections and lattice vibrations.

If a band of energy states is completely empty, there can, of course, be no contribution to an electric current by that band. Similarly, if a band is completely filled, there can be no contribution to an electric current by the band. By symmetry, when all the states of a band are filled, the average value of the vector velocity of the wavepackets in the band is zero; there are just as many wavepackets traveling in one direction as in the opposite direction. Crystals which contain only filled and empty bands are very poor conductors of electricity and are known as insulators.

If a crystal (for example, sodium) contains a band which is partially filled, an externally applied electric field can shift the occupation of the energy levels and cause a current to flow. This situation is illustrated for one dimension in Fig. 12.12 for an applied field in the negative direction. The force on the wavepackets urges them to the right by equation 12.13, but reflections from imperfections and lattice

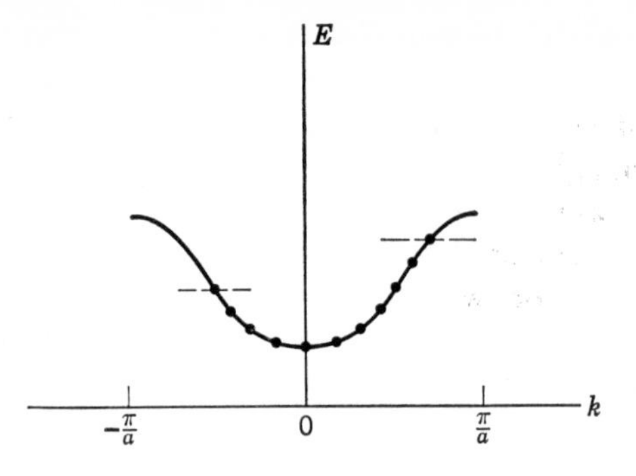

Fig. 12.12. A partially filled band under the influence of an electric field in the negative direction.

vibrations tend to return the distribution to a symmetric one. The result is a steady-state situation like that in Fig. 12.12 in which the average velocity of the wavepackets is positive.

In Chapter 8 conductivity was defined as the ratio of the current density to the applied electric field.

$$\mathbf{J} = \sigma \mathcal{E} \tag{8.15}$$

From equation 8.16 the conductivity can be expressed in terms of the mobility μ and concentration of charge carriers n.

$$\sigma = |\rho|\mu = n|q|\mu \tag{12.16}$$

In most metals it is convenient to think of the charge carriers as electrons (there are, however, a few exceptions, notably zinc, beryllium, and cadmium, in which the charge carriers are more conveniently treated as holes). In most metals, then, n represents the number of electrons per unit volume and is independent of temperature. Any temperature dependence of σ, therefore, arises from the temperature dependence of the mobility. The mobility decreases with increasing temperature because the amplitudes of the lattice vibrations increase, resulting in larger deviations from periodicity and causing more frequent scattering of electrons. From equation 8.19 a shorter average time between collisions results in a lower value of mobility. The decrease of mobility and conductivity in metals with increasing temperature is observed experimentally. The fractional decrease per degree centigrade is on the order of 10^{-3}.

In Chapter 13 we will see that both holes and electrons may carry current in semiconductors. When this is so, the total current density is the sum of the hole and electron current densities.

$$\mathbf{J} = \sigma_n \mathcal{E} + \sigma_p \mathcal{E} = \sigma_{\text{total}} \mathcal{E} \tag{12.17}$$

The electron and hole conductivities σ_n and σ_p can be written in terms of the electron and hole mobilities μ_n, μ_p, and densities n_n, n_p.

$$\sigma_n = n_n e \mu_n \qquad \text{and} \qquad \sigma_p = n_p e \mu_p \tag{12.18}$$

Therefore,

$$\sigma_{\text{total}} = n_n e \mu_n + n_p e \mu_p \tag{12.19}$$

12.9 The Hall effect

The best experimental evidence for the existence of holes is the Hall effect, the production of a transverse electric field by the motion of charge carriers in a material in a magnetic field. The geometry of a Hall effect experiment is shown schematically in Fig. 12.13. A magnetic field is imposed on a current-carrying bar in a direction perpendicular to the current, causing a deflection of the charge carriers to one side of the bar. The Hall effect for negative charge carriers is shown in Fig. 12.13*a* and that for positive charge carriers in Fig. 12.13*b*. It is important to realize that for a given direction of conventional current and external magnetic field, positive and negative current carriers are deflected *in the same direction.* The deflection of the carriers builds up a charge on one side of the bar. Therefore in Fig. 12.13*a*, point A has a negative potential with respect to A' and in Fig. 12.13*b*, A is positive with respect to A'. By determining the polarity of this potential, called the Hall potential, one may determine whether the current carriers are predominantly positive holes or negative electrons.

The deflection of charge carriers cannot continue indefinitely because the build-up of charge creates a transverse electric field in the crystal. When the force on the charge carriers due to this transverse electric field just balances the magnetic force, equilibrium occurs. If we denote the magnitude of the transverse electric field by $\mathcal{E}_T$ the condition for equilibrium is

$$e\mathcal{E}_T = Bev_D \tag{12.20}$$

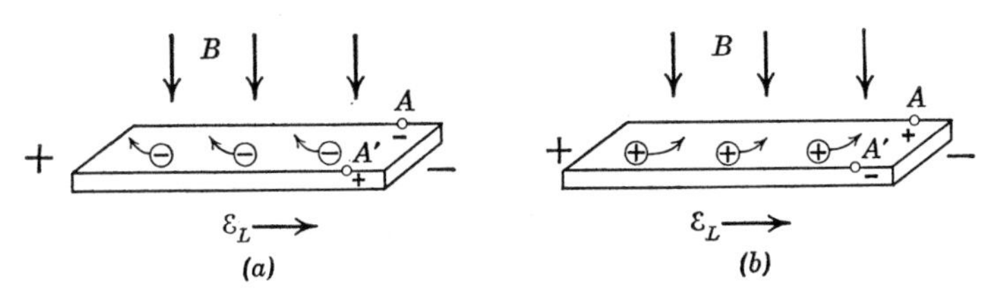

Fig. 12.13. The Hall effect. (*a*) For negative carriers. (*b*) For positive carriers.

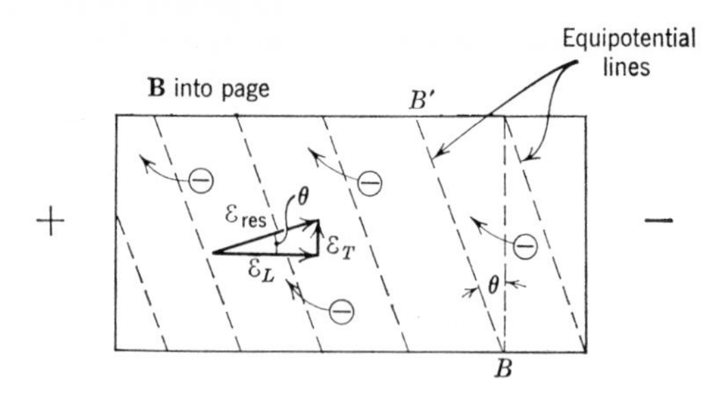

Fig. 12.14. Top view of the bar in Fig. 12.13*a*.

where v_D is the average drift velocity of the holes or electrons longitudinally along the bar. Since the mobility μ is, by definition, equal to $v_D/\mathcal{E}_L$, where $\mathcal{E}_L$ is the magnitude of the longitudinal field, we can eliminate the non-directly measurable quantity v_D and arrive at

$$\mu = \frac{\mathcal{E}_T}{\mathcal{E}_L B} \tag{12.21}$$

The above elementary theory is applicable only when the density of one type of carrier is negligible. The mobility can be determined experimentally by finding the ratio of transverse to longitudinal electric fields. Figure 12.14 shows a top view of the bar of Fig. 12.13.

Since surfaces of constant potential are always perpendicular to lines of electric field, pairs of points such as B–B' have zero potential difference between them. It is evident from Fig. 12.14 that $\mathcal{E}_T/\mathcal{E}_L = \tan\theta$, where θ is the "tilt" angle or Hall angle of the equipotentials, so

$$\mu = \frac{\tan\theta}{B} \tag{12.22}$$

A measure of the magnitude of the Hall effect is often given in terms of a quantity called the Hall coefficient. Using equation 8.14

$$\mathbf{J} = |\rho|\mu\boldsymbol{\mathcal{E}} = ne\mu\boldsymbol{\mathcal{E}}_L \tag{12.23}$$

Rearranging 12.21 and using 12.23, we write

$$\mathcal{E}_T = \mu\mathcal{E}_L B = \frac{J}{ne} B = R_H J B \tag{12.24}$$

R_H, the Hall coefficient, is defined by

$$R_H \equiv \frac{\mathcal{E}_T}{JB} = \frac{1}{ne} \tag{12.25}$$

The measured Hall coefficients for several solids are listed in Table 12.1. The carrier density n is obtained from these experimental coefficients using 12.25.

Table 12.1. Hall coefficients for several metals

	$R_H \left(\frac{m^3}{\text{coulomb}}\right)$
Li	-17.0×10^{-11}
Be	$+24.4$
Na	-25.0
K	-42.0
Cu	$-\ 5.5$
Zn	$+\ 3.3$
Ag	$-\ 8.4$
Cd	$+\ 6.0$
Cs	-78.0
Au	$-\ 7.2$

(− sign indicates electron conduction; + sign indicates hole conduction.)

It is possible to explain the Hall effect entirely in terms of electron flow. At first this seems paradoxical because in Fig. 12.13*b*, the flow of holes to the right corresponds to a flow of electrons to the left. The magnetic force on leftward moving electrons is toward the back of the bar, but if electrons move toward the back then holes must move toward the front. This contradicts Fig. 12.13*b*. The resolution of this apparent paradox is that the electrons which are flowing to the left in Fig. 12.13*b* are those near the top of a band, where the E versus k curve is concave downward. This means that their effective masses are negative and the magnetic force toward the back of the bar causes these negative-mass electrons to drift to the front of the bar. In the more common case of Fig. 12.13*a* the electrons which participate in the current flow are those near the bottom of a band, where the effective mass is positive.

12.10 Superconductivity

Superconductivity is an important electrical property of some materials at very low temperatures. This phenomenon occurs for about 23 elements, none of which is one of the group I metals (the best conductors at ordinary temperatures). Some of the more well-known elements which exhibit superconductivity are aluminum, zinc, tin, mercury, lead, and uranium. Superconductivity is a property which is becoming increasingly important in electronics.

The important experimental aspects of superconductivity are as follows: As the temperature of the material is reduced below room temperature, the resistance gradually decreases and then levels off to a value called the residual resistance. Then at a temperature of the order of 1° to 10° K the resistance abruptly drops to zero and the material is said to be in the superconducting state. Circulating currents set up in a superconducting toroid have been observed to continue for years. For a given material the temperature at which the transition to the superconducting state occurs is found to be dependent on the magnetic field in which the material is immersed. The stronger the applied field the lower is the transition temperature. An empirical relation which describes the dependence of the transition temperature T on the magnetic field B is

$$B = B_0\left(1 - \frac{T^2}{T_c^{\,2}}\right) \tag{12.26}$$

where T_c represents the critical temperature (transition temperature at zero field). B_0 is usually of the order of a few hundred gauss. Equation 12.26 with appropriate values for B_0 and T_c is accurate to within a few percent.

Another aspect of superconductivity is that when a material is in the superconducting state it is impossible for a magnetic field to penetrate very far into the material. Thus the material becomes, in the superconducting state, an almost perfect diamagnet. (Contrast the magnetic field inside iron in the presence of an external magnetic field.)

A small effect known as the isotope effect is thought to give an important clue to the mechanism by which superconductivity occurs. It is found that for a given element such as tin, which has many stable isotopes, the critical temperature is lower for samples composed mainly of the heavier isotopes than for samples composed mainly of the lighter isotopes. This and the fact that the group I metals with loosely bound valence electrons do not exhibit superconductivity are felt to be convincing arguments that superconductivity depends on interactions of electrons with the vibrating lattice ions. In 1957, Bardeen, Cooper, and Schrieffer proposed a mathematical theory of superconductivity which is successful in predicting many of the features of the superconducting phenomenon. A Russian physicist, Bogoliubov, immediately pointed out mathematical similarities between the B.C.S. theory and the theory of superfluidity.

One application of superconductivity is in the achievement of very strong magnetic fields with a relatively small supply of d-c power. Another very important application of the superconducting phenomenon is in the field of memories for digital computers. Figure

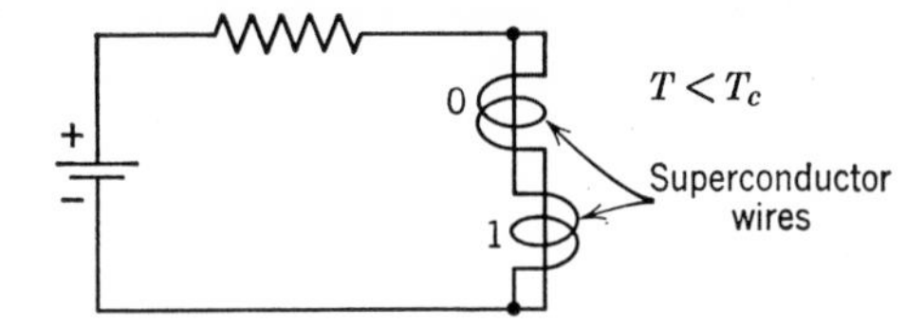

Fig. 12.15. Schematic representation of a superconductor memory element.

12.15 shows, schematically, one possible arrangement. The memory element consists of a battery connected to two wires each made of a superconductor. The wires spiral around one another as shown. The temperature of each wire is a little less than T_c, so that if a large current is flowing, say, in wire 0, which is in the superconducting state, the magnetic field due to that current prevents wire 1 from superconducting. If, however, by some means (not illustrated) the current in wire 0 is reduced, wire 1 will become superconducting. Thus we have a device which has two stable states and can therefore represent the 0 or 1 of a binary digit. The advantage of superconducting memories is that an enormous number of digits can be stored in an extremely small volume.

Suggested References

C. Kittel, *Introduction to Solid State Physics*, 2nd ed. John Wiley and Sons, 1956. Chapter 11 gives a more advanced but, for the most part, an easily understood account of wave propagation in a periodic lattice, the formation of energy bands, effective masses, holes, and the Hall effect.

A. J. Dekker, *Solid State Physics*, Prentice-Hall, 1957. Chapter 10 is the equivalent, both in level and subject matter, of Kittel's Chapter 11. Much of both chapters should be understandable and helpful to a student at the advanced undergraduate level.

N. F. Mott and H. Jones, *The Theory of the Properties of Metals and Alloys*, Dover Publications, 1958. Parts of Chapter II, although on a more advanced level and quite tightly written, may prove helpful to the more mathematically inclined student. In particular, the wavefunctions and energy levels for electrons in periodic structures are derived for several different approximations.

A. T. Goble and D. K. Baker, *Elements of Modern Physics*, The Ronald Press, 1962. A detailed, elementary discussion of the formation of bands in the Kronig-Penney model is given in Chapter 14.

B. T. Mathias, *Superconductivity*, Scientific American, November 1957. This article presents a simple account of the experimental aspects of superconductivity.

PROBLEMS

12.1. Sketch the three lowest-energy standing-wave patterns for a group of three rectangular, one-dimensional potential-energy wells which are joined together to form a ring. Do these wavefunctions represent states in the same band or in different bands? Which of the three represents a state at the bottom of a band and which represents a state at the top of a band?

12.2. (*a*) Sketch the lowest energy wavefunction for each of the first four bands for the one-dimensional lattice shown below.

(*b*) Express the wavelength and wavenumber of each wave in terms of the lattice constant a.

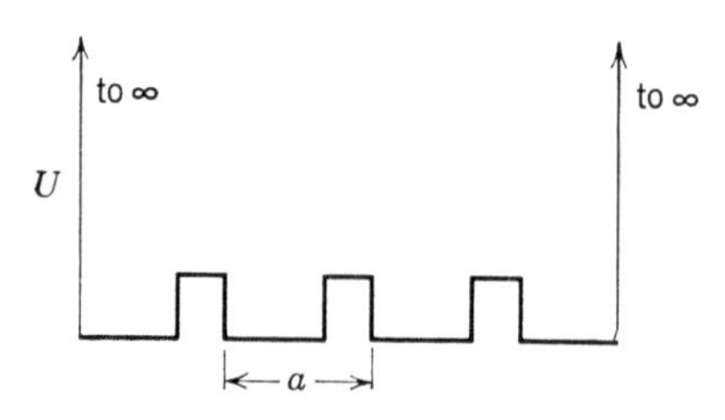

Prob 12.2

12.3. Given the E–k diagram for a band with the electric field in the negative direction (force on electrons in positive direction), (*a*) give the polarity of the effective masses of the four wavepackets made up of groups of states near A, B, C, D.

(*b*) In what direction is the velocity of each of the four wavepackets?

(*c*) In what direction is the acceleration for each?

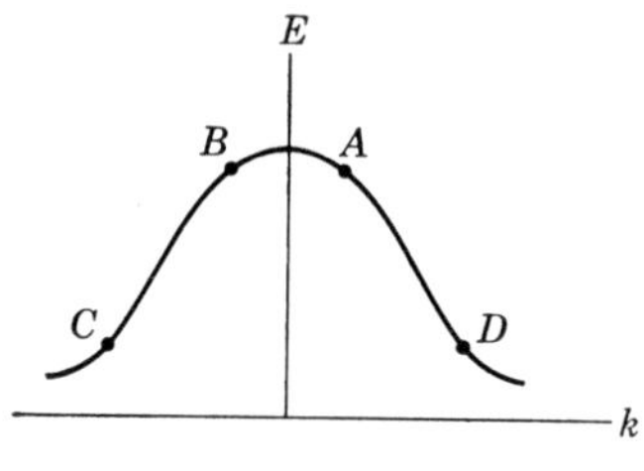

Prob. 12.3

12.4. A Hall effect experiment on a rectangular block of copper 0.1 meter long (in the direction of **J**), 0.001 meter thick (in the direction of **B**), and 0.01 meter wide gives a Hall potential of V_1, when B is 1.5 weber/meter^2 and the current is 40 amp. Reversing the direction of B gives a Hall potential V_2. What is the value of $V_2 - V_1$?

12.5. Show that the Hall angle θ for a semiconductor containing both electrons and holes is given by

$$\tan\theta = \pm \frac{(n_p\mu_p{}^2 - n_n\mu_n{}^2)}{n_p\mu_p + n_n\mu_n} B$$

Hint: In the steady state the total transverse current density must be zero. In the equation $\mathbf{J} = \sigma\boldsymbol{\mathcal{E}}$ replace $\boldsymbol{\mathcal{E}}$ by the total force (electric *and* magnetic) per unit charge.

12.6. Determine the cyclotron resonance frequency for the motion of free carriers in a conductor (or semiconductor) in the presence of a magnetic field, (that is, the frequency at which the electromagnetic radiation energy will be strongly absorbed by the carriers moving in synchronous "cyclotron" paths). This phenomenon gives a means of determining the effective masses m^* of the electrons and holes.

12.7. In order to obtain a sharp cyclotron resonance the mean free path $\bar{l}$ of the carriers must be long compared with the circumference of the cyclotron orbit. What magnetic field is needed to satisfy this condition when (*a*) $\bar{l} = 10^{-5}$ cm, $T = 300°$ K (*b*) $\bar{l} = 10^{-4}$ cm, $T = 10°$ K, and effective mass $m^* =$ free electron mass m in both cases?

13. semiconductors

In this chapter we present both a qualitative discussion of the nature of intrinsic and impurity semiconductors and a quantitative discussion of the distribution of electrons and holes among energy levels. The temperature dependence of semiconductor conductivity is described and compared with that for metals, and a discussion of electrical contacts is begun.

13.1 Conductors, insulators, and semiconductors

The conductivities of solid materials vary over an enormous range. Representative values are from less than 2×10^{-17} mhos/meter for fused quartz, a good insulator, to about 6×10^{7} mhos/meter for silver, a good conductor. Materials with intermediate conductivity values are called semiconductors. The distinguishing features of conductors, insulators, and semiconductors are best explained in terms of the energy band concept developed in Chapters 2 and 12. Energy band diagrams for a conductor, insulator, and semiconductor are shown in Fig. 13.1.

In Chapter 12 we learned that currents can flow only in crystals which contain a band partly filled with electrons. No current can be carried by electrons in a completely filled band. Using this concept we can explain the electrical conductivites of metals, insulators, and semiconductors. A metal always contains a partly filled band, and the occupation of states is easily altered to produce a current by the application of an electric field. In insulators at temperatures up to several hundred degrees Kelvin and in semiconductors at temperatures approaching absolute zero, all bands are either practically com-

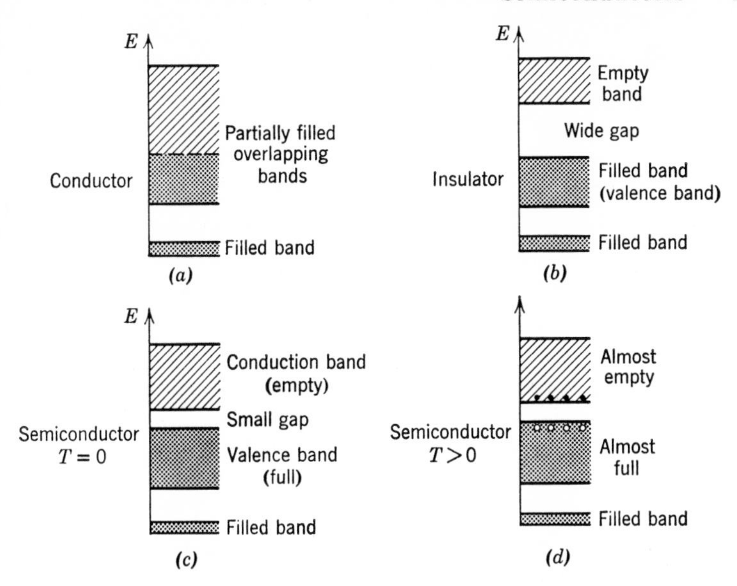

Fig. 13.1. Energy-level diagrams for: (*a*) conductor, (*b*) insulator, (*c*) intrinsic semiconductor at $T = 0$, (*d*) intrinsic semiconductor at $T > 0$.

pletely filled or practically completely empty. In these circumstances the very low conductivity is due to a relatively small statistical distribution of electrons excited from the uppermost "filled" band into the "empty" band above. The uppermost "filled" band is usually called the valence band, and the "empty" band just above it is called the conduction band.

The intermediate conductivities of semiconductors at room temperatures are also due to this thermal excitation of electrons from the valence band into the conduction band. However, many more electrons are excited into the conduction band at room temperatures than at low temperatures. Note that, except for the magnitude of the energy gap between the valence and conduction bands, insulators and semiconductors have similar band diagrams. Thus an insulator at high temperatures behaves like a semiconductor at lower temperatures.

13.2 Intrinsic semiconductors

The word "intrinsic" is used to describe semiconductor crystals which contain such a small concentration of chemical impurities that

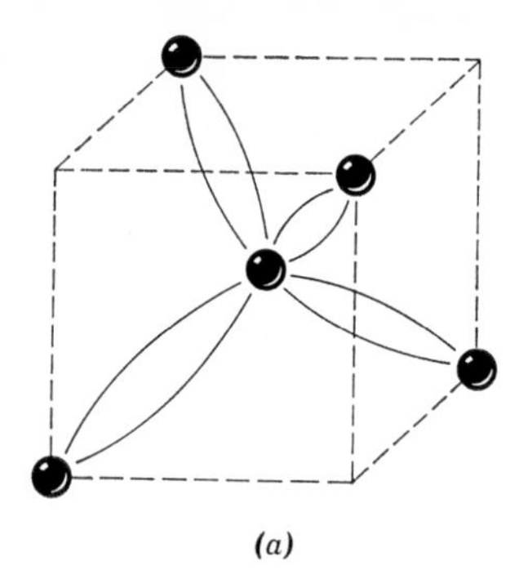

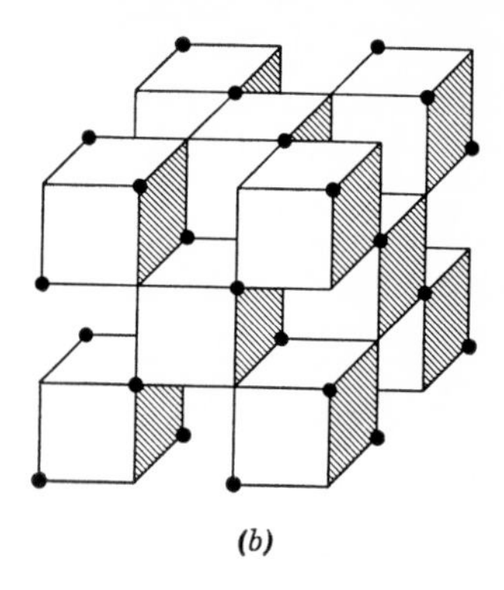

Fig. 13.2. Diamond crystal structure. (*a*) Unit cube containing 5 atoms. (*b*) Packing arrangement of unit cubes (atoms at centers of unit cubes not shown).

the impurities do not affect the electrical characteristics. Intrinsic semiconductors are characterized by the band structure shown in Fig. 13.1*c* or *d*, in which the valence band is separated from the conduction band by a relatively narrow energy gap. Typical gap widths for semiconductor crystals range from 0.2 to 1.5 ev.

Semiconductor crystals can be made from both single elements (for example, silicon and germanium) and compounds (for example, gallium arsenide, GaAs, and indium antimonide, InSb). The crystal structure of both silicon and germanium is the so-called diamond lattice. (Diamond itself is usually considered to be an insulator; its band gap is about 6 ev.) The diamond lattice is illustrated in Fig. 13.2. The entire crystal is exactly half filled with the "unit cubes" illustrated in part (*a*) of this figure. Each unit cube contains five atoms, one at each of four of its eight corners and one at its center. The packing arrangement of the unit cubes is shown in part (*b*) of the figure. An important characteristic of this structure, which may be verified by a study of Fig. 13.2, is that each atom has *four* nearest neighbors.

The double lines joining the atoms of the unit cube in Fig. 13.2*a* are intended to represent covalent bonds which hold the crystal together. Each atom has four valence electrons and contributes one of these to each of its four bonds. In a perfect crystal at absolute zero all bonds are complete and no electrons are available to participate in the conduction of current. At temperatures above absolute zero, thermal vibrations shake loose some of the electrons from the covalent bonds. The electrons which have been shaken loose have energies within the conduction band and can carry current. Furthermore, the vacancies in the covalent bonds, which in the previous chapter were called holes, can carry current. In this pictorial treatment hole conduction may be viewed as a successive filling of the vacant covalent bonds by electrons from neighboring bonds. The above discussion has treated electrons and holes as particles and vacancies. It is more correct to treat electrons and holes as wavepackets. The wavepackets representing electrons and holes move in *opposite* directions in the crystal. This behavior in real space should be contrasted with the behavior in k-space, where the electron and hole wavepackets move in the *same* direction (see section 12.6).

13.3 Impurity semiconductors

The electrical properties of semiconductor crystals can be drastically altered by the addition of a small amount of either of two types of impurities. The two types are designated n-type or donor and p-type or acceptor. These are illustrated in Fig. 13.3 for a germanium crystal. In part (a) of the figure a unit cube containing an n-type or donor impurity atom at its center is illustrated. The donor atom normally has five valence electrons. When the donor atom substitutes for a germanium atom in the crystal, four of its five valence electrons share in the covalent bonds and are relatively tightly bound. The fifth valence electron can occupy a less tightly bound state in which its wavefunction is essentially localized around the donor atom. However, this extra electron can also receive energy from thermal vibrations, be excited into the conduction band, and contribute to the

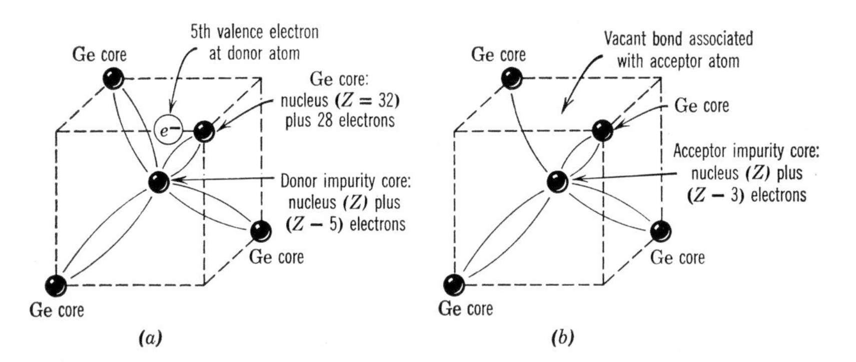

Fig. 13.3. Unit cubes of germanium containing (a) a donor or n-type impurity atom, and (b) an acceptable acceptor or p-type impurity atom.

conduction of current. Some pentavalent atoms which are often used as donor impurities in germanium and silicon are phosphorus, arsenic, and antimony. In germanium the energies of the bound states of the fifth valence electrons of these impurities lie about 0.01 ev below the bottom of the conduction band. This small energy difference should be contrasted with the band-gap energy, which is about 0.72 ev for germanium. The energy of the bound state of the fifth valence electron is called the donor energy or donor level. The donor level is illustrated on an energy-level diagram for n-type germanium in Fig. 13.4a.

In contrast with an intrinsic semiconductor, which contains equal numbers of conduction electrons and holes, an n-type semiconductor contains more conduction electrons than holes. This is true because the "ionization" of an n-type impurity atom produces a conduction electron without the simultaneous production of a hole in the valence band. (The vacancies created in the donor level are too far apart to contribute to the conduction of current.) Finally, it should be pointed out that, when the fifth valence electron is excited into the conduction band and wanders away from the donor atom, the region surrounding the donor atom is left with a net positive charge of e. We call the donor nucleus (atomic number Z) and its remaining $Z - 1$ electrons a donor ion.

A unit cell of germanium containing a p-type or acceptor impurity atom at its center is illustrated in Fig. 13.3b. The acceptor atom normally has only three valence electrons and, when it substitutes for a germanium atom in the crystal, one of the four covalent bonds joining it to the neighboring atoms has a vacancy. This vacancy can be filled by an electron (either from one of the nearby filled bonds or from elsewhere in the crystal). The energy of the state associated with the vacancy adjacent to the impurity atom is higher than that of any ordinary germanium-germanium covalent-bond state which lies in the valence band. If an electron is thermally excited from one of the ordinary covalent bonds into this localized vacancy state, a hole remains in the valence band. This hole, which has been produced without the production of a conduction electron, can contribute to the conduction of current.

Some trivalent atoms which are often used as acceptor impurities in germanium and silicon are boron, aluminum, gallium, and indium. The energy of the localized "acceptor state" (the acceptor level) associated with any of these atoms in germanium lies about 0.01 ev above the top of the valence band. The acceptor level is illustrated on an energy-level diagram for p-type germanium in Fig. 13.4b.

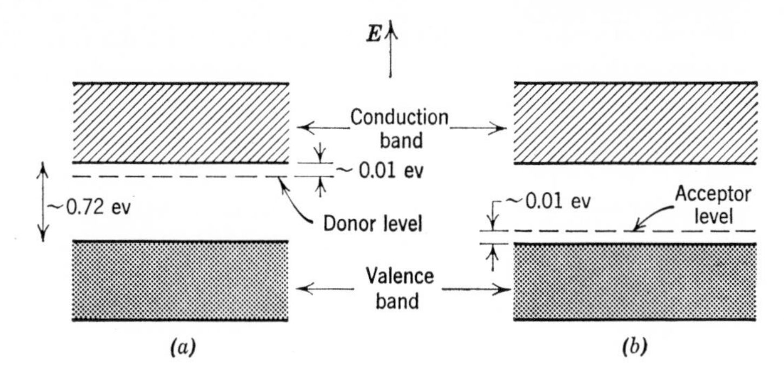

Fig. 13.4. Energy-level diagrams of (*a*) *n*-type and (*b*) *p*-type germanium.

When a valence electron is excited into an acceptor state and the hole has wandered away, the region surrounding the acceptor atom is left with a net negative charge of $-e$. The acceptor nucleus (atomic number Z) and its $Z + 1$ electrons are called an acceptor ion.

As we shall see in the next section it takes only a very small percentage of an n- or p-type impurity to modify the conductivity of a semi-conductor crystal a great deal. Impurity concentrations of one part per ten million are typical. The way in which n- and p-type semiconductor crystals are utilized to construct the solid-state equivalents of the vacuum diode and triode is discussed in Chapter 14.

13.4 Electron and hole concentrations in semiconductors

It is important to know how many electrons there are in the conduction band of a semiconductor and how many holes there are in the valence band, for it is these electrons and holes that carry current. The calculation of these numbers involves a straightforward application of equation 3.12 using the Fermi factor and an appropriate density of states function. In order to obtain numerical values for the numbers of electrons and holes, the position of the Fermi level must be known. In the next section we show how to find the position of the Fermi level.

The number of electrons N_n in the conduction band of a semiconductor is found from equation 3.12 by taking the integral over all conduction band states. Thus,

$$N_n = \int\limits_{\substack{\text{all conduction} \\ \text{band states}}} P_{\text{FD}} \frac{dS}{dE}\, dE \approx \int_{E_g}^{\infty} \frac{dS/dE}{1 + e^{(E-E_F)/kT}}\, dE \qquad (13.1)$$

Here, the zero of energy is arbitrarily taken to be at the top of the valence band so that the band-gap energy E_g is the energy of the lowest state in the conduction band. Although the conduction band does not extend to $E = \infty$, the value of the integral from E_g to ∞ will not be significantly larger than the value of the integral from E_g to the top of the conduction band because of the rapid decrease of the Fermi factor with increasing energy. The form of the density of states function near the bottom of the conduction band is usually taken to be a ½ power function of the energy relative to the bottom of the conduction band. The same constant is usually adopted for the conduction band density of states as was found in Chapter 2 for the density of states for electrons in a box. Hence,

$$\frac{dS}{dE} \text{(conduction band)} = AV(E - E_g)^{1/2}$$

where (13.2)

$$A \equiv \frac{8\pi m^{3/2}\sqrt{2}}{h^3}; \qquad V = \text{volume of crystal}$$

The mass appearing in equation 13.2 is really the effective mass of an electron wavepacket and has a slight dependence on energy. However, we shall disregard this energy dependence and treat m as a constant which is equal to the ordinary mass of an electron.

Substituting equation 13.2 into 13.1 we have

$$N_n = \int_{E_g}^{\infty} \frac{AV(E - E_g)^{1/2}}{1 + e^{(E-E_F)/kT}}\, dE \tag{13.3}$$

Usually the Fermi level E_F lies at least several kT below the bottom of the conduction band. Hence, over the entire range of integration, the 1 in the denominator may be neglected and 13.3 may be rewritten

$$N_n = AVe^{-(E_g-E_F)/kT} \int_{E_g}^{\infty} e^{-(E-E_g)/kT}(E - E_g)^{1/2}\, dE \tag{13.4}$$

This integral may be evaluated by making the substitution

$$u = \frac{E - E_g}{kT} \tag{13.5}$$

and then referring to tables of definite integrals.[1] The result is $(kT)^{3/2}\sqrt{\pi}/2$. Substituting the value of the integral into 13.4 we have

[1] See, for example, Dwight, *Tables of Integrals and Other Mathematical Data*, Nos. 850.1 and 850.7.

$$N_n = A(kT)^{3/2}\,\frac{\sqrt{\pi}}{2}\,Ve^{-(E_g-E_F)/kT} = GT^{3/2}Ve^{-(E_g-E_F)/kT}$$

where (13.6)

$$G \equiv Ak^{3/2}\,\frac{\sqrt{\pi}}{2} = 4.83 \times 10^{21}\,\frac{\text{electrons}}{\text{meter}^3(°\,\text{K})^{3/2}}$$

The above expression for N_n still contains E_F, which will be evaluated in section 13.5.

The number of holes N_p in the valence band of a semiconductor may be found by a procedure analogous to the one just carried out for N_n. However, instead of using in 3.12 the Fermi factor P_{FD} for the probability that a state is occupied by an electron, we must use $(1 - P_{\text{FD}})$ as the probability that a state is *not* occupied by an electron, that is, occupied by a hole. $(1 - P_{\text{FD}})$ is sometimes called the Fermi factor for holes and may be written

$$1 - P_{\text{FD}} = 1 - \frac{1}{1 + e^{(E-E_F)/kT}} = \frac{1}{e^{(E_F-E)/kT} + 1} \tag{13.7}$$

The value of the Fermi factor for holes decreases rapidly toward zero as the energy E decreases below the Fermi level (see Fig. 13.6*a*). For this reason, the density of states need only be known for the states near the top of the valence band and, furthermore, the integration over the valence band can be imagined to extend from $E = -\infty$ to $E = 0$, without significantly changing the value of the integral. The density of states in the top of the valence band is usually taken to be a ½ power function of the energy measured relative to the top of the valence band, again with the same constant as for particles in a box. Hence

$$\frac{dS}{dE}\,(\text{valence band}) = AV(-E)^{1/2}$$

where (13.8)

$$A \equiv \frac{8\pi m^{3/2}\sqrt{2}}{h^3}; \qquad V = \text{volume of crystal}$$

Here, we shall treat m as the mass of an electron rather than as the effective mass of a hole.

Substituting 13.7 and 13.8 into equation 3.12 we have

$$N_p = \int_{-\infty}^{0} (1 - P_{\text{FD}})\,\frac{dS}{dE}\,dE = AV\int_{-\infty}^{0} \frac{(-E)^{1/2}\,dE}{e^{(E_F-E)/kT} + 1} \tag{13.9}$$

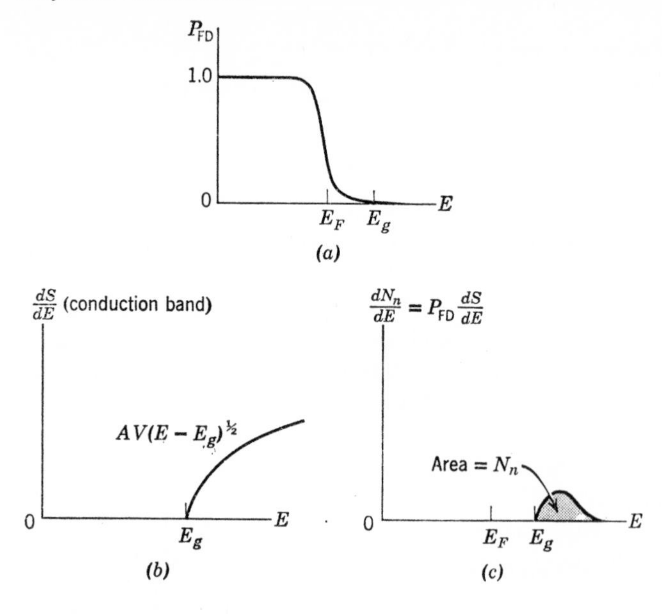

Fig. 13.5. The calculation of N_n. (a) Fermi factor for electrons versus E. (b) Density of states in conduction band versus E. (c) Number of electrons per unit energy dN_n/dE versus E.

If, as is usually the case, the Fermi level lies more than a few kT above the top of the valence band, the 1 in the denominator may be neglected, yielding

$$N_p = AVe^{-E_F/kT} \int_{-\infty}^{0} e^{E/kT}(-E)^{1/2}\, dE \tag{13.10}$$

The substitution

$$u = \frac{-E}{kT} \tag{13.11}$$

reduces the integral in 13.10 to the same form as that obtained after using the substitution 13.5 in the integral of equation 13.4. Using the result of the earlier integration we have,

$$N_p = A(kT)^{3/2} \frac{\sqrt{\pi}}{2} Ve^{-E_F/kT} = GT^{3/2}Ve^{-E_F/kT}$$

where (13.12)

$$G \equiv Ak^{3/2} \frac{\sqrt{\pi}}{2} = 4.83 \times 10^{21} \frac{\text{holes}}{\text{meter}^3(^\circ\text{K})^{3/2}}$$

An interesting result is obtained by taking the product of the electron and hole concentrations n_n and n_p. Thus, using 13.6 and 13.12.

$$n_n n_p = \frac{N_n}{V}\frac{N_p}{V} = G^2 T^3 e^{-E_g/kT} \tag{13.13}$$

The product of the electron and hole concentrations is constant for a given temperature and band-gap energy and is independent of the position of the Fermi level or the impurity concentration. (This is an example of what is called the "law of mass action" in chemical thermodynamics.) Since the derivations of equations 13.6 and 13.12 relied on the approximation that the Fermi level lies within the energy gap and at least several kT from either the valence band or conduction band, equation 13.13 is strictly true only when these conditions are satisfied.

Figures 13.5 and 13.6 illustrate the procedure we have applied in calculating N_n and N_p. In Fig. 13.6, for example, the Fermi factor for holes and the density of states in the valence band are drawn and the product of these (the integrand in equation 13.9) is shown as a function

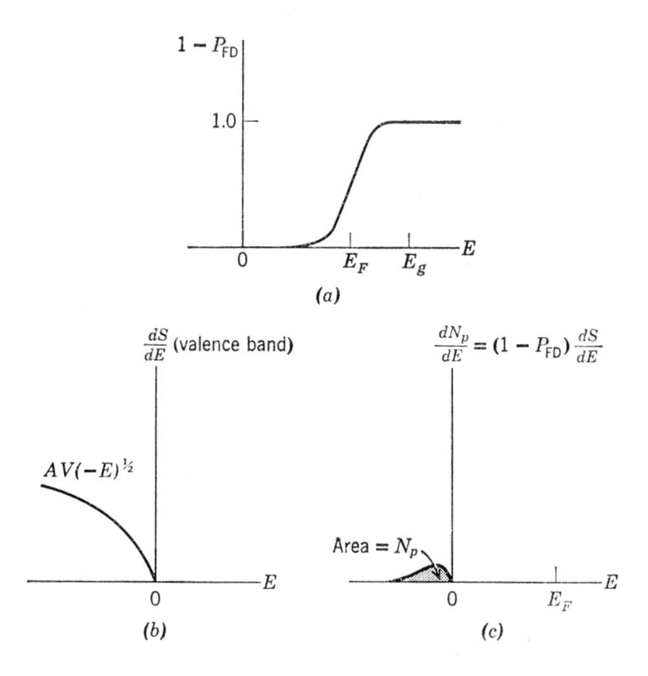

Fig. 13.6. The calculation of N_p. (*a*) Fermi factor for holes versus E. (*b*) Density of states in valence band versus E. (*c*) Number of holes per unit energy dN_p/dE versus E.

of energy. The number of holes in the valence band is equal to the area under the product curve. The functions involved in the calculation of the number of electrons in the conduction band are shown in Fig. 13.5. From these figures and from equations 13.6 and 13.12 it should be evident that raising the Fermi level leads to an increase in N_n and a decrease in N_p and that lowering the Fermi level leads to an increase in N_p and a decrease in N_n.

13.5 The Fermi level in semiconductors

In Chapter 3 we pointed out that both the total number of fermions and their total energy must be specified to determine the average or most probable distribution of the fermions among energy states. Thus two parameters, either α and β or E_F and T, appear in the Fermi factor. The calculation of the Fermi level E_F for semiconductors shows, as did the calculation for metals in section 3.5, how the position of the Fermi level depends on the number of fermions present.

In the interior of a crystal there must be enough electrons to make the interior electrically neutral. (Any excess charge placed on a crystal in which charges are free to move resides on the surface of the crystal, as may be shown using Gauss' law.) The condition for electrical neutrality for any volume inside a crystal may be written

$$N_n + N_A^- = N_p + N_D^+ \tag{13.14}$$

where N_A^- is the number of acceptor ions in that volume and N_D^+ is the number of donor ions. The left side of (13.14) is the number of negative charges within the volume and the right side is the number of positive charges. N_n and N_p have already been written in terms of the Fermi energy in 13.6 and 13.12. Since the Fermi factor is the probability that a state contains an electron, N_A^- and N_D^+ are expressed in terms of E_F by

$$N_A^- = N_A P_{\text{FD}}\Big|_{EA} = \frac{N_A}{1 + e^{(E_A - E_F)/kT}} \tag{13.15}$$

$$N_D^+ = N_D\left(1 - P_{\text{FD}}\Big|_{ED}\right) = \frac{N_D}{e^{(E_F - E_D)/kT} + 1} \tag{13.16}$$

Here, N_A = total number of acceptor atoms, N_D = total number of donor atoms, E_A = energy of acceptor states (all assumed to have the same energy), and E_D = energy of donor states (all assumed to have the same energy). Substituting 13.6, 13.12, 13.15, and 13.16 into the conservation of charge equation

$$\underset{\text{(No. electrons in C.B.)}}{GT^{3/2}Ve^{-(E_g-E_F)/kT}} + \underset{\text{(No. acceptor ions)}}{\frac{N_A}{1+e^{(E_A-E_F)/kT}}} = \underset{\text{(No. holes in V.B.)}}{GT^{3/2}Ve^{-E_F/kT}} + \underset{\text{(No. donor ions)}}{\frac{N_D}{e^{(E_F-E_D)/kT}+1}} \tag{13.17}$$

Equation 13.17 may be solved for E_F if all the other parameters are known. To facilitate the solution for E_F we put 13.17 in a more attractive form by defining some new constants and a new variable. Letting $GT^{3/2}e^{-E_g/kT} = C_n$, $N_A/V = n_A$, $e^{E_A/kT} = C_A$, $GT^{3/2} = C_p$, $N_D/V = n_D$, $e^{-E_D/kT} = C_D$, and $e^{E_F/kT} = x$, 13.17 becomes

$$\underset{\substack{\text{(Concentration}\\ \text{of electrons}\\ \text{in C.B.)}}}{C_n x} + \underset{\substack{\text{(Concentration}\\ \text{of acceptor}\\ \text{ions)}}}{\frac{n_A}{1+C_A/x}} = \underset{\substack{\text{(Concentration}\\ \text{of holes in}\\ \text{V.B.)}}}{\frac{C_p}{x}} + \underset{\substack{\text{(Concentration}\\ \text{of donor ions)}}}{\frac{n_D}{C_D x+1}} \tag{13.18}$$

which is a fourth degree algebraic equation for x.

Often a crystal contains a negligible number of either donor or acceptor atoms. In such a case either the term involving n_D or the term involving n_A may be neglected, which reduces 13.18 to a cubic equation for x. Furthermore, if the Fermi level lies more than a few kT above the middle of the gap, which is usually the case for an n-type semiconductor, the concentration of holes in the valence band, C_p/x, becomes negligibly small. Correspondingly, if the Fermi level lies more than a few kT below the middle of the gap, which is usually the case for a p-type semiconductor, the concentration of electrons in the conduction band, $C_n x$, becomes negligibly small. In either of the latter cases 13.18 becomes approximately a quadratic or even a linear equation. A numerical example will help clarify these statements.

Example. Calculate the position of the Fermi level and the densities N_n/V and N_p/V of conduction electrons and holes in an n-type germanium crystal at room temperature, $T = 300°$ K, containing 10^{22} donor atoms/meter³ and no acceptors. The band-gap is $E_g = 0.72$ ev and the donor level lies at $E_D = 0.71$ ev.

In equation 13.18, since $kT = 0.026$ ev for $T = 300°$ K,

$$C_n = 4.83 \times 10^{21}(300)^{3/2} \cdot e^{-0.72/0.026} \approx 2.41 \times 10^{13} \text{ electrons/meter}^3$$

$$n_A = 0$$

$$C_p = 4.83 \times 10^{21}(300)^{3/2} \approx 2.51 \times 10^{25} \text{ holes/meter}^3$$

$$n_D = 10^{22} \text{ donor atoms/meter}^3$$

$$C_D = e^{-0.71/0.026} \approx 1.4 \times 10^{-12}$$

Substituting these into 13.18

$$2.41 \times 10^{13}x = \frac{2.51 \times 10^{25}}{x} + \frac{10^{22}}{1.4 \times 10^{-12}x + 1} \tag{13.19}$$

A useful method of attack on such an equation is to estimate the answer by a cut-and-try process. Thus, trying $x = 1$ we find the left side is far smaller than the right side, so $x = 1$ is too small. Trying $x = 10^{10}$ we find the left side is somewhat larger than the right side, so $x = 10^{10}$ is too large. Trying $x = 10^9$ we have

$$2.41 \times 10^{22} > 2.51 \times 10^{16} + \frac{10^{22}}{1.4 \times 10^{-3} + 1} \tag{13.20}$$

so that $x = 10^9$ is still a little too large. An important by-product of our estimation is that we have shown that the first term on the right in 13.19 is completely negligible and so is the term involving x in the denominator of the last term. Hence, a precise value of x may be found by solving the linear approximation to equation 13.19

$$2.41 \times 10^{13}x \approx 10^{22} \tag{13.21}$$

$$x \approx 4.17 \times 10^8$$

The Fermi level may be found using

$$x = 4.17 \times 10^8 = e^{E_F/kT} = e^{E_F/0.026\text{ev}} \tag{13.22}$$

from which $E_F \approx 0.52$ ev.

Finally, the number of electrons per unit volume in the conduction band (the first term in 13.19) becomes

$$\frac{N_n}{V} = 2.41 \times 10^{13} \times 4.17 \times 10^8 = 10^{22} \frac{\text{electrons}}{\text{meter}^3} \tag{13.23}$$

Similarly, the number of holes per unit volume in the valence band (the second term in 13.19) is

$$\frac{N_p}{V} \approx \frac{2.51 \times 10^{25}}{4.17 \times 10^8} \approx 6.0 \times 10^{16} \frac{\text{holes}}{\text{meter}^3} \tag{13.24}$$

a result which could also have been obtained by using 13.23 in 13.13.

The third term in 13.19 is equal to the number of positive donor ions per unit volume and is seen to be very little smaller than the number of donor atoms per unit volume. We may conclude that in this particular crystal at room temperature, nearly all of the "fifth valence electrons" of the donor atoms have been shaken loose and appear in the conduction band. Furthermore, only a small percentage of the electrons in the conduction band is due to thermal excitation of valence band electrons to the conduction band.

13.6 Temperature dependence of the conductivity of a semiconductor

The conductivity of a semiconductor depends on temperature, not only because the mobility depends on temperature but also because the densities of the charge carriers (holes and conduction electrons) depend on temperature. The carrier densities depend on temperature in an even more complicated way than shown explicitly in equations 13.6 and 13.12 because E_F is a function of temperature. (For example, for the n-type semiconductor of the previous example, the Fermi level at absolute zero would have to lie somewhere between the donor level, $E_D = 0.71$ ev, and the bottom of the conduction band, $E_g =$ 0.72 ev, to account for the fact that, at $T = 0$, all the donor states are full and all the conduction band states are empty. This position of E_F should be compared with our calculated value, $E_F \approx 0.52$ ev at $T = 300°$ K.)

We present here a qualitative explanation of the temperature dependence of the charge-carrier density. Specifically, we shall treat an n-type semiconductor. Typical experimental results are shown in Fig. 13.7. The conductivity is plotted on a logarithmic scale as a function of $1/T$ in part (a). If the mobility is measured as a function of temperature, for example, by a Hall effect experiment, then a graph of N_n/V versus $1/T$ may be constructed using equation 12.18.

$$\sigma \approx n_n e \mu_n = \frac{N_n}{V} e \mu_n \qquad \text{(for } n\text{-type semiconductors)} \quad (12.18)$$

There are three distinct regions in the curve of n_n versus $1/T$. For large $1/T$ (small T) n_n increases as T increases as a result of thermal excitation of more and more electrons from donor states into the conduction band. For $1/T \approx 0.04$ ($T = 50°$ K) practically all the donor atoms are ionized and a further increase in temperature causes no more electrons to be excited into the conduction band. Finally, at $1/T \approx$ 0.005 ($T \approx 200°$ K) the sample becomes intrinsic; that is, appreciable numbers of electrons begin to be excited from the valence band into the conduction band. For temperatures higher than about 200° K the concentrations of conduction electrons and holes become approximately equal; then, using equation 13.13 both N_n and N_p should be proportional to $T^{3/2}e^{-E_g/2kT}$. In this region the temperature dependence is dominated by the exponential factor which explains the straight-line dependence of log n_n on $1/T$ at the high temperature end of Fig. 13.7b.

It is found experimentally that the mobility is approximately proportional to the $-3/2$ power of the absolute temperature. This $-3/2$ power dependence can also be obtained theoretically. Hence the conductivity in the intrinsic range is proportional to $e^{-E_g/2kT}$ which is borne out by the straight-line portion at the high-temperature end of

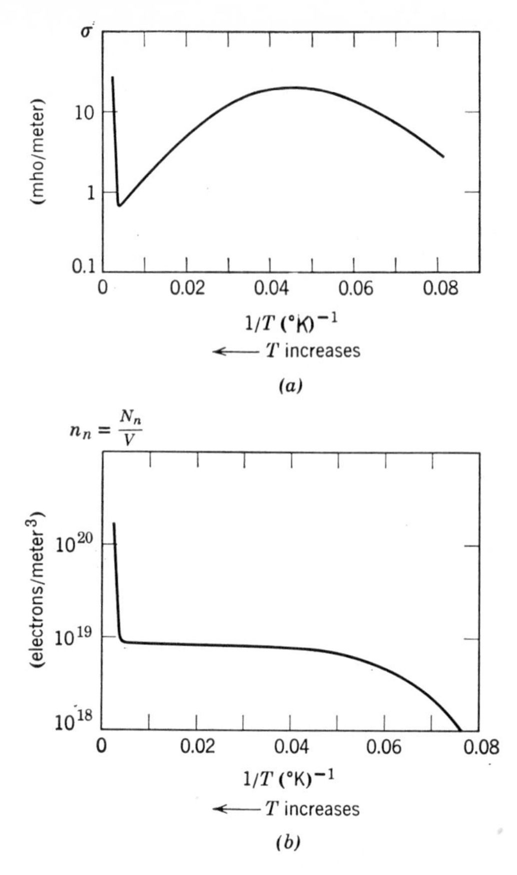

Fig. 13.7. Conductivity (*a*) and conduction-electron concentration (*b*) in a *n*-type semiconductor sample. [After Debye and Conwell, *Phys. Rev.*, **93,** 693 (1954).]

the log σ versus $1/T$ graph in Fig. 13.7*a*. Note that in the room temperature region the conductivity of a semiconductor increases with increasing temperature, whereas the conductivity of a metal decreases with increasing temperature.

13.7 Crystals in contact

Whenever two different crystals are first placed in contact, there is likely to be a flow of electrons from one to the other. The flow occurs because the electrons that strike the boundary from one side have more energy on the average than those striking the boundary from the other side.

Figure 13.8*a* is an energy-level diagram showing two different metal crystals (box models) before contact. Note that the Fermi level of A lies further below zero energy than the Fermi level of B.

In Fig. 13.8*b* the metals have been touched together. Electrons near the Fermi level in B can cross the boundary to A because there are empty states available to them in A. On the other hand, electrons in A "see" mostly filled states in B and hence cannot cross into B. Thus the net flow of electrons from B to A is basically due to the prevention of flow in the other direction by the exclusion principle.

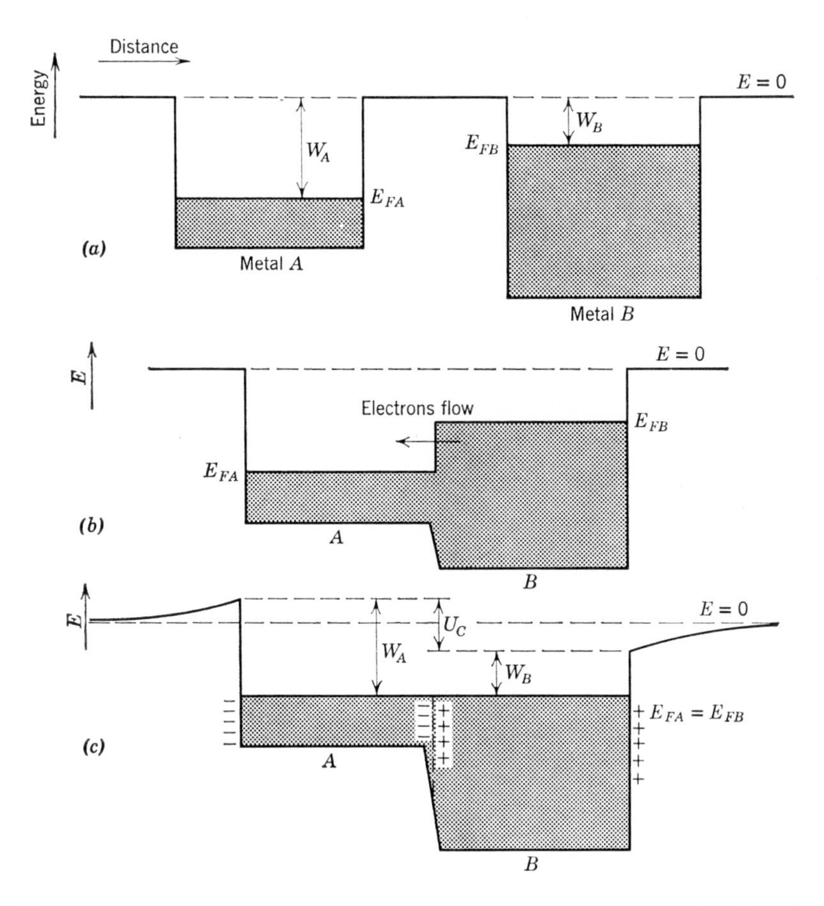

Fig. 13.8. Energy-level diagram of the contact between two metals using the box model. (*a*) Before contact. (*b*) Immediately after contact. (*c*) Equilibrium.

Since the two metals together comprise a single system of fermions, the flow of electrons continues until there is a single Fermi level, that is, until the Fermi levels in A and B are at the same energy. However, the position of the Fermi level in each metal cannot change relative to the potential energy inside the metal because the interior of each metal must remain electrically neutral. Therefore the energies of all the levels in A must shift upward and those of all the levels in B must shift downward to allow the Fermi levels to line up. The upward shift in A occurs because of the excess negative surface charge on A which lowers A's potential and raises the potential energy of every level in A. Likewise the downward shift in B occurs because of the excess positive surface charge on B which raises B's potential and lowers the potential energy of every level in B. The relative amount by which the levels in A shift with respect to the levels in B is called the contact potential-energy difference U_C. From a study of Fig. 13.8*c* one can see that the relative shift in energy levels is equal to the difference in the work functions of A and B.

$$U_C = eV_C = |W_A - W_B| \tag{13.25}$$

The material with the smaller work function becomes positively charged and has a higher potential than the other by the contact potential V_C.

The lining-up of Fermi levels at equilibrium is a general result. It applies to any number of metals and/or semiconductors in contact.

13.8 Photoconductivity

Electrons in a crystal can be excited to higher energy levels by photons as well as by collisions with each other and with thermally vibrating lattice ions. The increase in conductivity due to holes in the valence band produced by photon excitation of valence electrons to higher lying states is one form of photoconductivity. Similarly, conduction electrons can be produced by photon excitation of electrons from lower energy states. It is usually not necessary for a photon to have an energy as great as the width of the energy gap between valence and conduction bands in order to produce current carriers, for excitations can occur to and from the localized energy levels associated with imperfections in the crystal. There are many types of imperfections in crystals besides the intentional replacement of a normal atom of the crystal by an impurity atom. For example, in a valence crystal such as NaCl, which consists of an interlaced array of positive sodium ions and negative chlorine ions, a Cl^- ion can be missing. This negative-ion vacancy acts like a region of positive charge because of the Na^+ ions surrounding it and the vacancy can attract and bind an electron. A negative-ion vacancy which contains a bound electron is called an *F*-center. The electron of an *F*-center can be released by thermal excitation, by absorption of a photon or even by recombination of this electron with a hole in the valence band. The strong absorption of photons at some frequencies and not at others in the visible spectrum is the reason for the colors of crystals. Clear crystals do not readily absorb visible light. It should be noted that semiconductor crystals become essentially transparent to photons in the infrared where photon energies are less than the band-gap energy.

Suggested References

R. L. Sproull, *Modern Physics*, John Wiley and Sons, 1956. Chapter 11 treats the distributions of electrons and holes in semiconductors from the band theory point of view and at about our level.

C. Kittel, *Introduction to Solid State Physics*, 2nd ed, John Wiley and Sons, 1956. Kittel's Chapter 13 is an illuminating account of conductivity, mobility, and the ionization of impurities in semiconductor crystals. The various photoconductivity processes are described in detail in Chapter 18.

PROBLEMS

13.1. (*a*) Estimate the energy required to "ionize" a donor atom in a germanium crystal ($\kappa = 16$) by assuming that the nucleus Z and innermost $Z - 1$ electrons are equivalent to a heavy point nucleus of charge $+e$, and that the remaining electron is in the ground state for this hydrogen-like atom.
(*b*) How can this simple approach be modified to give a result more in accord with experiment?

13.2. The calculation in Problem 13.1 of the donor ionization energy ignores the difference between free and effective mass of an electron. (*a*) Explain why a smaller effective mass increases the radius of the first Bohr orbit, and by what factor. (*b*) How does this alter the ionization energy?

13.3. For what photon wavelengths would you expect a piece of intrinsic germanium to become optically transparent?

13.4. What purity (in parts per million) must a germanium crystal have in order that there is no more than one "impurity carrier" for every 100 "intrinsic carriers." Assume that the impurity atoms are all ionized and that the intrinsic carrier density is 2.5×10^{13} carrier/cm^3. The density and atomic weight of germanium are 5.36 gm/cm^3 and 72.6.

13.5. (*a*) Write $E = E_F + \delta$, and find δ for $P_{FD} = \frac{1}{4}, \frac{3}{4}$, expressing δ in units of kT.
(*b*) Show also for any δ, $P_{FD}(E_F + \delta) = 1 - P_{FD}(E_F - \delta)$. (*c*) Evaluate P_{FD} at room temperature for $\delta = 0.1, 0.2$, and 1.0 ev.

13.6. (*a*) Sketch the density of states factor versus energy for an intrinsic semiconductor.

(*b*) Sketch the Fermi factor versus energy. (Where is the Fermi level?)

(*c*) Find the numbers of conduction electrons and holes per unit volume if the energy gap is 1.0 ev, at absolute temperatures of 0°, 30°, 300°, 400° K.

(*d*) Sketch the number of electrons per unit volume in the conduction band of this intrinsic semiconductor as a function of T.

13.7. In a certain n-type semiconductor at 300° K, 24% of the donor atoms are ionized. Does the Fermi level lie above or below the donor level and by how much?

13.8. In a certain p-type semiconductor at 300° K, 32% of the acceptor states are filled. Does the Fermi level lie above or below the acceptor level and by how much?

13.9. A certain semiconductor contains both p-type and n-type impurities. The donor and acceptor levels are 0.12 ev apart.

(*a*) Show that, if at 300° K the acceptor levels are about 97% full, then the donor levels are about 76% ionized.

(*b*) Where is the Fermi level?

13.10. In a certain intrinsic semiconductor, the density of states factor is given by the shape below rather than by equations 13.2 and 13.8. Show that

$$E_F = \frac{E_g}{2} - \frac{kT}{2} \ln 10$$

provided E_F lies in the gap far from the top of the valence band or the bottom of the conduction band.

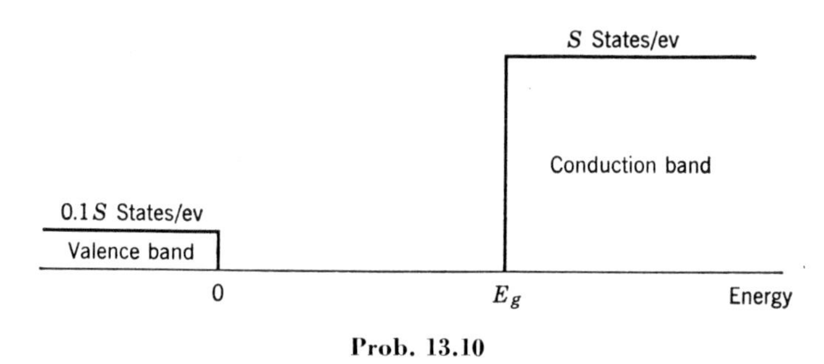

Prob. 13.10

13.11. Using equations 12.19 and 13.13, show that a semiconductor will have a minimum conductivity at a given temperature when

$$n_n = n_i \sqrt{\mu_p/\mu_n} \qquad \text{and} \qquad n_p = n_i \sqrt{\mu_n/\mu_p}$$

where $n_i = \sqrt{n_n n_p}$ = constant.

13.12. (*a*) Find the numerical values of the intrinsic and minimum conductivities (see Problem 13.11) for germanium at a temperature such that $n_i = 2.5 \times 10^{13}/\text{cm}^3$, $\mu_n = 0.38$ meter²/volt-sec, $\mu_p = 0.19$ meter²/volt-sec.

(*b*) For what values of n_p and n_n (other than $n_p = n_n = n_i$) does this crystal have a conductivity equal to the intrinsic conductivity?

13.13. A semiconductor with energy gap 1.0 ev has 10^{18} acceptors per cubic centimeter at 0.5 ev above the valence band. If the hole mobility is 0.01 meter²/volt-sec, calculate the position of the Fermi level and the conductivity of the material at room temperature (300° K) and at liquid oxygen temperature (90° K).

13.14. Where is E_F relative to E_g for an n-type semiconductor in which:

$$E_g > 4 \text{ ev}, E_D = E_g - 1.5 \text{ ev}, n_D = 10^{22} \frac{\text{donor atoms}}{\text{meter}^3}, n_A \ll n_D, T = 1000° \text{ K}$$

14. semiconductor devices

Now that we are familiar with the production and motion of charge carriers in solids, we are in a position to study some solid-state devices. A detailed discussion of the *p-n* junction is given and used in the description of the Zener diode, tunnel diode, and junction transistor. Some other semiconductor devices are briefly described.

14.1 The *p-n* junction

The *p-n* junction is an important building block in the fabrication of the solid-state equivalents of the vacuum diode and triode. A *p-n* junction is made by growing a *single semiconductor crystal*, part of which is *n*-type and part *p*-type. The boundary inside the crystal between the *p*- and *n*- regions is called a *p-n* junction. A *p-n* junction must be fabricated as a single crystal in order for the junction to have interesting electrical properties. A junction formed by merely pressing together an *n*-type crystal and a *p*-type crystal would have too many imperfections to be of interest.

The most important electrical property of a *p-n* junction is its property of rectification. That is, if the *p*- side of the junction is biased at a higher potential than the *n*- side (forward bias), an appreciable current flows across the junction. On the other hand, if the *n*-side of the junction has the higher potential (reverse bias), very little current flows. A *p-n* junction, then, acts like a diode vacuum tube.

In Chapter 6 we showed that the current in a space-charge-limited vacuum diode is proportional to the $\frac{3}{2}$-power of the plate voltage when

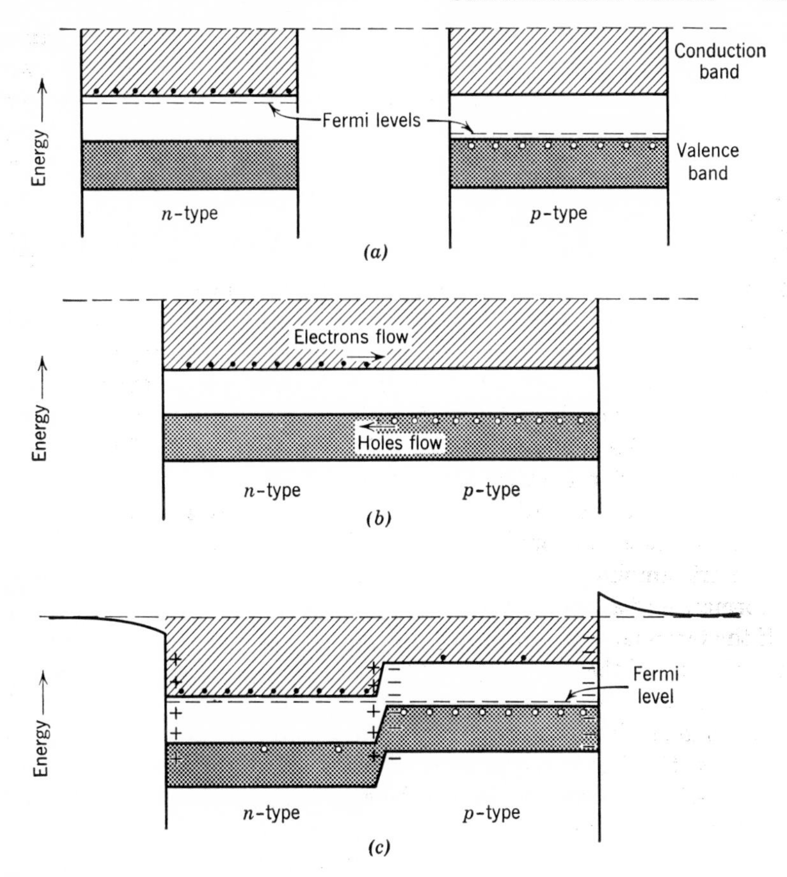

Fig. 14.1. The lining-up of Fermi levels at equilibrium for semiconductors. (*a*) Isolated *n*- and *p*-type semiconductors, identical except for impurity content. (*b*) Situation immediately following contact. (*c*) Equilibrium condition.

the plate is positive and is zero when the plate is negative. We now examine how the current across a *p-n* junction depends on the potential of the *p*-side relative to the *n*-side.

The two sides of a *p-n* junction are very much like any other two noninsulators in contact. Although a *p-n* junction is *not* actually made by pressing together *p*-type and *n*-type crystals, it is nevertheless instructive to *imagine* that it can be made that way. Figure 14.1 is very much like Fig. 13.8, except that the crystals are *n*-type and *p*-type semiconductors rather than two different metals.

In Fig. 14.1*a* the crystals are shown before contact. Since they are identical except for impurity content, the bands occur at the same energies in each crystal and the Fermi levels are *not* aligned. (As we learned in Chapter 13 the Fermi level in an n-type crystal lies nearer the conduction band than the valence band; the opposite is true for a p-type crystal.) In part (b) of the figure the crystals have been pushed together; electrons spill over from the higher levels on the n-side to the p-side and holes spill over the other way. The diffusion of electrons and holes stops when the Fermi levels are lined up. Figure 14.1c represents the equilibrium situation when no net current flows across the junction. The excess positive charges that accumulate on the n-side and the negative charges that accumulate on the p-side reside on the surfaces of the crystals and on both sides of the junction. The double layer of charge at the junction consists of negative acceptor ions on the p-side and positive donor ions on the n-side. This double charge layer region is called the depletion layer and is responsible for the depletion-layer capacitance discussed in section 14.4. This capacitance is an important factor in the operation of the solid-state parametric amplifier and can be a limiting factor in the high frequency performance of a transistor.

If the terminals of a battery of voltage V are connected to the crystal on both sides of the p-n junction, the energy levels on the two sides will all shift relative to one another by the amount eV. The direction of the shift depends on the polarity of the battery connections. Figure 14.2 shows the shift in energy levels when the p-side is biased positively. On the p-side the battery reduces the excess negative charge, *raises the potential,* and therefore *lowers the potential energy of electrons.* On the n-side the excess positive charge is reduced, the *potential is lowered,* and the *potential energy is raised.* Since, for this "forward bias,"

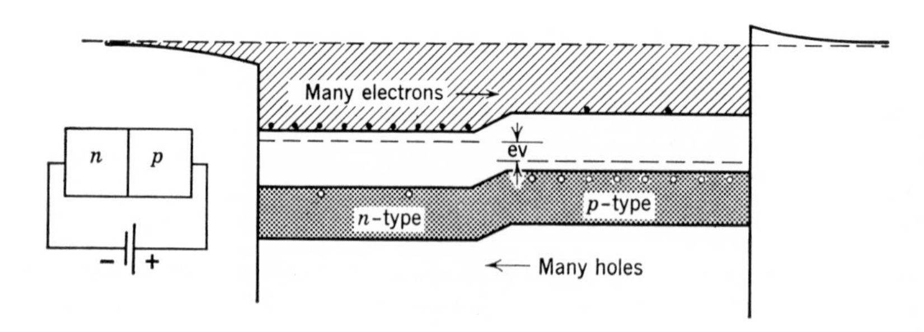

Fig. 14.2. Energy levels in a forward biased p-n junction.

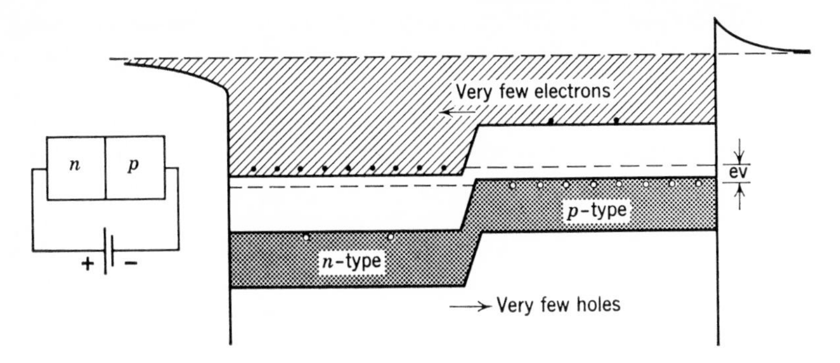

Fig. 14.3. Energy levels in a reverse biased p-n junction.

the Fermi level[1] on the n-side is raised above the Fermi level on the p-side, electrons flow from the n-side to the p-side.

Figure 14.3 shows the shift in energy levels when the p-side is connected to the negative terminal of the battery. The battery, in this "reverse-biased" situation, raises the energy levels on the p-side and lowers them on the n-side, so that electrons tend to spill over from the p-side to the n-side. However, since there are very few electrons in the conduction band on the p-side which are available to spill over, the electron current is very small. A similar argument shows that very few holes spill over from the n-side to the p-side.

In the following two sections we derive the current-voltage relationship for a p-n junction. The derivation consists of two parts. First, in section 14.2 we find that the *form* of the relation is

$$i = i_0(e^{eV/kT} - 1) \tag{14.1}$$

where i_0 is a constant called the reverse saturation current. The second part of the derivation consists of finding, in section 14.3, how i_0 depends on parameters that have simple physical interpretations in terms of a microscopic view of a semiconductor.

14.2 Current-voltage characteristic of a *p-n* junction

The following derivation of the form of the current-voltage relation is based on the fact that for every range of energy dE the net electron current flow across the junction is the difference between the rates of flow or currents in

[1] Fermi levels in nonequilibrium situations such as this are sometimes called quasi-equilibrium Fermi levels.

each direction. The *net* electron current from the n-side to the p-side produced by electrons in an energy range dE will be designated as di. Thus

$$di = di_{n \to p} - di_{p \to n} \tag{14.2}$$

where $di_{n \to p}$ and $di_{p \to n}$ are the components of the electron current flowing from the n-side to the p-side and vice-versa.

We assume that the electron current $di_{n \to p}$ from the n-side to the p-side is proportional to three separate factors: (1) the number of electrons per unit energy on the n-side $P_n dS_n/dE$ which are available to cross the junction, (2) the number of vacant states per unit energy on the p-side $(1 - P_p)dS_p/dE$ which are available to receive the electrons, and (3) the width dE of the energy interval. The constant of proportionality, which plays the role of a transition probability, may be a function of energy; we write it as $Z_{n \to p}(E)$. Thus

$$di_{n \to p} = Z_{n \to p}(E) \frac{dS_n}{dE} \frac{dS_p}{dE} P_n(1 - P_p)\, dE \tag{14.3}$$

in which the symbols are defined as:

$di_{n \to p}$ ≡ electron current from n-side to p-side in the energy range dE
$Z_{n \to p}(E)$ ≡ "transition probability," (electronic charge included)
$\frac{dS_n}{dE}$ ≡ density of states on n-side
$\frac{dS_p}{dE}$ ≡ density of states on p-side
P_n ≡ Fermi factor on n-side
P_p ≡ Fermi factor on p-side

Similarly, the electron current from the p-side to the n-side is proportional to the density of electrons on the p-side $P_p dS_p/dE$ and to the density of vacant states on the n-side $(1 - P_n)dS_n/dE$. Thus,

$$di_{p \to n} = Z_{p \to n}(E) \frac{dS_n}{dE} \frac{dS_p}{dE} P_p(1 - P_n) \tag{14.4}$$

We substitute 14.3 and 14.4 into 14.2 to find the *net* electron current di due to electrons in the energy range dE. Thus

$$di = \frac{dS_n}{dE} \frac{dS_p}{dE} [Z_{n \to p}(E)(P_n - P_n P_p) - Z_{p \to n}(E)(P_p - P_n P_p)]\, dE \tag{14.5}$$

The total net electron current from the n-side to the p-side due to the electrons in all energy states is the integral of 14.5 over all energies.

$$i = \int di = \int_{-\infty}^{\infty} \frac{dS_n}{dE} \frac{dS_p}{dE} [Z_{n \to p}(P_n - P_n P_p) - Z_{p \to n}(P_p - P_n P_p)]\, dE \tag{14.6}$$

If the Fermi levels and therefore the Fermi factors P_n and P_p are equal, we know that equilibrium exists and therefore i must be zero. If we set $P_n = P_p$ and $i = 0$ in 14.6 we obtain

$$0 = \int_{-\infty}^{\infty} \frac{dS_n}{dE} \frac{dS_p}{dE} (P_n - P_n^2)(Z_{n \to p} - Z_{p \to n})\, dE \tag{14.7}$$

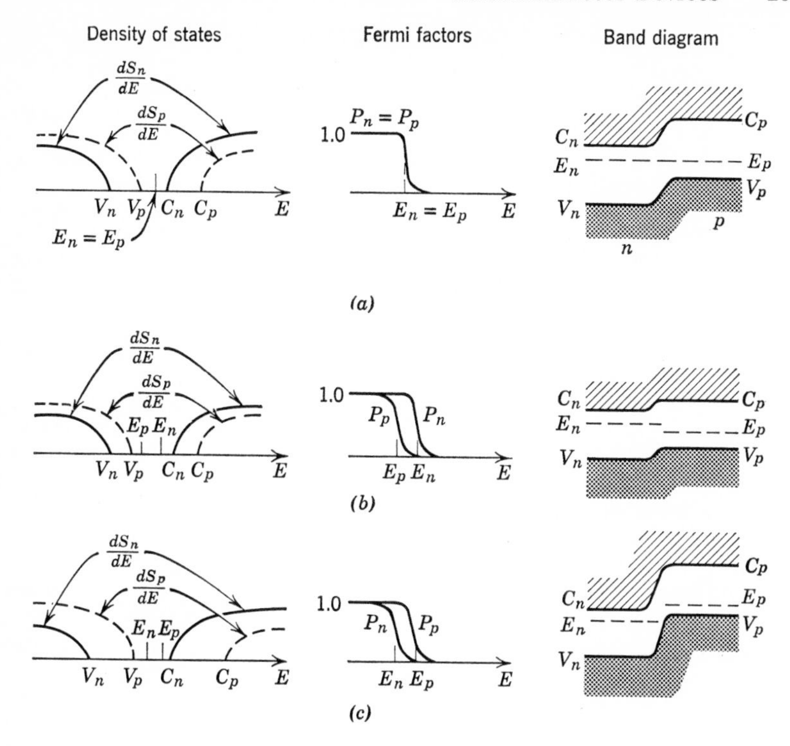

Fig. 14.4. Density of states, Fermi factors, and energy-level diagrams for *p-n* junction. (*a*) No bias. (*b*) Forward bias ($E_n > E_p$). (*c*) Reverse bias ($E_p > E_n$).

In general, this integral is zero only if $Z_{n \to p}$ equals $Z_{p \to n}$, that is, if the transition probabilities in both directions between states of equal energy on opposite sides of the junction are equal. We assume in what follows that these transition probabilities are equal and we relable each with the symbol $Z(E)$. Applying this simplification to equation 14.6 and simplifying slightly, we have

$$i = \int_{-\infty}^{\infty} Z(E) \frac{dS_n}{dE} \frac{dS_p}{dE} (P_n - P_p) \, dE \tag{14.8}$$

Although the integral looks quite formidable, especially when expressions for dS_p/dE, dS_n/dE, P_n, and P_p as functions of energy are substituted, it is possible to find how the integral depends on the voltage of a bias battery connected across the junction without actually performing the integration. To see what would be involved in performing the integral we plot in Fig. 14.4 graphs of dS_p/dE, dS_n/dE, P_n, and P_p for the cases of no bias, forward bias, and reverse bias. The relative positions of the conduction and valence bands and the Fermi levels on the two sides of the junction are shown in band diagrams for convenience. The density of states factors are again assumed to be ½-power functions of energy as in Chapter 13. In Fig. 14.4 the symbols denoting the various energies are intended to convey their meanings and are somewhat different from symbols used earlier. The definitions are:

$E_n, E_p \equiv$ Fermi levels on n- and p-sides.
$V_n, V_p \equiv$ tops of valence bands on n- and p-sides.
$C_n, C_p \equiv$ bottoms of conduction bands on n- and p-sides.

It will be noticed from the density of states graphs that the product $dS_n/dE \cdot dS_p/dE$ is nonzero only below $E = V_n$ and above $E = C_p$. Thus the integral in 14.8 may be split into two integrals

$$i = \int_{-\infty}^{V_n} Z(E) \frac{dS_n}{dE} \frac{dS_p}{dE} (P_n - P_p)\, dE + \int_{C_p}^{\infty} Z(E) \frac{dS_n}{dE} \frac{dS_p}{dE} (P_n - P_p)\, dE \tag{14.9}$$

The expression $(P_n - P_p)$ will now be evaluated. We make the assumption that the Fermi energies lie several times kT above V_n and several times kT below C_p. Over the range of integration from $-\infty$ to V_n, one approximation is valid in the computation of $(P_n - P_p)$; over the range of integration from C_p to a different approximation is valid. Thus using 3.42

$$P_n - P_p = \frac{1}{1 + e^{(E-E_n)/kT}} - \frac{1}{1 + e^{(E-E_p)/kT}} \tag{14.10}$$

Over the range of integration from C_p to ∞, $E - E_n \gg kT$ and $E - E_p \gg kT$. Hence the unity in each denominator may be neglected and we have

$$P_n - P_p \approx e^{-(E-E_n)/kT} - e^{-(E-E_p)/kT} \qquad (C_p < E < \infty) \tag{14.11}$$

Factoring $e^{-(E-E_p)/kT}$ from each term we obtain

$$P_n - P_p = e^{-(E-E_p)/kT}[e^{(E_n-E_p)/kT} - 1] \tag{14.12}$$

It is to be emphasized that equation 14.12 is the correct expression for $(P_n - P_p)$ only for the integration between C_p and ∞, (that is, where $E - E_n$ and $E - E_p$ are $\gg kT$). In a similar way it follows that an approximate expression for $P_n - P_p$ for the integration between $-\infty$ and V_n (that is, where $(E_n - E)$ and $(E_p - E)$ are both $\gg kT$) is

$$P_n - P_p = e^{-(E_n-E)/kT}[e^{(E_n-E_p)/kT} - 1] \tag{14.13}$$

Substituting 14.12 and 14.13 into 14.9 and factoring we have

$$i = [e^{(E_n-E_p)/kT} - 1] \left\{ \int_{C_p}^{\infty} Z(E) \frac{dS_n}{dE} \frac{dS_p}{dE} e^{-(E-E_p)/kT}\, dE + \int_{-\infty}^{V_n} Z(E) \frac{dS_n}{dE} \frac{dS_p}{dE} e^{-(E_n-E)/kT}\, dE \right\} \tag{14.14}$$

From a study of Figs. 14.2 and 14.3 it can be seen that

$$E_n - E_p = eV \tag{14.15}$$

where $E_n - E_p$ is the difference between the Fermi levels and V is the potential difference of the p-side relative to the n-side.

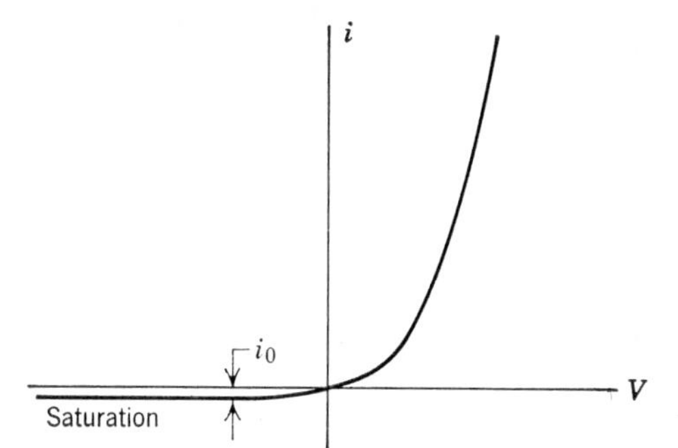

Fig. 14.5. Graph of equation 14.1, theoretical current-voltage relation for a p-n junction diode.

The largest contribution to the first integral in 14.14 arises from the states near the bottom of the conduction band on the p-side. This is true because the factor $e^{-(E-E_p)/kT}$ falls off rapidly with increasing energy. This first integral depends on the bias potential V only by virtue of the fact that dS_n/dE shifts with respect to C_p when V is changed. However, the value of dS_n/dE at the important energies just above C_p is not a strong function of energy, and therefore this integral is not a strong function of V.

A similar argument can be made to show that the second integral is not a strong function of V. The slight dependence of these integrals on V can be exhibited by numerical or graphical integration techniques.

To the approximation that the integrals in 14.14 are independent of V, and that their sum can be represented by the constant i_0, we may write 14.14 as

$$i = i_0(e^{eV/kT} - 1) \tag{14.1}$$

This equation is plotted in Fig. 14.5. Notice that a reverse saturation current is predicted. That is, for negative V's (reverse biases) i quickly approaches $-i_0$ as the reverse-bias voltage is increased. Generally, except for some important special effects to be discussed in sections 14.5 and 14.6, the experimental current-voltage characteristics for p-n junction diodes agree quite well with the theoretical shape given by 14.1.

14.3 Reverse saturation current in a p-n junction

The constant i_0 of equation 14.1 can be expressed in a more illuminating way than by the sum of the integrals in equation 14.14. We now calculate i_0 from a consideration of the conditions existing in the crystal when this reverse saturation current flows.

For reverse bias, the p-side of the junction is negatively biased and the Fermi level on the p-side lies higher than the Fermi level on the n-side. Conduction electrons (minority carriers) on the p-side and holes (minority carriers) on the n-side spill over the junction and contribute to the reverse current. However, there are relatively few conduction electrons on the p-side and holes on the n-side, and "satu-

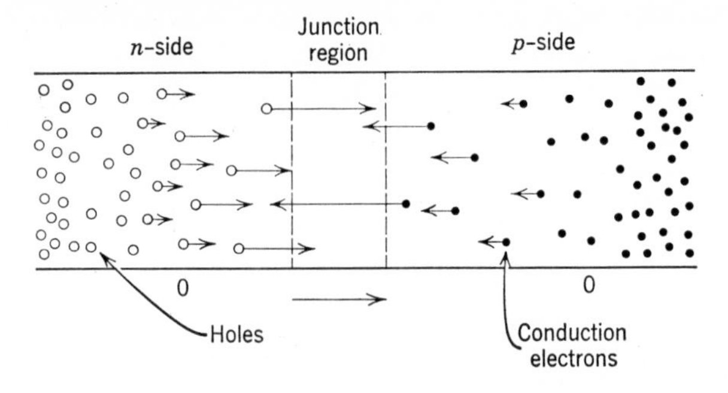

Fig. 14.6. Enlarged view of junction with reverse bias, showing diffusion of both types of "minority" carriers toward the junction. Majority carriers are not illustrated.

ration" occurs if the rate at which these carriers reach the junction is independent of reverse bias voltage. The reverse saturation current i_0 is therefore composed of an electron component i_{0n} and a hole component i_{0p}.

$$i_0 = i_{0n} + i_{0p} \tag{14.16}$$

The following analysis applies to the electron flow component i_{0n}.

The iR drops across the p- and n-regions of a junction diode are relatively small, so that almost the entire bias-voltage drop occurs at the junction, a narrow region at most a few hundred atomic spacings wide. Hence a large electric field exists within the junction. To a good approximation the electrons and holes move in a field-free region except when they happen to wander near the junction itself. If a conduction electron on the p-side wanders too close to the (reverse-biased) junction, it is pulled across the junction by the strong field there. Saturation occurs if the field at the junction is strong enough to maintain essentially a zero concentration of conduction electrons at the p-edge of the junction (and a zero concentration of holes at the n-edge of the junction). The concentration of conduction electrons far from the junction must be the equilibrium concentration n_∞ due to thermal production of conduction electrons in the p-region (such as we calculated in sections 13.4 and 13.5). Since the concentration of conduction electrons far from the junction is greater than that at the junction, a diffusional flow of electrons toward the junction occurs. The diffusion current of electrons right at the p-edge of the junction is equal to the conduction-electron contribution i_{0n} to the reverse saturation current. Figure 14.6 illustrates the diffusion of minority carriers toward a reverse-biased junction.

Since the diffusional rate of flow is proportional to the concentration gradient of the conduction electrons, we must first find how the concentration n_n of conduction electrons depends on distance x from the junction. This derivation is an example of the use of the one-dimensional, steady-state continuity equation when the flow occurs by diffusion only. Hence from 8.24

$$\frac{\partial n_n}{\partial t} = D \frac{\partial^2 n_n}{\partial x^2} + C = 0 \tag{14.17}$$

In the steady state the rate of flow due to diffusion is given by $D\, dn_n/dx$, the current density due to the flow of electrons is $eD\, dn_n/dx$, and the electron current i_{0n} across the junction of area A is

$$i_{0n} = eDA \left.\frac{dn_n}{dx}\right|_{x=0} \tag{14.18}$$

where $x = 0$ represents the p-edge of the junction region. Since the electric field within the junction maintains a zero concentration of conduction electrons at $x = 0$ and since the concentration far from the junction is the equilibrium concentration n_∞, the boundary conditions which must be satisfied by a solution of 14.17 are:

$$\begin{aligned} n_n &= 0 \qquad \text{at } x = 0 \\ n_n &= n_\infty \qquad \text{at } x = \infty \end{aligned} \tag{14.19}$$

The net rate of creation of electrons per unit volume (the net result of thermal production and recombination) is assumed to be proportional to $(n_\infty - n_n)$, that is, to the difference between the equilibrium concentration n_∞ and the actual concentration n_n. Hence the creation term in 14.17 is

$$C = c(n_\infty - n_n) \tag{14.20}$$

where the constant of proportionality c is positive. Hence, substituting into equation 14.17 we obtain, for a steady state situation

$$0 = D \frac{d^2 n}{dx^2} + c(n_\infty - n) \tag{14.21}$$

The solution of 14.21 which satisfies boundary conditions 14.19 is

$$n_n = n_\infty(1 - e^{-\sqrt{c/D}\,x}) = n_\infty(1 - e^{-x/L}) \tag{14.22}$$

in which $L(\equiv \sqrt{D/c})$ is a constant having the units of length. This constant is sometimes called the diffusion length. The diffusion length is somewhat analogous to a mean free path. Differentiating 14.22

and evaluating at $x = 0$, we find

$$\left.\frac{dn_n}{dx}\right|_{x=0} = \left.\frac{n_\infty}{L} e^{-x/L}\right|_{x=0} = \frac{n_\infty}{L} \tag{14.23}$$

Substitution into 14.18 yields an expression for i_{0n}.

$$i_{0n} = \frac{eDAn_\infty}{L} \tag{14.24}$$

In this expression,

$D \equiv$ diffusion constant for conduction electrons on the p-side
$n_\infty \equiv$ equilibrium concentration of conduction electrons on the p-side
$L \equiv$ diffusion length for conduction electrons on the p-side
$e \equiv$ electronic charge
$A \equiv$ area of junction

A similar expression holds for i_{0p} except that D, n_∞, and L are for holes on the n-side. The two components of the saturation current are not necessarily equal.

The diffusion constant may be expressed in terms of the temperature and mobility using the Einstein relation (see Chapter 8)

$$D = \frac{kT\mu}{e} \tag{8.35}$$

Using 8.35 equation 14.24 becomes

$$i_{0n} = \frac{\mu kTA}{L} n_\infty \tag{14.25}$$

It should be remembered that n_∞ and μ are functions of temperature so that i_{0n} is not just directly proportional to T.

14.4 Depletion-layer capacitance

We learned in section 14.1 that a narrow double charge layer exists at a p-n junction. The positive charge layer on the n-side of the junctions consists of donor ions, and the negative charge layer on the p-side of the junction consists of acceptor ions. When the potential difference between the n- and p-sides is changed, the thickness of the depletion layer must change; relatively thick depletion layers occur with large reverse bias, thin depletion layers occur with forward bias. Since charge must flow in order to change the potential difference

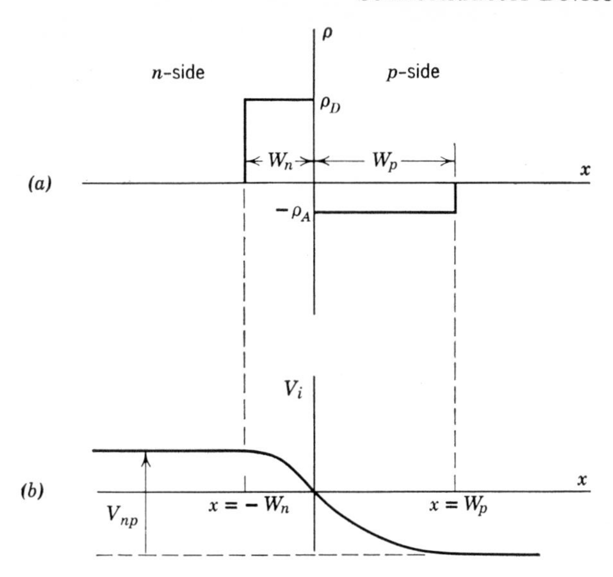

Fig. 14.7. Variation of (*a*) charge density ρ, (*b*) internal potential V_i in a junction diode.

across the junction, the junction behaves somewhat like a capacitor. However, unlike an ordinary capacitor the charge stored in the depletion layer is not directly proportional to the potential difference. For analysis in the presence of small a-c signals, a useful parameter for measuring this depletion-layer capacitance effect is the so-called incremental depletion-layer capacitance, C_D, defined by

$$C_D \equiv \frac{|dQ|}{|dV_{np}|} = \frac{|dQ|}{|dV|} \tag{14.26}$$

Here V_{np} is the internal junction potential difference, which differs from the applied bias voltage V by the contact potential difference V_c (a constant). We now examine the dependence of this incremental capacitance on the junction potential difference V_{np}. The form of this dependence depends on the particular variation of the depletion-layer charge density ρ with distance. We assume a step-function variation of charge density with distance as shown in Fig. 14.7*a*. The charge density on the *n*-side (due to positive donor ions) is ρ_D within a distance W_n of the junction, and the charge density on the *p*-side is $-\rho_A$ (due to negative acceptor ions) within a distance W_p

of the junction. Since equal amounts of positive and negative charge must reside at the junction,

$$\rho_D W_n = \rho_A W_n = \frac{Q}{A} \tag{14.27}$$

where Q is the magnitude of the charge on either side of the junction and A is the junction area. The potential difference V_{np} between the n-side and the p-side can be calculated from Poisson's equation for the internal potential V_i using the charge distribution of Fig. 14.7*a* and appropriate boundary conditions, which may be written

$$V_i \text{ and } dV_i/dx \text{ are continuous at } x = 0$$

$$\begin{aligned} \frac{dV_i}{dx} &= 0 \qquad \text{at } x \geq W_p \\ \frac{dV_i}{dx} &= 0 \qquad \text{at } x \leq -W_n \end{aligned} \tag{14.28}$$

The second and third boundary conditions arise from the fact that no significant electric fields can exist inside the electrically neutral conducting regions. An electric field can exist only in the depletion layers and at the surfaces of the crystal. Poisson's equation may be written for negative and positive values of x as

$$\begin{aligned} \frac{d^2V}{dx^2} &= -\frac{\rho_D}{\epsilon}, \qquad x < 0 \\ \frac{d^2V}{dx^2} &= \frac{\rho_A}{\epsilon}, \qquad x > 0 \end{aligned} \tag{14.29}$$

The solution of Poisson's equation which satisfies the boundary conditions 14.28 is

$$\begin{aligned} V_i &= \frac{-\rho_D}{2\epsilon} x^2 - \rho_D \frac{W_n}{\epsilon} x + C, \qquad W_n < x < 0 \\ V_i &= \frac{\rho_A}{2\epsilon} x^2 - \frac{\rho_A W_p}{\epsilon} x + C, \qquad 0 < x < W_p \end{aligned} \tag{14.30}$$

In equation 14.30 C is an arbitrary constant whose value depends on the reference point for the zero of potential. The variation of internal potential given in 14.30 is sketched in Fig. 14.7*b* for the case $C = 0$.

The internal potential difference between the n-side and the p-side is found by evaluating V_i at $x = -W_n$ and at $x = W_p$ and subtracting. Thus, after some simplification,

$$V_{np} \equiv V_i \bigg|_{x=-W_n} - V_i \bigg|_{x=W_p} = \frac{\rho_D W_n{}^2}{2\epsilon} + \frac{\rho_A W_p{}^2}{2\epsilon} \qquad (14.31)$$

The potential difference V_{np} may be expressed in terms of the charge Q on either side of the junction by using 14.27.

$$V_{np} = \frac{\rho_D{}^2 W_n{}^2}{2\epsilon\rho_D} + \frac{\rho_A{}^2 W_p{}^2}{2\epsilon\rho_A} = \frac{Q^2}{2\epsilon A^2}\left(\frac{1}{\rho_D} + \frac{1}{\rho_A}\right) \qquad (14.32)$$

Solving for Q we have,

$$Q = A\left(\frac{2\epsilon\rho_D\rho_A}{\rho_A + \rho_D}\right)^{1/2} V_{np}{}^{1/2} \qquad (14.33)$$

and using (14.26) to calculate the incremental depletion-layer capacitance we find

$$C_D = \frac{A}{2}\left(\frac{2\epsilon\rho_D\rho_A}{\rho_D + \rho_A}\right)^{1/2} V_{np}{}^{-1/2} \qquad (14.34)$$

It is important to realize that the potential difference V_{np} in 14.34 is not the same as the bias voltage V of the previous sections. When the bias voltage V is zero, the potential difference V_{np} is the contact potential V_c (see section 13.7), which is usually of the order of 0.5 volt. When a positive bias is applied (p-side connected to the positive terminal of a battery and n-side to the negative terminal), V_{np} is reduced. The correct expression for V_{np} in terms of V may be written

$$V_{np} = V_c - V \qquad (14.35)$$

Equations 14.34 and 14.35 indicate that when a junction is forward biased ($V > 0$), V_{np} may become small and the incremental depletion-layer capacitance may become large. When a junction is reverse biased, ($V < 0$), V_{np} is relatively large and C_D is small. These results may be obtained qualitatively by recognizing that a reverse-biased junction has a wide depletion layer, and is effectively a capacitor of relatively large "plate" separation and therefore small capacitance. On the other hand, a forward-biased junction has a narrower depletion layer and is effectively a capacitor of smaller "plate" separation and larger capacitance.

14.5 The Zener diode

As the reverse bias voltage across a junction diode is increased, the electric field at the junction increases. If the electric field is strong

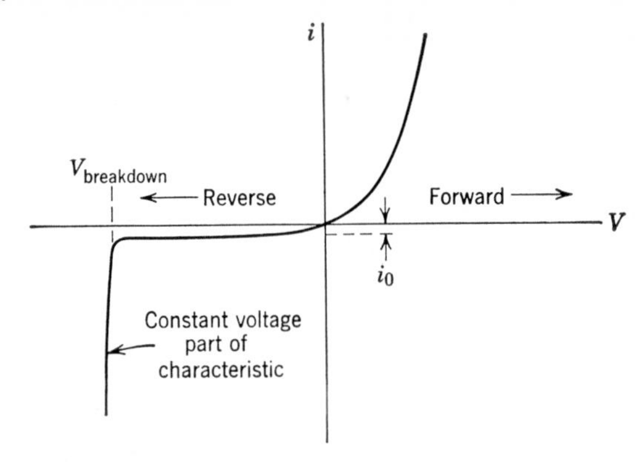

Fig. 14.8. Current-voltage characteristic of a Zener diode.

enough, an avalanche process occurs, which is much like the avalanche process in a Townsend discharge (see Chapter 9). An avalanche in a *p-n* junction diode occurs when electrons and holes crossing the junction acquire enough energy from the electric field to collisionally excite electrons from the valence band to the conduction band. Since such a process produces additional hole and electron current carriers, the reverse current increases above the normal reverse saturation current. A very rapid increase in reverse current occurs as the reverse voltage across the diode is increased above a critical "breakdown" voltage, and an external series resistor is usually required in order to avoid burning-out the diode. "Zener" diodes are built specifically to utilize the nearly vertical current-voltage characteristic exhibited after breakdown (see Fig. 14.8). They are used as voltage regulator devices and can be made with a wider range of breakdown voltages than gaseous voltage regulator tubes (see Chapter 10). The type of circuit in which a Zener diode is employed is that shown in Fig. 10.4.

14.6 The tunnel diode

In 1958 Esaki published a paper[1] on *p-n* junctions in which the *p*- and *n*-type regions had exceptionally large concentrations of acceptor and donor impurities. He reported that a segment of the current-voltage characteristic of his junctions had a negative slope (see Fig. 14.9).

[1] L. Esaki, "New Phenomenon in Narrow Germanium *p-n* Junctions," *Phys. Rev.*, **109,** 603 (1958).

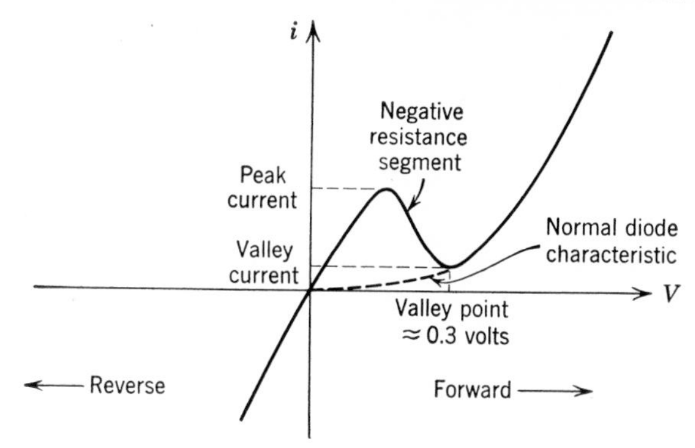

Fig. 14.9. Current-voltage characteristic of a tunnel diode.

Now that we have built up rather detailed mathematical and physical models of p- and n-type semiconductors and p-n junctions it is easy to understand why a tunnel diode exhibits such an unusual characteristic.

Energy-level diagrams of a tunnel diode encompassing the tops of the valence bands and the bottoms of the conduction bands are drawn in Fig. 14.10. An essential feature is that the Fermi level on the n-side lies above the bottom of the conduction band, and the Fermi level on the p-side lies below the top of the valence band. This is a consequence of the very large concentration of donor and acceptor impurity atoms. (For these concentrations, the integrals in equations 13.1 and 13.9 cannot be simplified and must be calculated numerically

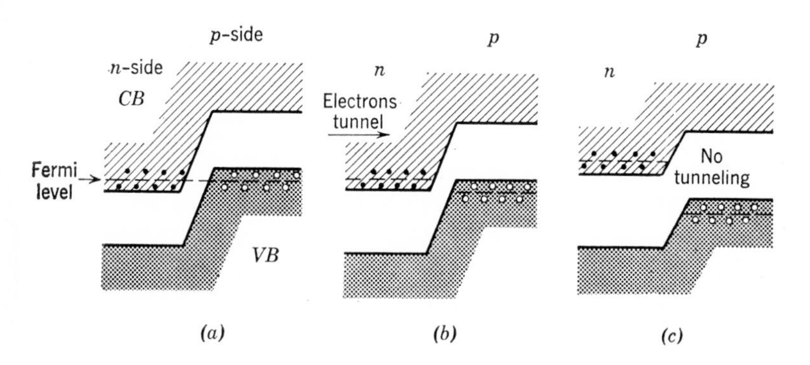

Fig. 14.10. Energy-level diagram for a tunnel diode. (*a*) No bias. (*b*) Small forward bias $V = 0$ to valley point in Fig. 14.9. (*c*) Larger forward bias (to right of valley point).

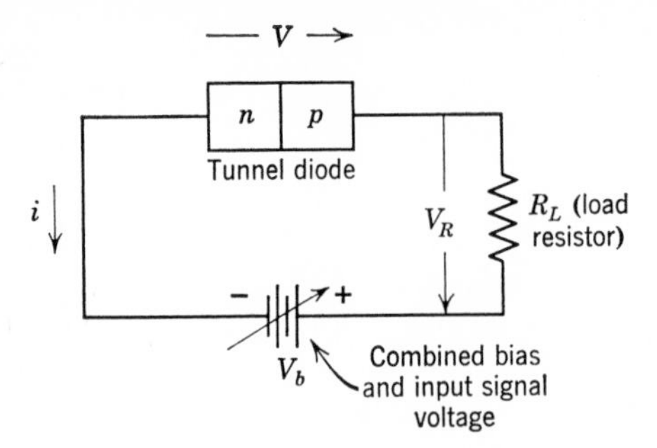

Fig. 14.11. Possible circuit for a tunnel-diode amplifier or bistable element.

or graphically.) For a small forward bias (see Fig. 14.10*b*) *electrons from the conduction band on the n-side cross the junction into vacant valence-band states on the p-side at the same energy.* The electrons cross the junction via the quantum-mechanical tunneling process described in Chapter 1.

For a larger forward bias (see Fig. 14.10*c*), tunneling ceases because there are no longer any conduction-band states on the *n*-side at the same energy levels as valence-band states on the *p*-side. In the terminology of section 14.2, either dS_p/dE or $dS_n/dE = 0$ for every energy level between V_n and C_p, and the current becomes the normal forward current given by 14.1. The presence of the normal forward current accounts for the nonzero valley current of Fig. 14.9.

Another unusual feature of the tunnel diode characteristic of Fig. 14.9 is the nonsaturating behavior for reverse voltages. In view of the energy-level diagram in Fig. 14.10 this behavior exists because tunneling also occurs when the Fermi level on the *p*-side is higher than the Fermi level on the *n*-side. In fact, the higher the reverse voltage, the wider the range of levels that participate in tunneling and the larger the reverse current.

The negative resistance segment of the tunnel diode's current-voltage characteristic can be utilized to make an amplifier or a bistable device for use in computer switching circuits.

Voltage amplification by a negative resistance device such as a tunnel diode can easily be explained in terms of the load line construction of Fig. 14.12, which applies to the circuit of Fig. 14.11. In the circuit of Fig. 14.11 the load resistor is chosen so that the load-line slope is slightly steeper than that of the negative resistance part of the characteristic.[1] A slight change ΔV_b of bias voltage produced, for example,

[1] In practice severe precautions are required in order to maintain a stable operating point.

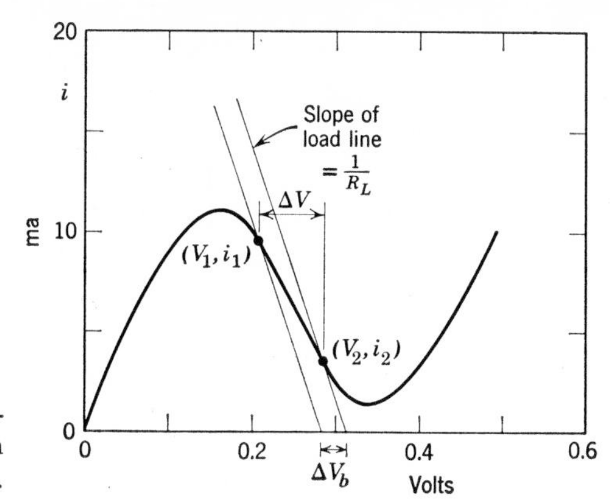

Fig. 14.12. Load line construction to show amplification by a negative resistance device.

by an input signal shifts the load line slightly to the right or left. This slight shift of the load line can cause a relatively large change ΔV in the voltage across the diode. In this manner a voltage gain is achieved.

If the load resistor R_L in Fig. 14.11 is chosen so that the slope of the load line is flatter than the negative resistance slope, the load line can intersect the characteristic curve of the tunnel diode in three places as shown in Fig. 14.13. In Fig. 14.13 the points labeled A and C are stable operating points and in practice point B is unstable. Thus, for sufficiently large values of R_L, the series circuit of Fig. 14.11 can become a bistable circuit suitable for use in computers.

The most important reason for the enthusiasm for tunnel diodes is their extreme speed. The rate of tunneling can change as fast as the energy levels can be shifted. On the other hand, in devices such as the

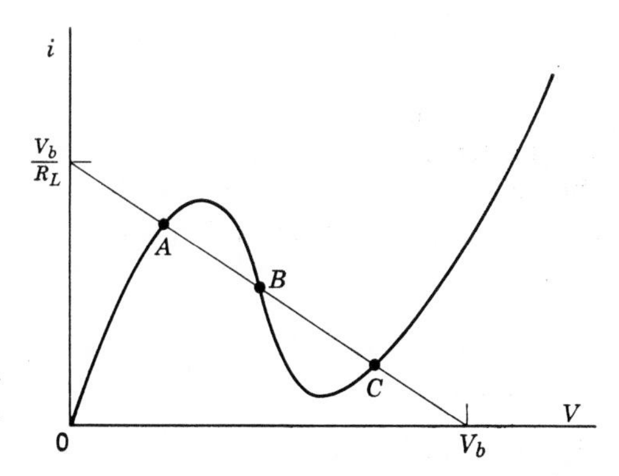

Fig. 14.13. Load line construction for bistable tunnel diode circuit.

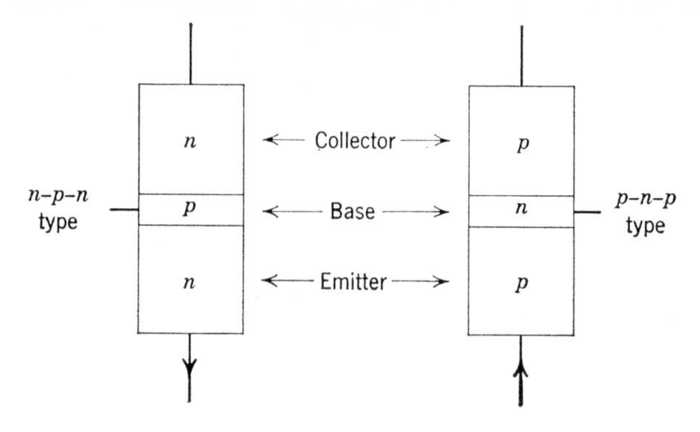

Fig. 14.14. Schematic representation of junction transistors.

transistor the electrical signal is carried by diffusing charge carriers. The rate of diffusion can change only as fast as the charge distribution can be shifted. It is difficult to make transistors that will operate at more than a few hundred megacycles per second. Tunnel diodes have been operated as oscillators at frequencies in excess of 10^5 megacycles per second and in bistable circuits with switching times shorter than 10^{-9} sec.

14.7 The junction transistor

The transistor is the solid state analogue of the vacuum triode.[1] In this section we discuss the physics of the junction transistor (the most commonly used type) and show how a transistor can be used to achieve amplification.

The junction transistor consists of a single semiconductor crystal containing two junctions between *p*- and *n*-type regions. The two possible configurations, *p-n-p* and *n-p-n*, are illustrated schematically in Fig. 14.14. The *n-p-n* or *p-n-p* sandwich can be viewed as two *p-n* junctions back to back. The ends of a transistor sandwich, known as the emitter and collector, are heavily "doped" with impurity atoms. The middle of the sandwich, known as the base, is thin and contains a relatively small concentration of impurity atoms. Since the emitter and collector regions usually contain from twenty to one hundred times the impurity atom concentration of the base region, in the *n-p-n* type transistor most of the current is carried by electrons, and in the *p-n-p* type transistor most of the current is carried by holes.

[1] In 1956 J. Bardeen, W. Brattain, and W. Shockley received the Nobel prize for their contributions to the development of the transistor.

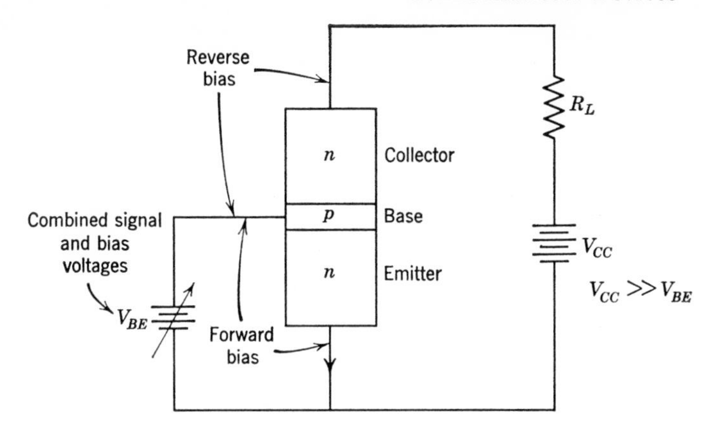

Fig. 14.15. Simplified transistor amplifier circuit.

In the operation of either type of junction transistor, the emitter-base junction is usually forward biased and the collector-base junction is reverse biased, as shown in the simplified amplifier circuit of Fig. 14.15. Figure 14.15 and the following discussion apply to an *n-p-n* transistor. An analogous amplifier can be made from a *p-n-p* transistor by reversing the polarities of the batteries V_{BE} and V_{CC}.

Figure 14.16 shows energy-level diagrams for an *n-p-n* junction transistor. In part (*a*) the transistor is unbiased and in part (*b*) it is biased as in the amplifier circuit of Fig. 14.15. When the junction between the emitter and base regions is forward biased ($V_{BE} > 0$), conduction electrons spill over from the *n*-type emitter region into the *p*-type base region. The resulting forward current between emitter

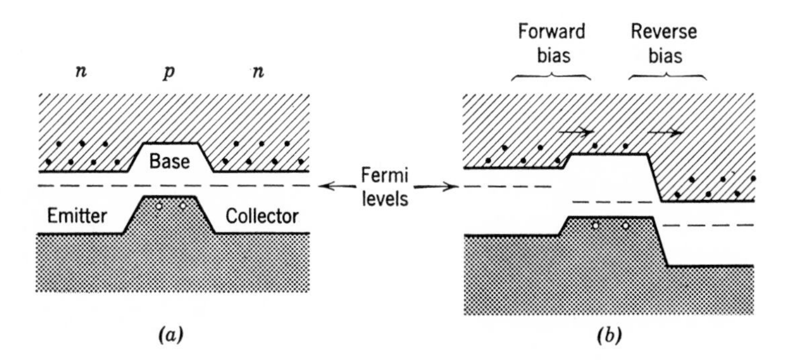

Fig. 14.16. Energy-level diagrams for *n-p-n* transistor. (*a*) Unbiased. (*b*) Biased for normal operation.

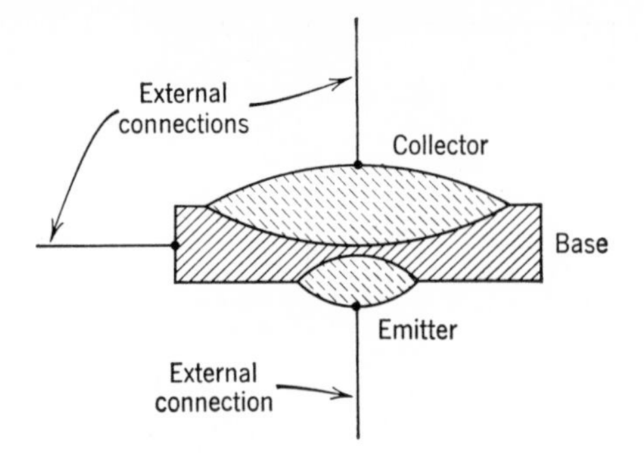

Fig. 14.17. Typical geometry of a junction transistor.

and base is described by equation 14.1 with $V > 0$. Because of the exponential nature of equation 14.1, a small change in forward voltage produces a large change of current into the base. Once inside the base, the electrons diffuse away from the emitter-base junction. Some of these electrons recombine with holes in the *p*-type base and a few diffuse to and flow out through the external base lead. Both of these effects lead to base current. However, because of the narrowness of the base region (typically of the order of 10^{-3} in. thick) and the geometry of the collector (see Fig. 14.17), the majority of the electrons diffuse to the base-collector junction. Here they are pulled across into the collector by the electric field existing between the positive donor ions in the depletion layer on the collector side and the negative acceptor ions in the depletion layer on the base side. Typically 95% or more of the electrons entering the base reach the collector. The relatively large collector bias voltage V_{CC} does work on the electrons arriving from the base and causes them to flow through and deliver power to an external load. Amplification is possible because relatively little power is required from the signal source to modulate the electron current crossing from the emitter through the base to the collector.

Since the transistor is a three-terminal device,[1] two independent relations among the voltages and currents must be specified (in addition to the relations which may be obtained from Kirchhoff's laws) in order that its behavior in a circuit can be determined. It is common to treat the base current i_B as a function of the base-emitter voltage V_{BE} and collector-emitter voltage V_{CE}, and the collector current i_C as a function of the base current i_B and the collector-emitter

[1] A triode is also a three-terminal device. For negative grid voltages the grid current is zero, and a grid current characteristic is not needed. However, for positive grid voltages the grid draws current, and grid characteristics as well as plate characteristics are needed for analysis.

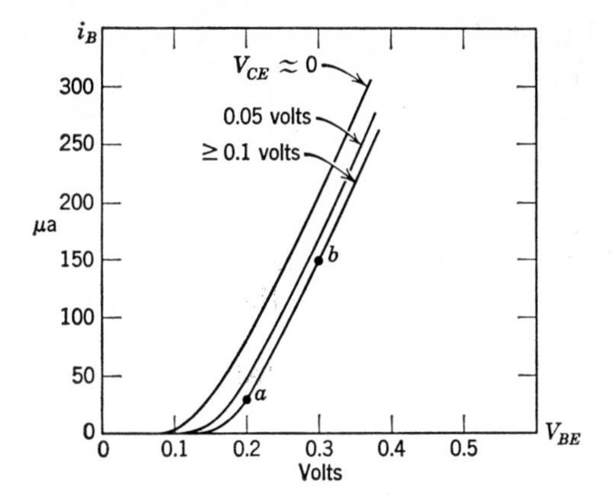

Fig. 14.18. Base characteristics: i_B versus V_{BE} with V_{CE} as parameter (equation 14.36).

voltage. That is,

$$i_B = f_1(V_{BE}, V_{CE}) \tag{14.36}$$

and

$$i_C = f_2(V_{CE}, i_B) \tag{14.37}$$

These two functions are called the base and collector characteristics respectively and are plotted in Figs. 14.18 and 14.19 for a typical transistor.

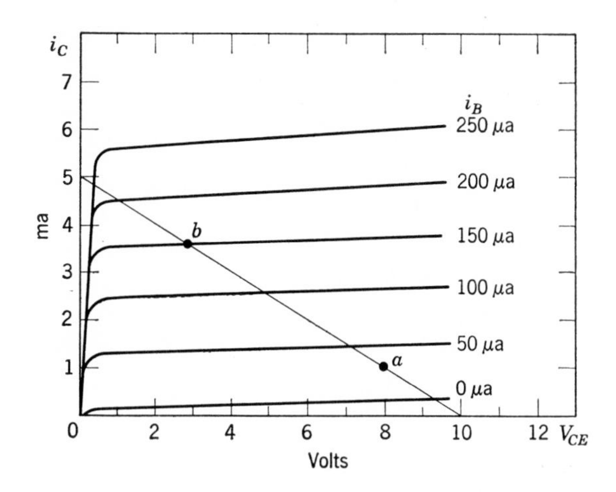

Fig. 14.19. Collector characteristics: i_C versus V_{CE} with i_B as parameter (equation 14.37).

The base characteristic is plotted as i_B versus V_{BE} with V_{CE} as parameter. The base current is approximately a constant (small) fraction of the current injected into the base from the emitter. Since this injected current is determined almost entirely by the base-emitter voltage, the i_B versus V_{BE} dependence has approximately the form of the forward current-voltage characteristic of a *p-n* junction diode. Furthermore, the base current is practically independent of the collector-junction reverse voltage and is therefore practically independent of V_{CE}.

The collector characteristic is plotted as i_C versus V_{CE} with i_B as parameter. The collector current is approximately a constant (large) fraction of the current injected into the base and is relatively independent of V_{CE} except at low values of V_{CE}. The behavior of both sets of characteristics at low values of collector-emitter voltage is explained by the fact that for small V_{CE} the collector junction has zero bias or even a slight forward bias, and electrons begin to be injected from the collector into the base.

Example. Determine the change in the output voltage ΔV_{CE} and the voltage gain $\Delta V_{CE}/\Delta V_{BE}$ in the simplified amplifier circuit of Fig. 14.15 when V_{BE} changes from 0.2 volt to 0.3 volt, $V_{CC} = 10$ volts and $R_L = 2000$ ohms.

Figure 14.18 may be used to calculate i_B for each value of V_{BE}. We tentatively assume that V_{CE} is greater than 0.1 volt so that the base characteristic for $V_{CE} > 0.1$ volt may be used. Our result will verify this assumption. Hence from Fig. 14.18, we have

$$i_B = 30\ \mu\text{a} \quad \text{for } V_{BE} = 0.2 \text{ volt}$$

and

$$i_B = 150\ \mu\text{a} \quad \text{for } V_{BE} = 0.3 \text{ volt} \tag{14.38}$$

Next the collector characteristics are used to determine the collector-emitter voltages corresponding to the base currents of equation 14.38. As in section 6.5 a load line is drawn, with intercepts $V_{CE} = V_{CC} = 10$ volts and $i_c = V_{CC}/R_L = 5$ ma. From the intersections (points *a* and *b*) of the load line with the characteristics for $i_B = 30\ \mu$a and $150\ \mu$a, we find that

$$\begin{aligned} V_{CE} &= 8.0 \text{ volts} \quad \text{for } i_B = 30\ \mu\text{a} \\ V_{CE} &= 2.9 \text{ volts} \quad \text{for } i_B = 150\ \mu\text{a} \end{aligned} \tag{14.39}$$

Note that the assumption which enabled us to use the base characteristic for $V_{CE} > 0.1$ volt is validated by these results. The change in output voltage is

$$\Delta V_{CE} = 2.9 - 8.0 = -5.1 \text{ volts} \tag{14.40}$$

Then, since

$$\Delta V_{BE} = 0.3 - 0.2 = 0.1 \text{ volt} \tag{14.41}$$

the voltage gain is

$$\frac{\Delta V_{CE}}{\Delta V_{BE}} = -51 \tag{14.42}$$

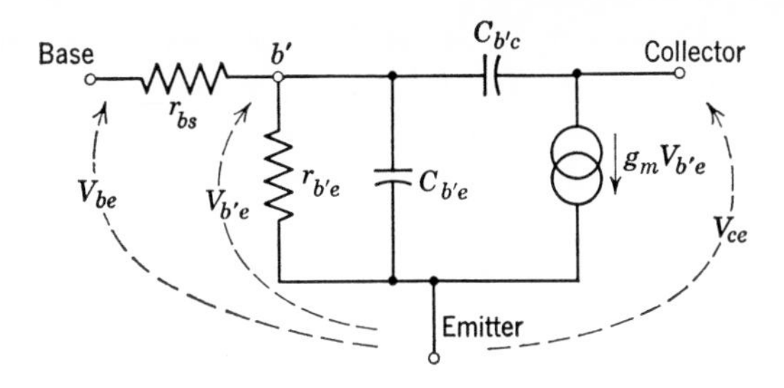

Fig. 14.20. A useful a-c equivalent circuit for a junction transistor.

14.8 Equivalent circuit of a junction transistor

The search for an equivalent circuit to replace the transistor in small-signal circuit analysis is complicated by the fact that there are a number of effects which occur in transistors in addition to those mentioned earlier. These effects manifest themselves in the various parameters of the equivalent circuit. Unfortunately, no one equivalent circuit is "best" because different effects dominate others for different types of junction transistors,[1] which leads to different simplifying assumptions for each type. A group of workers headed by Pritchard[2] has attacked the equivalent-circuit problem in terms of so-called internal parameters by concentrating on the flow of electrons and holes as a function of the "junction" voltages $V_{B'E'}$ and $V_{C'B'}$. These junction voltages may be somewhat different from the external voltages V_{BE} and V_{CB} measured between the leads of the transistor but are not to be confused with the internal potential V_i used in section 14.4.

One of the more useful a-c equivalent circuits for transistors is shown in Fig. 14.20. In this circuit $r_{b'e}$ indicates the variation of a-c emitter-junction current with a-c emitter-junction voltage $V_{b'e}$. The ideal current generator $g_mV_{b'e}$ describes the dependence of the collector current on the emitter-junction voltage $V_{b'e}$. A list of some of the more important physical effects responsible for the equivalent circuit parameters follows. This list is stated in terms of an *n-p-n* transistor.

1. The finite resistances of the emitter, base, and collector regions cause the lead voltages to differ from the junction voltages. Usually

[1] We have omitted any discussion of the various types of junction transistors. Discussion of the different techniques of manufacture and the particular characteristics of each type of transistor may be found in books on transistor technology.

[2] Pritchard, Angell, Adler, Early, and Webster, *Proc. IRE*, **49**, 725 (1961).

the collector and emitter resistances can be neglected, but the base resistance, known as the base spreading resistance r_{bs}, cannot be neglected and appears in the equivalent circuit.

2. The junction voltage $V_{B'E'}$ which causes the injection of electrons from emitter into base also causes the injection of holes from the base into the emitter. These holes are undesirable because they do not contribute to the collector current. The number of injected holes is made small by doping the base lightly as compared with the emitter.

3. Recombination of injected electrons with holes in the base reduces slightly the number of injected electrons that reach the collector. This effect was mentioned earlier.

4. There are dispersion and delay associated with the diffusion of electrons through the base, giving rise to phase shifts and reduction of gain at high frequencies. This effect may be represented by a capacitance called the emitter-junction diffusion capacitance. In the equivalent circuit $C_{b'e}$ is mainly due to this diffusion capacitance.

5. Avalanche multiplication in the collector-base depletion layer tends to increase the electron current to the collector and creates holes which flow into the base from the depletion layer.

6. There is a depletion layer capacitance associated with each junction. The contribution of the emitter-base depletion layer capacitance to $C_{b'e}$ is usually negligible in comparison with the emitter-junction diffusion capacitance. The collector-base depletion layer capacitance is not negligible and is the main contributor to $C_{b'c}$.

14.9 Comparison of transistors with vacuum tubes

A list of some advantages and disadvantages of transistors as compared with ordinary vacuum tubes follows.

Advantages

1. Small size.
2. Mechanical ruggedness.
3. No power required to heat a filament. In complex installations such as computers this can mean a substantial saving in air-conditioning equipment.
4. Long life, primarily due to the fact that there is no "evaporation" of a cathode.
5. No warm-up time required.
6. Low-voltage power supplies are sufficient. In many cases batteries are cheaper to use than rectified a-c power supplies.
7. The existence of both *p-n-p* and *n-p-n* transistors gives more versatility in circuit design.

Disadvantages

1. Transistor characteristics are strong functions of temperature. Sometimes air-conditioning might be required in a transistor circuit when it would not be required in an equivalent tube circuit.

2. Transistors in general cannot operate at as high frequencies as vacuum tubes.

3. Transistors are limited in power output compared with vacuum tubes.

The emitter, base, and collector of a transistor are roughly analogous to the cathode, grid, and anode respectively of a vacuum triode. Thus, like a triode, a transistor is a three-terminal device and the output and input circuits can be fairly well isolated. On the other hand, the tunnel diode, which has a great advantage in speed over a transistor, is a two-terminal device and it is difficult to isolate the input from the output.

14.10 Other semiconductor devices

In this section we briefly describe several additional semiconductor devices. Although these devices may not have the importance of the devices previously described, they provide additional simple illustrations of the principles of solid-state electronics.

Solar battery

Solar batteries are used to convert radiant energy directly to electrical energy. The efficiency of a solar cell is usually between 6 and 8% although efficiencies as high as 11% have been attained. A diagram of a solar cell connected to an external resistor is shown in Fig. 14.21.

The cell consists of a thin layer of p-type silicon on an n-type silicon base. The n- and p-regions are heavily doped so that the resistance of the cell is small. There is an optimum thickness of the p-region ($\approx$ 0.001 in.) so that as much as possible of the light is absorbed near the junction.

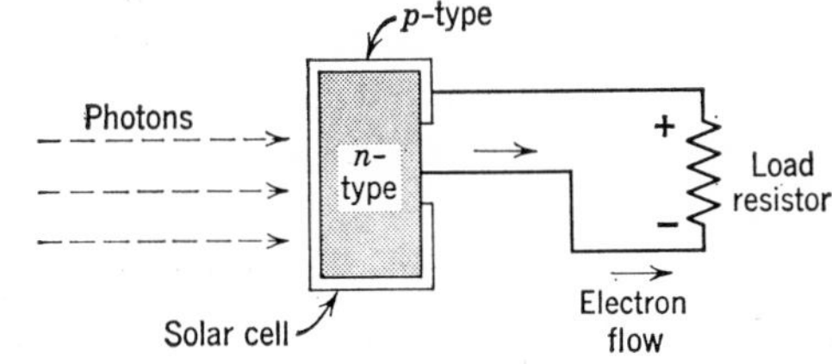

Fig. 14.21. A solar cell converts radiant energy directly to electrical energy.

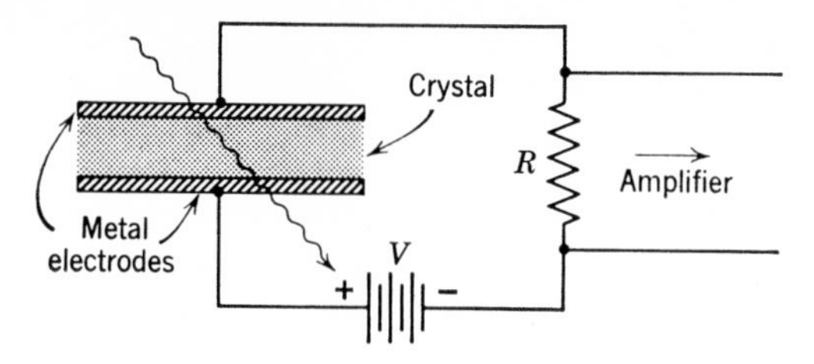

Fig. 14.22. Crystal counter.

When a photon is absorbed in the p- or n-region, it can create a hole-electron pair. Usually the hole and electron quickly recombine, but in a solar cell the internal electric field in the depletion layer at the p-n junction (directed from the n-side to the p-side) can separate the hole and electron before they have a chance to recombine. Electrons produced in the p-side that wander near the junction are pulled into the n-side, and holes produced near the junction in the n-side are pulled into the p-side resulting in current across the junction. In flowing through the external resistor, the charge carriers do work, which has come directly from the energy of the incident photon.

Although the open circuit voltage of a solar cell is about 0.5 volt, the maximum power is delivered to the load when the voltage is about 0.3 volt. This voltage and the efficiency are practically independent of the intensity of the incident light. This behavior makes solar batteries useful for charging storage batteries. Solar batteries are also used to power electronic equipment in artificial satellites.

Crystal counter

Consider a flat crystal of diamond with two metal electrodes evaporated on two parallel-plane faces, connected in the series circuit shown in Fig. 14.22.

A diamond is an intrinsic semiconductor with a relatively large energy gap, and consequently has low conductivity at normal temperatures. If a high energy charged particle passes through the crystal, it will collisionally lift electrons into the conduction band and leave behind holes in the valence band, giving rise to a current pulse. This current pulse can be converted to a voltage pulse in the series resistor R and amplified. A crystal counter is basically a solid-state ionization chamber.

Thermistor

A thermistor is either an intrinsic semiconductor or an impurity semiconductor which is operated in a temperature range such that the conductivity increases strongly with increasing temperature. (See Fig. 13.7.)

Photodiode

A photodiode is the solid-state equivalent of a vacuum photocell. Basically it is a junction diode operated under reversed-bias conditions. Under these conditions, the reverse current will depend partly on the number of electrons which are elevated to the conduction band by absorbed photons. A photodiode requires an external battery for significant photoelectric currents.

Point-contact diode

If a phosphor-bronze point is fused electrically into a small *n*-type germanium crystal, some of the phosphorus atoms diffuse into the germanium converting the germanium into a *p*-type semiconductor in the vicinity of the point. The germanium then acts like a *p*-*n* junction of small cross-sectional area and correspondingly low "capacitance." High-frequency crystal diodes utilize these principles. The point-contact diode is a modern version of the temperamental "cat's whisker" detector so important for its rectification properties in the early days of radio communication. The first transistors utilized two point-contacts rather than two *p*-*n* junctions.

Suggested References

R. L. Sproull, *Modern Physics*, John Wiley and Sons, 1956. In Chapter 11 the *p*-*n* junction is treated from the standpoint of the Boltzmann relation, and the physical principles and characteristic curves are discussed.

D. M. Warschauer, *Semiconductors and Transistors*, McGraw-Hill Book Company, 1959. Chapters 9 and 10 are elementary treatments of the *p*-*n* junction and junction transistor. Chapter 11 reviews some of the methods of transistor construction.

Pritchard, Angell, Adler, Early, and Webster. *Proc. IRE*, **49**, 725. Although their task is primarily to develop useful transistor equivalent circuits, the authors present an excellent account of the physical processes occurring in transistors, including the many higher-order effects.

PROBLEMS

14.1. A certain *p*-*n* junction of area 1 mm^2 has a reverse saturation current of 10 μa at 300°K. Assuming the entire current is due to electrons, calculate the diffusion length for electrons on the *p*-side. The Fermi level lies 0.50 ev below the bottom of the conduction band on the *p*-side; the mobility of the electrons is 0.38 $meter^2$/volt-sec.

14.2. For a diode with a reverse saturation current of 10 μa, calculate the forward current and voltage of the diode when connected in series (at 300° K) with a 10-volt battery and 1-K resistor. (Use two unknowns, i and V, and two equations; solve graphically or by trial and error.)

14.3. When V is sufficiently positive, equation 14.1 becomes $i = i_0 e^{eV/kT}$. Show that under these conditions the a-c conductance of the diode is proportional to the current. What is the minimum voltage for 10% accuracy in neglecting unity compared with $e^{eV/kT}$, in equation 14.1, at room temperature?

14.4. If the impurity density (acceptors and donors) on either side of a germanium p-n junction is 10^{17} atoms/cm^3, determine the temperature at which the intrinsic-pair density is ten times the impurity density. (Use equations derived in Chapter 13, for example, 13.13.)

14.5. Make an order of magnitude estimate of the impurity concentration necessary to construct a tunnel diode in germanium with the donor level 0.01 ev below bottom of conduction band. Do this by finding the donor concentration necessary to put the Fermi level 0.01 ev *above* the bottom of the *conduction* band at 300° K. Use equation 13.14 and the density of states factor given by 13.2. For the integration necessary to find N_n use, as an approximation to the Fermi factor, its form at $T = 0$. For the calculation of $N_D{}^+$ the actual Fermi factor (not an approximation) must be used.

14.6. The B.C.S. theory (see Chapter 12) associates the phenomenon of superconductivity with the appearance, below the transition temperature, of a gap in the electron density of states function (analogous to that in, say, an intrinsic semiconductor), with the Fermi level in the center of the gap, and dS/dE tending to peak strongly near the edges of the gap as shown in the figure. Thin films of two such different superconducting metals separated by a dielectric insulating layer of 15 to 20 Å thick give the current voltage characteristic shown (see, for example, J. Nicol et al., *Phys. Rev. Letters*, **5,** 461, 1960) when small voltages are applied between the two metals. Arguing in the same way as for the semiconductor tunnel diode, explain the shape of the curve qualitatively, and show that $(V_2 - V_1)$ and $(V_1 + V_2)$ measure respectively the energy gaps of the metals with the smaller and larger gaps (that is, lower and higher transition temperatures). How does the reverse voltage characteristic compare with that for the semiconductor tunnel diode?

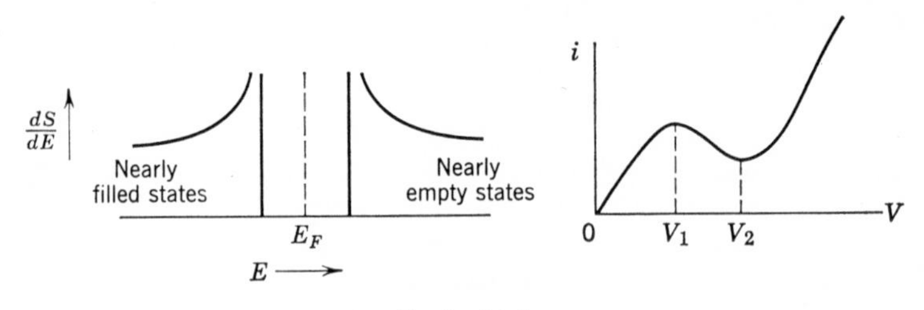

Prob. 14.6

14.7. Draw energy band diagrams, like those of Fig. 14.16, for a p-n-p type transistor. Indicate clearly the polarity of the battery voltages for normal operation.

14.8. Find the voltage gain of a transistor with the characteristics of Figs. 14.18 and 14.19 in a circuit with a 6-volt collector battery, a 1-K load resistor, and a 5-K input resistor in series with the signal and the base. Let the input voltage change from say 0.5 to 0.75 volt.

14.9. What current flows in each of the three external leads of the transistor of Figs. 14.18 and 14.19 when $V_{CE} = 5$ volts and $V_{BE} = 0.2$ volt?

14.10. If equation 14.36 is rewritten $V_{BE} = f_1(i_B, V_{CE})$, then it and equation 14.37 are called common-emitter hybrid characteristics whose slopes are the important parameters of the transistor: h_{11}, h_{12}, h_{21}, h_{22}, where $h_{11} = (\partial V_{BE}/\partial i_B)V_{CE\text{constant}}$, $h_{12} = (\partial V_{BE}/\partial V_{CE})i_{B\text{constant}}$, etc. Write down the corresponding transistor small-signal equations analogous to equation 7.21 for a triode tube, and draw an equivalent circuit for the transistor based on these equations.

14.11. Repeat Problem 14.10 for the common-base equations

$$V_{EB} = f_1(i_E, V_{CB}) \qquad \text{and} \qquad i_C = f_2(i_E, V_{CB})$$

14.12. From the two sets of small-signal equations derived in Problems 14.10 and 14.11 and the conditions $i_E + i_B + i_C = 0$ and $V_{CB} = V_{CE} + V_{EB}$, express the common-emitter parameters in terms of the common-base parameters.

14.13. The parameters h_{12e}, h_{22e}, h_{12b}, and h_{22b} (where the subscript *e* or *b* denotes which is the common electrode) are often negligibly small for junction transistors, so that $i_C \approx h_{21b}i_E = -\alpha i_E$ (where $\alpha \approx 0.98$) defines the common-base current gain α and $i_C \approx h_{21e}i_B = \beta i_B$ defines the common-emitter current gain β. Show that

$$\beta = \frac{\alpha}{1 - \alpha} \qquad \text{and} \qquad h_{11e} = \frac{h_{11b}}{1 - \alpha}$$

14.14. Show that the ratio $\Delta V_{CE}/\Delta V_{BE}$ (which may be considered the voltage gain of a common-emitter transistor amplifier) is given approximately by $-\beta R_L/h_{11e}$ where R_L is the load resistance and h_{11e} and β are defined in Problems 14.10 and 14.13.

14.15. The emitter current of a *p-n-p* transistor is approximately given by $i_E = i_0 e^{AV_{EB}}$ when V_{EB} is positive. Show that the rate of change of V_{EB} with i_E is inversely proportional to i_E.

15. physics of electron beams

This chapter presents the physics of electron beams largely through a discussion of the klystron. The concepts of velocity modulation, electron-beam plasma oscillations, and space-charge waves are introduced. Chapter 16 discusses modern amplifiers from a general point of view based on the concepts developed here. In order to have interactions with an electron beam, it is necessary to keep the beam from spreading. We begin by discussing the confinement of an electron beam by a magnetic field.

15.1 Beam confinement by magnetic fields

The Coulomb repulsive forces between electrons tend to cause a radial spreading of an electron beam. These electrostatic spreading forces can be compensated by either magnetic forces or electrostatic forces to confine the beam to a constant radius. We shall consider two types of *magnetic*-field confinement.

In one type of magnetic confinement, the beam is produced by a gun in a region free of magnetic field, but it is directed into a region in which there is a magnetic field parallel to the axis of the beam. In this case the electrons pick up an angular velocity about the magnetic field when they enter the field which results in an inward radial restoring force. This type of confinement is called "Brillouin flow."

In the other type of magnetic confinement the beam originates and remains in a longitudinal magnetic field. Here the necessary angular velocity is developed as the electrons attempt to spread radially and cross magnetic flux lines. This flow is known as magnetically confined or immersed flow.

We first calculate the radial force due to space charge on the outermost electrons of a cylindrical beam. Using Gauss' law the radial electric field $\mathcal{E}_r$ at the outer edge of a cylindrical beam having charge per unit length λ and radius a may be shown to be

$$\mathcal{E}_r = \frac{\lambda}{2\pi\epsilon_0 a} \tag{15.1}$$

Using equations 8.8 and 5.24 we may express λ in terms of the beam current i and the potential V through which the beam has been accelerated. Thus, if A represents the cross-sectional area of the beam

$$i = JA = \rho v A = \frac{\lambda}{A} vA = \lambda \sqrt{2\eta V} \tag{15.2}$$

or

$$\lambda = \frac{i}{\sqrt{2\eta V}} \tag{15.3}$$

The electric force F_r acting on an outermost electron becomes, using 15.1 and 15.3,

$$F_r = e\mathcal{E}_r = \frac{ei}{2\pi\epsilon_0 a \sqrt{2\eta V}} \tag{15.4}$$

Now that we have an expression for the spreading force on an outermost electron, let us consider the restoring force set up by the magnetic field under the conditions of Brillouin type flow. A permanent magnet circuit suitable for producing a longitudinal magnetic field which the beam enters is illustrated in Fig. 15.1.

We now examine the forces acting on the electrons as they pass through the left pole piece of the magnet. We assume that the beam axis coincides with the axis of symmetry of the magnetic circuit and that the electrons travel parallel to the beam axis as they pass through the pole piece. As an off-axis electron passes through the left pole piece it crosses magnetic flux lines that have components in the r-direction as well as in the z-direction. When the path of the electron is in the plane of the page, the electron experiences a force F_θ in a direction perpendicular to the page given by

$$F_\theta = ev_z B_r = e\frac{dz}{dt} B_r \tag{15.5}$$

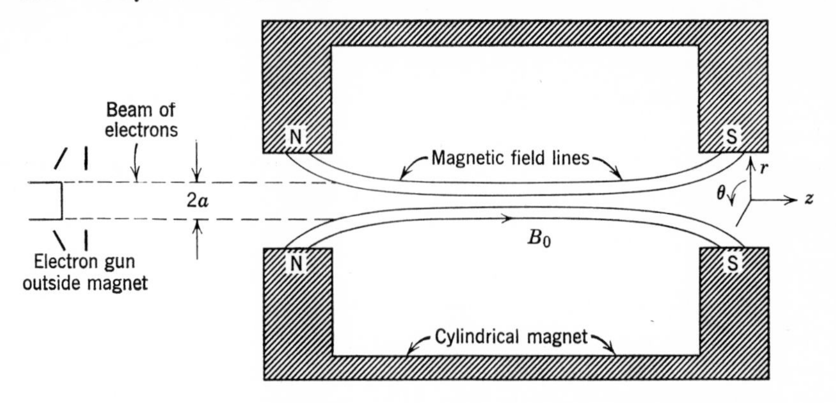

Fig. 15.1. Cylindrical permanent magnet circuit for Brillouin flow.

where B_r is the radial component of flux density at the position of the electron (see Fig. 15.2).

For mathematical convenience a further assumption is made; namely, that the electron travels through the pole piece in a short time, so that it is given only a short impulse directed perpendicularly outward from the page. When the electron reaches the region of longitudinal field, it has acquired a component of velocity which is perpendicular to the longitudinal magnetic field B_z.

Using equation 5.80 we may equate the torque about the z-axis to the time rate of change of angular momentum.

$$\frac{d}{dt} mr^2\dot{\theta} = rF_\theta = re\frac{dz}{dt} B_r \tag{15.6}$$

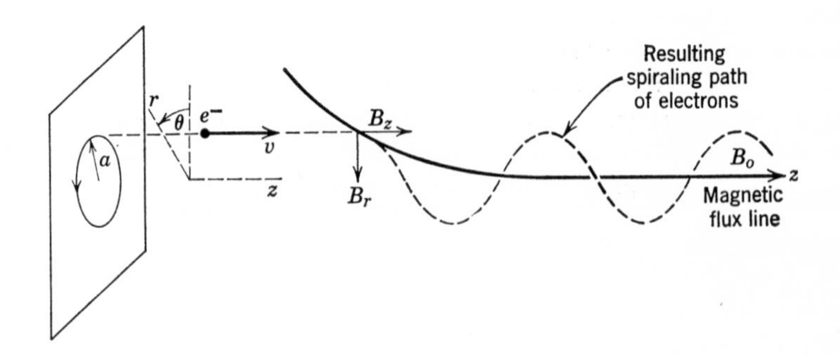

Fig. 15.2. Path of a single electron entering a magnetic field.

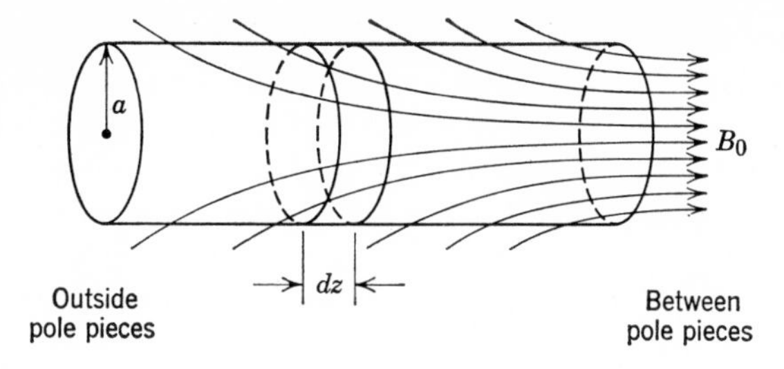

Fig. 15.3. Cylinder in space threading magnetic flux lines.

In beam confinement the distance of an outer electron from the axis is constant so that $r = a$ in equation 15.6. Multiplying both sides by 2π we have

$$2\pi ma^2 \, d\dot{\theta} = e2\pi aB_r \, dz \tag{15.7}$$

The expression $2\pi aB_r \, dz$ is the magnetic flux $d\phi$ crossing a length dz of a cylinder of radius a concentric with the axis of the beam (see Fig. 15.3). The total flux that crosses the side wall of the cylinder of radius a equals the total magnetic flux, $\pi a^2 B_0$, that comes out of the end of the cylinder. B_0 is the longitudinal flux density in the region between the pole pieces. Thus the integral of the right-hand side of 15.7 is

$$e \int_{\text{outside}}^{\text{inside}} 2\pi aB_r \, dz = e \int_{\substack{\text{cylindrical}\\ \text{surface}}} d\phi = e\pi a^2 B_0 \tag{15.8}$$

If the angular velocity $\dot{\theta}$ is zero outside the pole piece, the left side of 15.7 integrates to

$$2\pi ma^2 \int d\dot{\theta} = 2\pi ma^2 \omega \tag{15.9}$$

where ω is the resulting angular velocity about the beam axis after passing through the pole piece. Equating 15.8 and 15.9, we obtain

$$\omega = \frac{eB_0}{2m} = \frac{\omega_c}{2} \tag{15.10}$$

where ω_c is the cyclotron frequency defined by equation 5.49. Note that this initial angular frequency about the *axis* of the magnetic field is $\omega_c/2$ rather than ω_c; the difference is due to the presence of the radial electric field.

Since the beam is to be confined to a radius a, the magnetic force acting on an outermost electron must be sufficient not only to give it the centripetal acceleration to keep it moving in a helical path about the beam axis but also to counteract the radial electric field. Applying Newton's second law in the radial direction, we equate the resultant inward force to the mass times the centripetal acceleration required for a circular helix of radius a. We may also say we are equating the net inward force to the centrifugal force. The net inward force is the magnetic force $ev_\theta B_0$ minus the spreading electric field force (15.4).

$$ev_\theta B_0 - \frac{ei}{2\pi\epsilon_0 a\sqrt{2\eta V}} = ma\omega^2 \tag{15.11}$$

Substituting for the terms in 15.11, we obtain an expression for the magnetic field required to confine a beam current i to a cylinder of radius a.

$$B_0^2 = \frac{\sqrt{2}\, i}{\pi a^2 \epsilon_0 \eta^{3/2} V^{1/2}} \tag{15.12}$$

In terms of the current density J we write

$$B_0^2 = \frac{\sqrt{2}\, J}{\epsilon_0 \eta^{3/2} V^{1/2}} \tag{15.13}$$

This is the minimum value of the magnetic field which is required to confine the beam current density J accelerated by a voltage V.[1] The value of B_0 from 15.13 is known as the Brillouin field. It can be shown that equation 15.13 also applies to electrons inside the beam provided the current density is independent of radius. All electrons within the beam will rotate about the axis with the angular velocity $\omega_c/2$. The entire beam therefore twists about its axis, as if it were a rigid body, as it travels in the region of longitudinal magnetic field.

We now turn to the other type of beam confinement, known as magnetically confined flow. The angular velocity acquired by an electron which starts out in a magnetic field is given by equation 5.87.

$$\dot{\theta} = \frac{\omega_c}{2}\left(1 - \frac{r_c^2}{r^2}\right) \tag{5.87}$$

Using this expression for the angular velocity, one may calculate the restoring force from considerations similar to those for Brillouin flow. The important difference in the result is that the magnetic field

[1] This is not quite correct. The effective voltage V representing the axial velocity is generally less than the accelerating voltage. Some axial kinetic energy goes into rotational energy. For a more rigorous analysis see Pierce's "Beams," *op. cit.*, p. 153.

required for beam confinement for given beam parameters (i, a, V) is greater for magnetically confined flow than for Brillouin flow. The magnetic restoring force is

$$F_{\substack{\text{magnetic} \\ \text{restoring}}} = er\dot{\theta}B_0 = \frac{er\eta B_0^2}{2}\left(1 - \frac{r_c^2}{r^2}\right) \tag{15.14}$$

Examination of 15.14 indicates that if r is to be kept close to r_c in value, B_0 must be very large to provide the necessary restoring force.

The above analyses, developing expressions for the magnetic field needed to confine a beam to a constant diameter, are based on conditions too idealized to be achieved in practice. In an actual beam, the current density across the beam may be a function of radius and the outer edge of the beam poorly defined. A more general analysis shows that the beam envelope undergoes radial oscillations giving it a scalloped or sausage-like appearance. Magnetically immersed flow usually results in a more well defined, constant-diameter beam than does Brillouin flow.

15.2 Velocity modulation

In Chapter 7 we pointed out that a modulated beam which passes near an electrode connected to an impedance causes an induced current to flow through the impedance. This induced current may have an a-c component equal to the a-c component of the beam current. If the external impedance consists of a tuned circuit which is resonant at the frequency of the modulation, the tuned circuit becomes excited and oscillates at its resonant frequency. The energy of excitation is derived from the electrons' kinetic energy, and the a-c power delivered to the external impedance is proportional to the square of the a-c component of beam current (see equation 7.15). An unmodulated beam delivers no a-c power and no method for converting the kinetic energy of an unmodulated electron beam into useful a-c power is known.

Velocity modulation is a useful method of obtaining current modulation at high frequencies. Velocity modulation is achieved by impressing a small a-c component of velocity on a d-c electron beam. This may be done by allowing the beam to pass through two grids across which a small a-c voltage is applied. The density of electrons is not greatly affected immediately, but the velocity acquires an a-c component. The beam is now said to be velocity modulated. This velocity modulation is achieved with the expenditure of little or, ideally, no power.

As the electrons leave the modulating grids, the faster electrons move away from the slower electrons behind and overtake the slower electrons ahead. The numerical density of electrons further along the beam is no longer uniform, and the beam is said to be bunched. (Similar bunching effects may be observed in traffic density on a superhighway.) Because of this bunching the beam current has acquired an a-c component. Thus the velocity modulation imparted to the beam in passing through the grids gives rise to current modulation further along the beam. Klystron amplifiers and reflex klystron oscillators use velocity modulation and can be built for operation at frequencies in the range from 50 to 50,000 Mc.

A-c power may be extracted from a current-modulated electron beam by allowing it to pass through a second pair of grids connected to an external load impedance. The beam induces currents in the impedance and loses energy in a manner similar to that described in section 7.3.

In klystrons the grids and impedances generally have the physical form of resonant cavities in order to velocity modulate an electron beam and extract useful a-c power at high frequencies. Before considering the klystron in detail we discuss resonant cavities.

15.3 Resonant cavities

A resonant cavity is a high frequency descendent of the parallel resonant LC circuit. Such an LC circuit will resonate at a very high frequency ω_0 if the inductance L and capacitance C are very small since

$$\omega_0 = \frac{1}{\sqrt{LC}} \tag{15.15}$$

A relatively high frequency LC circuit might consist of two parallel plates joined by a single inductive turn of wire as shown in Fig. 15.4*a*. In order to reduce the inductance, more turns may be added in parallel as shown in Fig. 15.4*b*. The closed surface of Fig. 15.4*c* may be thought of as an infinite number of turns in parallel and represents a minimum value of inductance. A cavity such as that shown in Fig. 15.4*c* is a region of space surrounded by conducting walls; the space may be evacuated, or filled with a dielectric or air. The high frequency currents in a cavity flow effectively only in a narrow layer on the inner surface, the width of which is known as the skin depth. (At 10,000 Mc the skin depth is of the order of 10^{-4} cm for copper.) The energy stored in the electric and magnetic fields lies within the cavity.

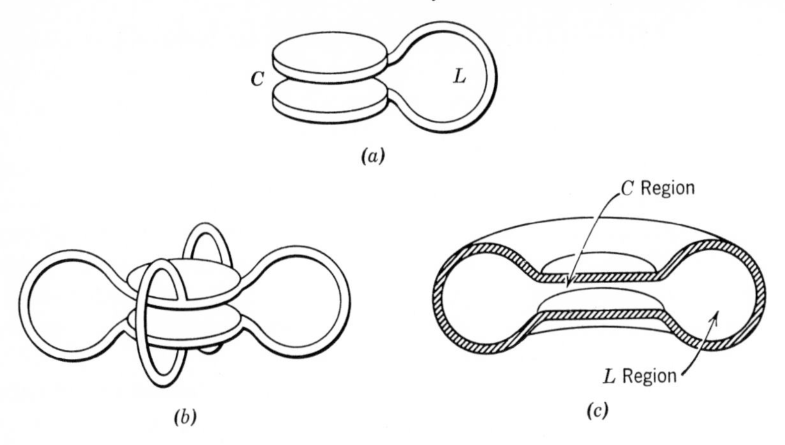

Fig. 15.4. Evolution of the resonant cavity from the parallel resonant circuit.

Field distributions for a typical resonant cavity are sketched in Fig. 15.5 for four phases of an oscillatory cycle. This cavity can be divided into two regions, one largely inductive (storing magnetic field energy), and one largely capacitive (storing electric field energy). The capacitive region is the short reentrant region C. The inductive region is largely the outer annular volume L. Not all cavities can be so clearly divided into these regions, but they still can act as resonators. Unlike an LC circuit, a cavity may have many resonant frequencies, each associated with a different mode of oscillation. These frequencies are functions of the cavity geometry, as are the fundamental frequency and harmonics of an acoustic organ pipe. The electromagnetic energy involved in the excitation of a mode of oscillation changes between energy stored in the magnetic field and energy stored in the electric field as the oscillations take place. The oscillating fields induce currents in the cavity walls, which may dissipate energy in the form of heat since the walls are resistive. In a steady-state condition, the supply of exciting energy must be equal to the power lost in the cavity walls. The ratio of the stored energy to the energy dissipated in a cycle of oscillation is often called the Q of a circuit. The Q's of cavities have typical values around 10^4, but may be as large as 10^5. A high Q value also means a sharp tuning or narrow bandwidth response.

When a cavity such as that shown in Fig. 15.5 is excited, we can speak of a "voltage" across the cavity. We define this voltage as the line integral of the electric field intensity from one plate of the capaci-

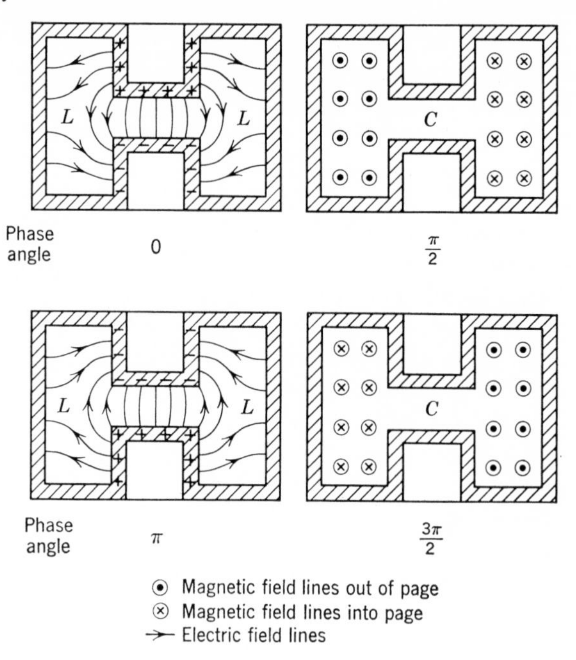

Fig. 15.5. Field distributions in a resonant cavity at phases spaced by $\pi/2$ radians during a cycle of oscillation in the principal mode.

tive section to the other. The usual scalar potential has less meaning here since the electric field is partly due to Faraday induced emfs.

Coupling of electromagnetic power into and out of resonant cavities is sometimes achieved by means of a small loop of wire which couples with the magnetic field within the cavity and joins to an external coaxial transmission line. Coupling can also be achieved by means of a probe which reaches into the cavity and couples with the electric field.

The preceding paragraphs have suggested that a cavity resonator is similar to an *LC* resonant circuit and can be treated as a complex impedance *Z*.

15.4 Klystron amplifier without space charge

A schematic representation of a klystron amplifier is shown in Fig. 15.6. The tube consists of two resonant cavities through which passes a cylindrical beam of electrons. The cavities are separated by a region called the drift space. The ends of the reentrant parts of the cavities (the capacitive sections of Fig. 15.4 and Fig. 15.5) may be wire grids. The cavity nearer the gun is called the input or buncher cavity. The signal couples to the r-f magnetic field of the input cavity by means of a coaxial line which has its center conductor joined to a small loop within the cavity. The input signal appears as an a-c voltage between the grids of the buncher cavity, and velocity modulates the beam.

In the drift space, bunching occurs. The beam then passes through the output cavity. The current modulated beam excites the output cavity by losing kinetic energy to the fields within the cavity. The output cavity is connected to a load impedance by means of a coaxial line so that when the cavity is excited, a-c power is delivered to the load impedance. A collector electrode, maintained at the output-cavity potential, intercepts the beam as it emerges from the output cavity. Both cavities generally have the same resonant frequency and are usually of the same construction. The beam may be prevented from spreading laterally by an axial magnetic field as described in section 15.1.

We next consider the details of the operation of the individual components of a klystron.

Input Cavity

Let us suppose that the electrons upon entering the input cavity have been accelerated through a potential V_0 and that a small a-c voltage $V_1 \cos \omega t$ is established between the grids of the cavity. The velocity v of the electrons as they emerge from the cavity is given by

$$v = \sqrt{2\eta V} = \sqrt{2\eta}\,(V_0 + V_1 \cos \omega t)^{1/2} \tag{15.16}$$

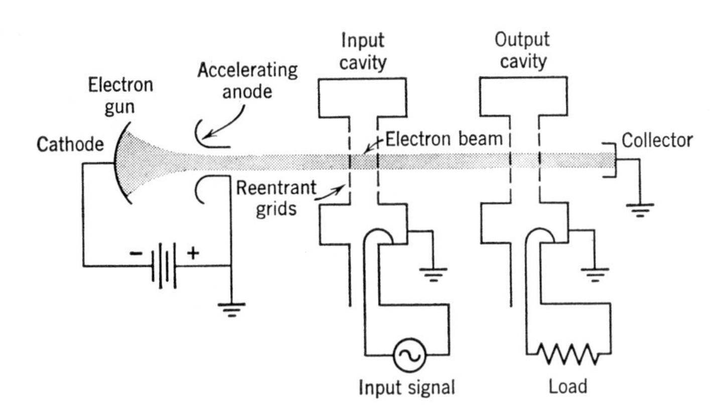

Fig. 15.6. Schematic representation of klystron amplifier.

If $V_1 \ll V_0$, the expression in parentheses may be expanded by the binomial theorem

$$v \approx v_0 \left(1 + \frac{V_1}{2V_0} \cos \omega t\right)$$

where (15.17)

$$v_0 = \sqrt{2\eta V_0}$$

Equation 15.17 gives the results of velocity modulation of the electron beam by the input cavity when the time for the electron beam to pass between the grids of the cavity is small compared with a period of an a-c cycle.

At extremely high frequencies while the electrons are passing between the grids, the voltage $V_1 \cos \omega t$ may change significantly during the time of transit and reduce the effectiveness of the velocity modulation. In conventional tubes of the triode type the acceleration to a relatively high velocity takes place after modulation; therefore the transit time from cathode to grid is relatively long and becomes important at moderately high frequencies. In a klystron electrons are accelerated to a high velocity before modulation, and the transit time through the input cavity is relatively short and becomes a limiting factor only at much higher frequencies.

Drift space

If the electron transit time in the input cavity is negligible, equal numbers of electrons emerge from the cavity in equal time intervals. Their velocities have the variation with time given by equation 15.17. It is instructive to plot the distance of an electron from the input or buncher cavity versus time for many individual electrons. Figure 15.7 shows distance versus time relations for individual electrons leaving the input cavity at equal time intervals. Zero distance corresponds to the position of the input cavity. The intersection of one of the sloping lines with the t-axis indicates the time of departure of that electron from the input cavity. The slope of the line is equal to the electron's velocity as given by equation 15.17. Plots of this type are known as Applegate diagrams.

If in Fig. 15.7 we pick a certain fixed z and examine the density of lines along a horizontal line, we see a periodic variation in the density of electrons with time. Between lines A and B the density variation is the largest. Faster electrons start to pass slower ones at a certain distance from the input cavity, with the result that the beam current at that distance reaches a large value once each cycle. Thus current

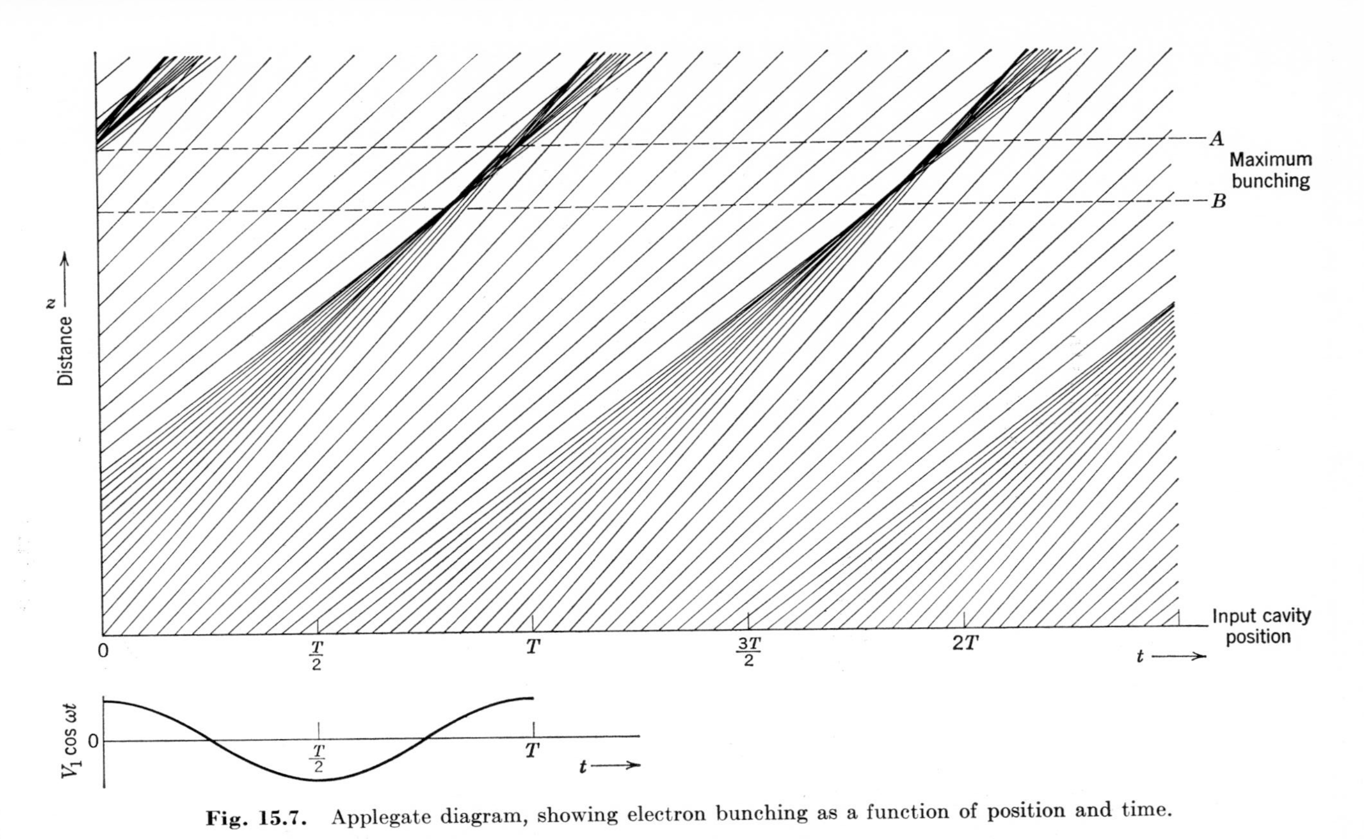

Fig. 15.7. Applegate diagram, showing electron bunching as a function of position and time.

modulation is achieved in the drift space by the density variations or bunching of the electrons in the beam.

From Fig. 15.7 it would appear that the output cavity of a klystron should be placed at the position of maximum bunching. This should be in the region between A and B in Fig. 15.7 in order to induce maximum a-c current in the cavity. However, the convection current as a function of time in this region may appear as in Fig. 15.8. The current is not sinusoidal and contains many harmonics. It turns out that the position of the maximum a-c current at the *fundamental* frequency is not located at the position of maximum bunching, but occurs at a position further from the cavity than A or B. We are generally most interested in the maximum fundamental current.

Output cavity

The modulated beam passing through the output cavity induces a net a-c current on the inside surface of the cavity walls. This induced current initiates the oscillations in the cavity when the modulation is first turned on. The amplitude of the output cavity oscillations builds up at the expense of the electrons' kinetic energy. In a steady-state condition, the energy lost by the electrons equals the sum of the energy delivered to the load and the energy dissipated in the cavity walls. The relative phase is such that when the number of electrons crossing the gap is largest, the oscillating electric field of the cavity retards the electrons and extracts energy from the beam. The path followed by the induced charges associated with a small bunch of electrons passing through a cavity is illustrated in Fig. 15.9. On the average, power is delivered to the output cavity because more than half the electrons pass through the cavity when the phase of the electric field is such as to decelerate the electrons and less than half the electrons pass through the cavity when the field is accelerating.

To summarize, a klystron is an energy converter. The d-c *kinetic* energy of the electrons is converted to the a-c energy of electromagnetic

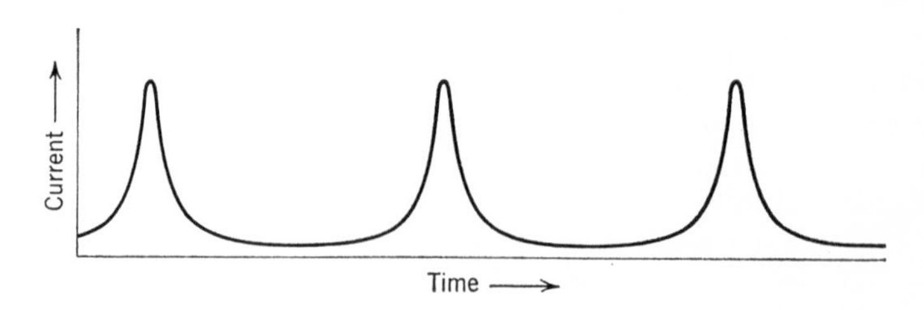

Fig. 15.8. Current as a function of time at position of maximum bunching.

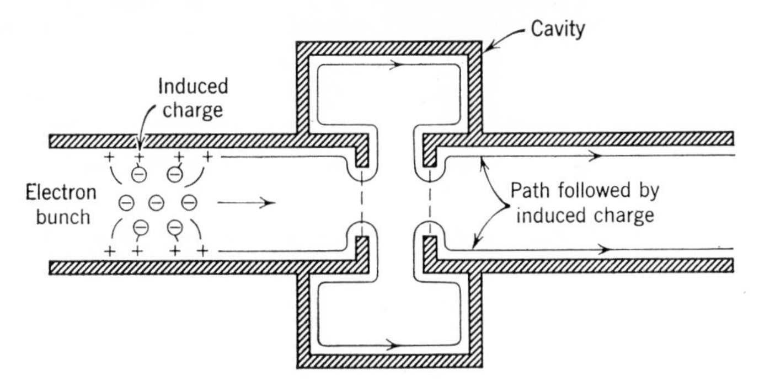

Fig. 15.9. Path followed by induced charges associated with a group of electrons passing through a cavity.

fields in a cavity. The magnetron (see section 5.7) converts the d-c *potential* energy of electrons to a-c energy. Power amplification in the klystron is achieved because only a small amount of a-c power is required to velocity modulate the electrons, and a large amount of output power is supplied by the kinetic energy of the electrons. The power amplification of a klystron can be very large, on the order of 1000 or greater.

The klystron amplifier has the unique property that it can be operated over a wide range of beam voltages. Both the reflex klystron oscillator and the traveling-wave tube which we shall discuss are quite sensitive to variations in d-c beam voltage. The chief limitation of the klystron as an amplifier is that the high-Q cavities necessary to extract appreciable power from the beam make the klystron a narrow bandwidth device.

15.5 Reflex klystron

The reflex klystron is perhaps the most widely used of all microwave tubes. Its chief application is as a low power source of microwave (high frequency) energy. A schematic illustration of the electrode arrangement for a reflex klystron oscillator is shown in Fig. 15.10*a*. This tube consists of an electron gun, a resonant cavity, and an electrode known as a repeller. No magnetic field is required because the interaction space is very short. Figure 15.10*b* indicates the d-c potentials between the electrodes as a function of distance. The resonant cavity and the accelerating electrode are operated at a positive potential with respect to the cathode, whereas the repeller is

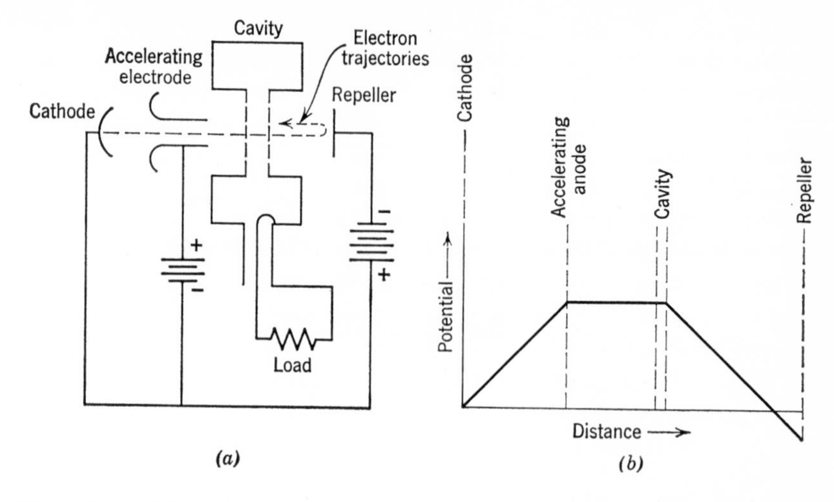

Fig. 15.10. The reflex klystron oscillator. (*a*) Electrode arrangement. (*b*) Plot of d-c potential along the axis of the tube.

negative with respect to the cathode. The retarding field between the repeller and the cavity causes the electrons to reverse their direction and pass through the cavity a second time. Thus in a reflex klystron a single cavity acts as both the input and output cavities. The electrons are finally collected on the accelerating electrode and on the walls of the cavity. The drift space in a reflex klystron is twice the distance from the cavity to the point at which the electrons are reflected. The time taken by the electrons to return to the cavity can be adjusted by changing the repeller voltage. If the timing is right, the current-modulated beam returns through the cavity in the right phase to add energy to the fields in the cavity, and maintains the oscillations which are normally started by random variations in beam density (noise). The frequency of operation of a reflex klystron thus depends on the elapsed time required for electrons to return to the cavity, and the resonant frequency of the cavity.

15.6 Space-charge effects

Let us examine an Applegate diagram representing only three electrons (Fig. 15.11): the slowest, the fastest, and one at the beam velocity. Their position-time lines would meet at a crossover point P in the absence of space charge. When one considers the repulsive forces of space charge, these lines may be modified as shown by the solid curves. We now consider the reasons for this in detail. The Coulomb forces between the electrons in a bunch tend to oppose the bunching. Since we may assume that the beam is confined in the radial direction by an axial magnetic field (section 15.1), the debunching of a beam occurs in the axial direction, and we have essentially a one-dimensional problem. As the charge density is increased by the bunching it becomes more difficult or even impossible for an individual electron to overtake the electrons just ahead of it. The electrons may not have sufficient velocity to overcome the Coulomb forces and the beam may become only longitudinally compressed. Thus no crossover or overtaking may occur, as indicated by the solid curves of Fig. 15.11. The compressed regions center around the electrons with the unperturbed velocities. We can imagine oscillations taking place in the beam in which the axial displacement of the electrons from their equilibrium positions varies periodically. The beam acts as an elastic medium which is capable of compression and rarefaction in the axial direction. In the next section, we examine the behavior of such oscillations, and later see how a disturbance (such as velocity modulation) given to a beam may be interpreted in terms of these oscillations.

We now present some background material on practical electron beams. Positive charges in the beam may be of great importance. At the gas pressure obtained in electron tubes (10^{-8} mm of mercury), there are on the order of 10^{10} gas molecules per cubic centimeter. Positively charged ions are produced at a constant rate by the electrons and the rate of recombination within the beam is small. A cylindrical beam of electrons causes a depression of the potential in

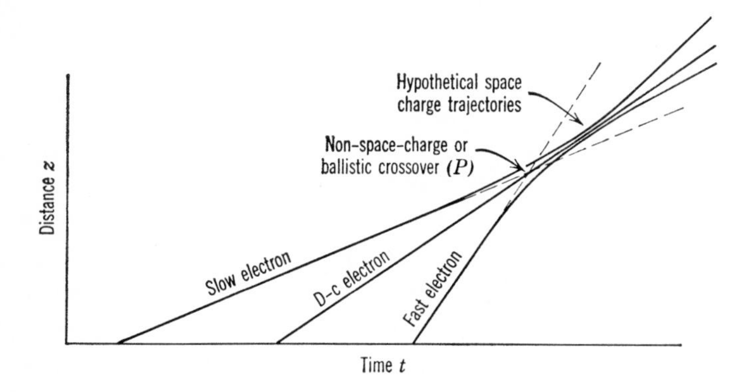

Fig. 15.11. Applegate diagram with three electron trajectories in the presence of space charge.

the region of the beam, with the result that a potential trough is formed with its lowest part along the axis of the beam. Positive ions of low kinetic energy are confined radially to this potential trough and can move only along the axis of the beam. It has been found that at normal tube pressures the rate of ion production may be sufficient to completely fill in the potential trough and neutralize the beam. If more ions are produced than are needed to neutralize the potential trough, they are free to escape to the walls of the tube and recombine.

If the Debye length of this neutralized beam is small compared with the dimensions of interest in the beam, the beam may satisfy the definition of a plasma (see section 11.4). Actually, even an unneutralized beam may behave like a plasma.[1]

15.7 Plasma oscillations

We wish to determine the frequency of the longitudinal oscillations of the electrons about their average positions in a neutralized beam or plasma. This frequency is called the plasma frequency ω_p. We assume:[2]

1. The electron-beam plasma is completely neutralized by positive ions, but the ions are immobile.
2. The amplitude of the oscillation is so small that the axial variation in charge density is small compared to the average charge density of the electrons.
3. The beam is considered to be infinite in cross section so that the electric field lies only in the axial direction (a one-dimensional problem).

When the electrons are in their equilibrium positions, the field lines from individual electrons terminate on adjacent ions and there is no net electric field within the plasma. If the electrons are displaced from equilibrium, there will be a net negative charge where they are bunched and a net positive charge where they are depleted. Electric field lines extend between concentrations of positive charge and adjacent concentrations of negative charge. This field provides the

[1] The motion of electrons in a neutralized plasma is similar to the motion of electrons in an unneutralized beam because in a plasma the ions are too heavy to follow the electron motion. The difference between an unneutralized beam and a neutralized plasma is mainly due to the d-c electric fields in the beam, whose tendency to spread the beam is counteracted by the application of a strong longitudinal confining magnetic field (see section 15.1).

[2] An assumption not explicitly used in the derivation is that the disturbances are zero at the axial ends of the plasma, that is, at $z = \pm\infty$.

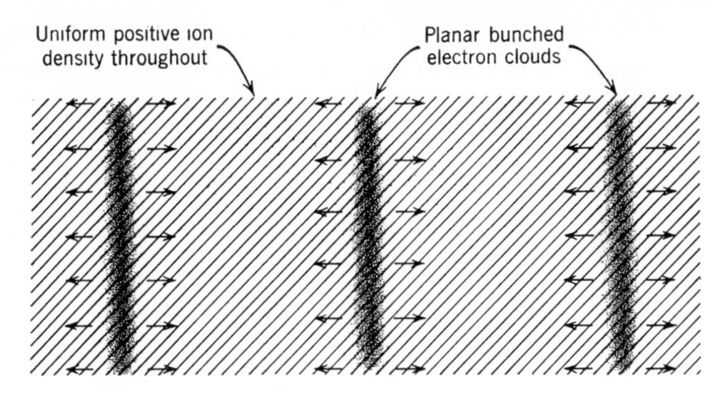

Fig. 15.12. Charge distribution in infinite bunched neutral beam indicating restoring forces on bunched electron clouds.

restoring force necessary for the plasma oscillations. Figure 15.12 portrays these concepts.

Let us calculate the restoring force on a displaced electron. The ions have an average charge density ρ_0, and the electrons have an average negative charge density $-\rho_0$. The average charge density ρ_0 is equal to the average numerical density of electrons n_0 times the electron charge

$$\rho_0 = n_0 e \tag{15.18}$$

In Fig. 15.13 we show a portion of an electron beam. Here the dots represent the mobile electrons. This figure is drawn from the point of view of an observer traveling with the beam, that is, with the average velocity of the electrons. In part (*a*) of this figure, the electrons are equally spaced. In part (*b*), a group of electrons in a plane (those marked 4) are displaced a distance s to the right from their equilibrium position with respect to the beam. The electrons to the right of number 4 are crowded together, producing a restoring force on each number 4 electron. We will show that the restoring force on an electron is proportional to its displacement s and therefore gives rise to a simple harmonic vibratory motion about its equilibrium position. We wish to consider a constant volume $A\,dz$ whose left face is at the equilibrium position of electrons number 4, and whose right face is at the equilibrium position of electrons number 7. Electrons 4 are considered to be moved to the right a distance s. The electrons in column 7, which were initially at the right face of the volume element, move a distance $s + ds$ to the right, where ds must be a negative quantity if there is a compression.

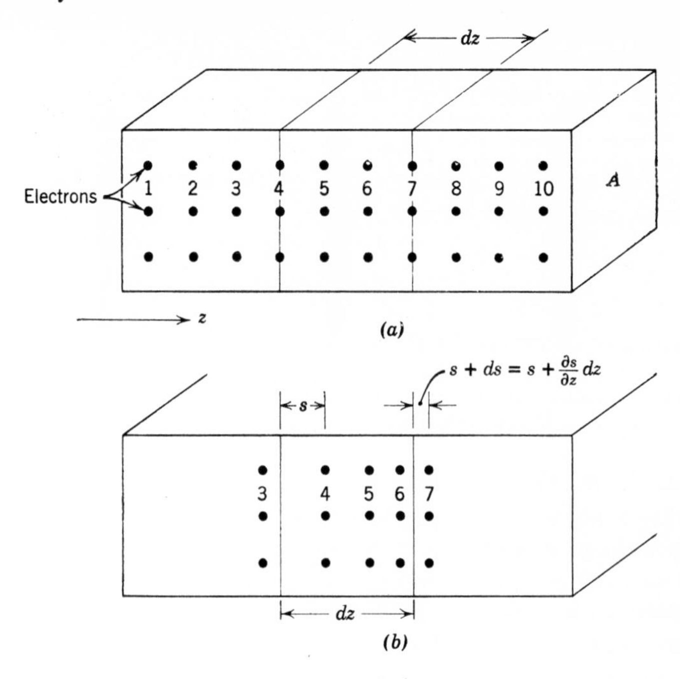

Fig. 15.13. Longitudinal displacement of electrons in a plasma.

Originally there was no net charge inside the volume element or slab $A\ dz$. Because of the disturbance, a net charge q is moved into the slab. If $\tilde{\rho}$ is the net charge density within the slab after displacement, then the net charge in the slab becomes

$$q = \tilde{\rho} A\ dz \tag{15.19}$$

At the position of the left face of the slab each electron is displaced a distance s. The charge moved into the slab through the left face is thus

$$q_{\text{in}} = -\rho_0 A s \tag{15.20}$$

(In Fig. 15.13 these are electrons 4 and others within a distance s to the left.) At the right face of the slab each electron moves a distance $s + ds$, and the charge moved out of the slab through the right face is

$$q_{\text{out}} = -\rho_0 A(s + ds) \tag{15.21}$$

(In Fig. 15.13 these are electrons 7 and others within a distance $s + ds$ to their left.) We note that the displacement from equilibrium s is both a function of position z and time t. We can write the total differential of s as

$$ds = \frac{\partial s}{\partial z} dz + \frac{\partial s}{\partial t} dt \tag{15.22}$$

If we consider the displacements of all the electrons in Fig. 15.13 at the same instant of time, dt is 0, and

$$ds = \frac{\partial s}{\partial z} dz \tag{15.23}$$

Substituting 15.23 into 15.21, we obtain

$$q_{\text{out}} = -\rho_0 A \left(s + \frac{\partial s}{\partial z} dz\right) \tag{15.24}$$

Hence, the net charge in the slab after the disturbance is

$$q = q_{\text{in}} - q_{\text{out}} = -\rho_0 A \left[s - \left(s + \frac{\partial s}{\partial z} dz\right)\right] \tag{15.25}$$

and combining 15.19 with 15.25, we have

$$\tilde{\rho} = \rho_0 \frac{\partial s}{\partial z} \tag{15.26}$$

Equation 15.26 is a basic equation relating $\tilde{\rho}$, the net charge density, to s. Note that if $\partial s/\partial z$ is negative as in Fig. 15.13, then $\tilde{\rho}$ is negative; that is, more electrons have moved in than have moved out.

We next calculate the electric field due to the net charge density $\tilde{\rho}$ by invoking Maxwell's first equation (see Appendix D) applied in one-dimension.

$$\nabla \cdot \mathcal{E} = \frac{\partial \mathcal{E}}{\partial z} = \frac{\tilde{\rho}}{\epsilon_0} \tag{15.27}$$

Substituting 15.26 into 15.27, we obtain

$$\frac{\partial \mathcal{E}}{\partial z} = \frac{\rho_0}{\epsilon_0} \frac{\partial s}{\partial z} \tag{15.28}$$

and integrating, we have

$$\mathcal{E} = \frac{\rho_0}{\epsilon_0} s \tag{15.29}$$

The constant of integration is 0 since $\mathcal{E} = 0$ when the electrons are not displaced. Equation 15.29 can be interpreted as describing the electric field seen by a displaced electron due to the organized bunching of the rest of the electrons. This *collective*[1] behavior has meaning only when the amplitude of the displacement s is greater than λ_D, the Debye length. This is equivalent to saying that the perturbation s is greater than the mean free path of the particles in the plasma (see equation 11.13).

The force F on an electron displaced a distance s from equilibrium is

$$F = -e\mathcal{E} = -\frac{e\rho_0}{\epsilon_0}s \tag{15.30}$$

Newton's second law for the electron becomes

$$-\frac{e\rho_0}{\epsilon_0}s = m\ddot{s} \tag{15.31}$$

Equation 15.30 is the familiar Hooke's law type of restoring force which is proportional to displacement, and 15.31 is the familiar differential equation of simple harmonic motion. The angular frequency of this motion, which we denote by ω_p, is known as the plasma angular frequency.

$$\omega_p = \sqrt{e\rho_0/m\epsilon_0} = \sqrt{\eta\rho_0/\epsilon_0} = \sqrt{\eta e n_0/\epsilon_0} \tag{15.32}$$

Equation 15.32 predicts that a plasma with an electron density of 10^{10} per cubic centimeter will have a plasma frequency of about 900 Mc. For electron beams having electron densities normally encountered in microwave tubes, the plasma frequency is of the order of a few hundred megacycles. The frequency of the oscillations of the electrons is a natural *resonant frequency* of the plasma, an "elastic" medium. In a stationary plasma electromechanical waves can propagate only with frequency ω_p in contrast to mechanical waves in air, water, or solids which can propagate with a continuous range of frequencies. The phenomenon of plasma oscillations was first discussed in 1929 by Tonks and Langmuir of the General Electric Research Laboratory.

Since the angular frequency ω_p given by equation 15.32 was derived for a beam with infinite cross section, it is sometimes called the infinite beam plasma frequency. A practical beam has a finite cross section and may be enclosed by a metal tube. In these circumstances the electric fields no longer lie only in the axial direction, the axial restoring forces are weaker, and the plasma frequency is smaller. Figure 15.14 illustrates this more practical situation. An important new feature in the three-dimensional case is that the differential equations have an infinite number of solutions involving an infinite number of

[1] D. Pines and D. Bohm, "A Collective Description of Electron Interactions," *Phys. Rev.*, **85**, 338, (1952).

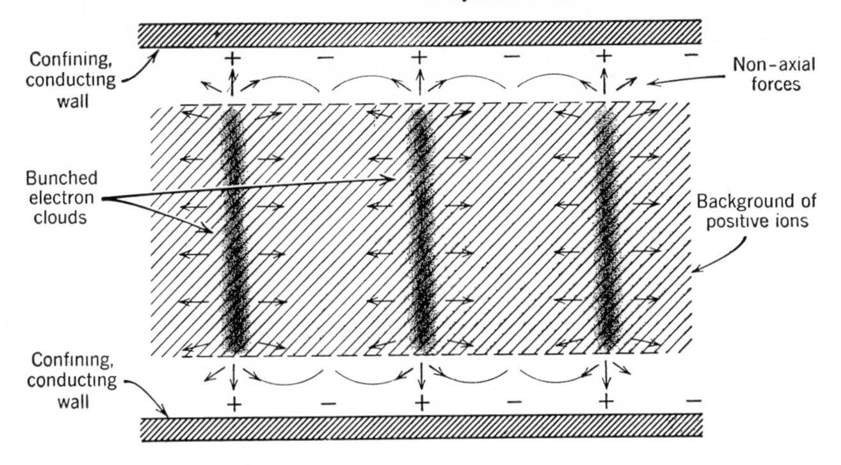

Fig. 15.14. Charge distribution in finite bunched neutral beam.

frequencies or modes. In simple cases the mode of vibration associated with the fundamental frequency is the only one excited with significant amplitude. The fundamental frequency is known as the "reduced" plasma frequency. In a practical beam the reduced plasma frequency is dependent on the geometry of the beam and metal tube, the average velocity at which the plasma is moving, and the externally applied a-c driving frequency which sets up the oscillation.

15.8 Space-charge waves

In this section we study the nature of the waves set up when an electron beam or a moving plasma is disturbed. Suppose we place a resonant cavity at a position $z = 0$ through which a uniform electron beam passes as shown in Fig. 15.15. A signal of frequency ω is fed into the cavity and provides an a-c voltage across the cavity grids. In section 15.4 we derived an expression for the velocity given to an electron beam by a sinusoidal modulating voltage of amplitude V_1.

$$v = v_0 + v_0 \frac{V_1}{2V_0} \cos \omega t \qquad (15.17)$$

An electron arriving at the cavity at time t_0 receives a velocity increment or "kick" $\tilde{v}(t_0)$ given by

$$\tilde{v}(t_0) = \frac{v_0 V_1}{2V_0} \cos \omega t_0 = v_1 \cos \omega t_0 \qquad (15.33)$$

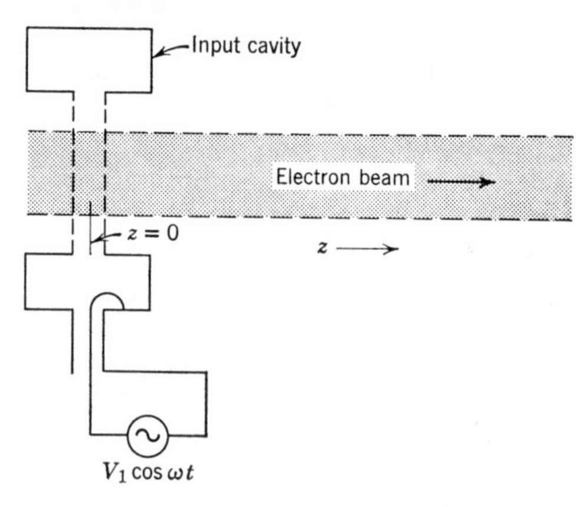

Fig. 15.15. A system for producing space charge waves in an electron beam.

After receiving a kick, each electron oscillates with simple harmonic motion about its equilibrium position in the moving beam. As pointed out in the previous section, such an oscillation can only be at the plasma frequency ω_p. An individual electron does *not* oscillate at the driving frequency ω. The amplitude of the plasma oscillation depends on the size of the velocity kick which, from 15.33, depends on the time t_0 at which the electron passes the input cavity. After an electron passes through the cavity, its equilibrium position continues to move with the beam at the constant velocity v_0.

To summarize, each individual electron oscillates with simple harmonic motion at the same frequency ω_p about its equilibrium position but with different amplitudes and phases. The set of conditions outlined above gives rise to unusual patterns of electron motion as viewed in a stationary laboratory system (fixed with respect to the input cavity). These patterns, which we call space-charge waves, are different from ordinary sound waves or electromagnetic waves largely because of the "resonant" property of the medium.

Space-charge waves will first be mathematically described in terms of the electron displacement s from its equilibrium position as the electron *vibrates* along the z-direction with frequency ω_p and also *translates* in the positive z-direction with velocity v_0. The equation of motion of the electron as viewed from the beam coordinate system (by an observer running alongside the beam) is 15.31, now written as

$$\ddot{s} + \omega_p^2 s = 0 \tag{15.34}$$

The solution of this equation (s as a function of t) can be expressed as

$$s = Ae^{j\omega_p t} + Be^{-j\omega_p t} \tag{15.35}$$

where the complex constants A and B are independent of time t. We wish to evaluate these constants A and B subject to the initial conditions that the electron has at its arrival time t_0 at the cavity. From 15.33 the velocity ds/dt at $t = t_0$ must be

$$\left.\frac{ds}{dt}\right|_{t=t_0} = \tilde{v}(t_0) = v_1 \cos \omega t_0 = \text{real part } (v_1 e^{j\omega t_0}) \tag{15.36}$$

(We choose to represent physical quantities by the real parts of complex expressions.) The displacement s for each electron at the modulating cavity is assumed to be zero. This is an approximation which is valid if the transit time through the cavity grids is negligible. Hence the initial conditions which 15.35 must satisfy are

$$\left.\frac{ds}{dt}\right|_{t=t_0} = v_1 e^{j\omega t_0} \tag{15.37}$$

$$\left. s \right|_{t=t_0} = 0 \tag{15.38}$$

Substituting 15.35 into 15.37 and 15.38, we find

$$A = \frac{v_1}{2j\omega_p} e^{j(\omega-\omega_p)t_0} \tag{15.39}$$

$$B = \frac{-v_1}{2j\omega_p} e^{j(\omega+\omega_p)t_0} \tag{15.40}$$

Using these expressions in 15.35, we obtain

$$s = \frac{v_1}{2j\omega_p} e^{j(\omega-\omega_p)t_0} e^{j\omega_p t} - \frac{v_1}{2j\omega_p} e^{j(\omega+\omega_p)t_0} e^{-j\omega_p t} \tag{15.41}$$

Equation 15.41 is the solution of the simple harmonic motion equation for the displacements of electrons about their equilibrium positions which satisfies the initial conditions 15.37 and 15.38. This equation describes the individual electron displacements about their equilibrium positions in the moving beam in terms of their times t_0 of passage through the modulating cavity. We now eliminate t_0 to obtain the displacements in terms of z, the distance of the equilibrium positions from this cavity. From Fig. 15.16, we may write

$$z = v_0(t - t_0) \tag{15.42}$$

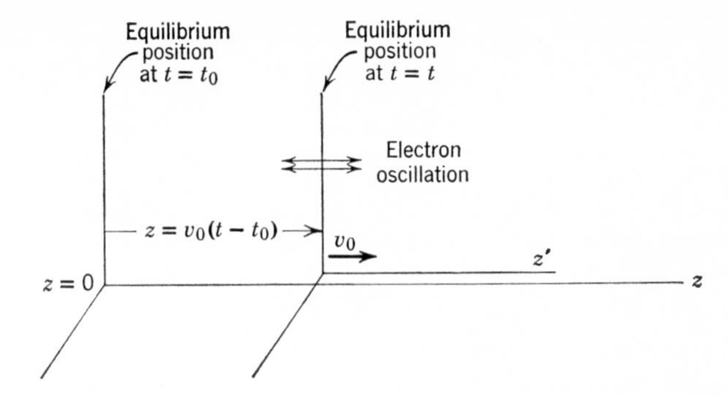

Fig. 15.16. Beam and laboratory coordinate relationships.

from which

$$t_0 = t - \frac{z}{v_0} \tag{15.43}$$

Substituting 15.43 into 15.41, we obtain

$$s = \frac{v_1}{2j\omega_p} e^{-j[(\omega-\omega_p)/v_0]z+j\omega t} - \frac{v_1}{2j\omega_p} e^{-j[(\omega+\omega_p)/v_0]z+j\omega t} \tag{15.44}$$

Equation 15.44 has the form of the algebraic sum of two traveling waves. Equation 15.44 may be rewritten as

$$s = \frac{v_1}{2j\omega_p} e^{-j\beta_f z+j\omega t} - \frac{v_1}{2j\omega_p} e^{-j\beta_s z+j\omega t} \tag{15.45}$$

where

$$\beta_f \equiv \frac{\omega - \omega_p}{v_0} \tag{15.46}$$

and

$$\beta_s \equiv \frac{\omega + \omega_p}{v_0} \tag{15.47}$$

These β's have the same significance as the propagation constant k used in equations 1.16 and 1.17. Hence using 1.12, the phase velocities of the two waves are

$$v_f = \frac{\omega}{k} = \frac{\omega}{\beta_f} = \frac{v_0}{1 - \dfrac{\omega_p}{\omega}} \tag{15.48}$$

and

$$v_s = \frac{\omega}{\beta_s} = \frac{v_0}{1 + \frac{\omega_p}{\omega}} \tag{15.49}$$

Thus if $\omega_p < \omega$ either 15.44 or 15.45 represents the difference of two displacement waves both traveling in the $+z$-direction, but with different velocities. One, called the fast wave, is traveling with phase velocity v_f which is greater than the beam velocity v_0. The other is called the slow wave and is traveling with a phase velocity v_s, which is less than the beam velocity. To get some idea of the velocity magnitudes involved, we recall that typical values of ω_p are a few hundred megacycles. For klystrons and other beam-type devices, ω is usually greater than a few thousand megacycles, so $\omega_p/\omega < 0.1$. Thus the velocities of the fast and slow waves generally differ from v_0 by less than 10%.

It is of interest to examine the velocities of these waves as viewed from a system moving with the beam. The velocity of the fast wave v_+ is then

$$v_+ = v_f - v_0 = \frac{v_0}{1 - \frac{\omega_p}{\omega}} - v_0 = v_0 \frac{\omega_p}{\omega - \omega_p} \tag{15.50}$$

and the velocity v_- of the slow wave becomes

$$v_- = v_s - v_0 = \frac{v_0}{1 + \frac{\omega_p}{\omega}} - v_0 = -v_0 \frac{\omega_p}{\omega + \omega_p} \tag{15.51}$$

We are led to the interesting conclusion that if we could run at a velocity v_0 and observe the waves, we would see two waves moving in opposite directions with *unequal* speeds ($|v_+| \neq |v_-|$). In contrast we recall that the more familiar types of waves propagate from a disturbance with equal speeds in opposite directions.

It is interesting that although the fast and slow waves travel at different phase velocities, their group velocities are equal (see equation 1.11)

$$v_g = \frac{d\omega}{dk} = \frac{d\omega}{d\beta} = v_0 \tag{15.52}$$

Since the energy carried by a wave usually propagates at the group velocity, this result implies that energy is transported mechanically by the oscillating electrons. We may speak of the space-charge waves as "electromechanical" in nature.

15.9 Frequency conversion of space-charge waves from beam coordinates to laboratory coordinates

In this section we show that we may think of the frequency ω of waves observed in the laboratory system as a Doppler shift of the plasma frequency ω_p of the waves seen by an observer in the beam coordinate system. The approach is to consider two waves, each having angular frequency ω_p in the beam coordinate system, one traveling to the right and one traveling to the left.

We start by writing down the equations of two oppositely directed traveling waves in the beam coordinate system which can be created from a disturbance in that system:

$$s_+ = s_1 e^{-j\beta_+ z' + j\omega_p t} \tag{15.53}$$

$$s_- = s_1 e^{j\beta_- z' + j\omega_p t} \tag{15.54}$$

where the propagation constants in the moving beam system are

$$\beta_+ = \frac{2\pi}{\lambda_+} \tag{15.55}$$

$$\beta_- = \frac{2\pi}{\lambda_-} \tag{15.56}$$

These two waves are illustrated in Fig. 15.17. For generality we let the β_+ and β_- be different; the frequency for both waves is ω_p. To express these equations in the laboratory coordinate system (that is, in terms of z and t), we use the Galilean transformation equation relating z and z' (see Fig. 15.16).

$$z' = z - v_0 t \tag{15.57}$$

Substituting 15.57 into 15.53 and 15.54, we have

$$s_+ = s_1 e^{-j\beta_+ z + j(\omega_p + \beta_+ v_0)t} \tag{15.58}$$

$$s_- = s_1 e^{+j\beta_- z + j(\omega_p - \beta_- v_0)t} \tag{15.59}$$

If we interpret these as traveling waves in the $+z$-direction with the same laboratory frequency ω, we have from 15.58

$$\omega = \omega_p + \beta_+ v_0 \tag{15.60}$$

and from 15.59

$$-\omega = \omega_p - \beta_- v_0 \tag{15.61}$$

Comparison of 15.60 and 15.61 with 15.46 and 15.47 verifies that β_f is the same as β_+, and β_s is the same as β_-. Thus we conclude that waves traveling in opposite directions in the beam coordinate system give rise to slow and fast space-charge waves in the laboratory coordinate system.

Equations 15.60 and 15.61 may also be derived by considering the frequency shift in transferring from one coordinate system to another. For a wave traveling with frequency ω_p, velocity v_+ to the right, and propagation constant β_+ in the beam system, we may write (using equation 1.12, and remem-

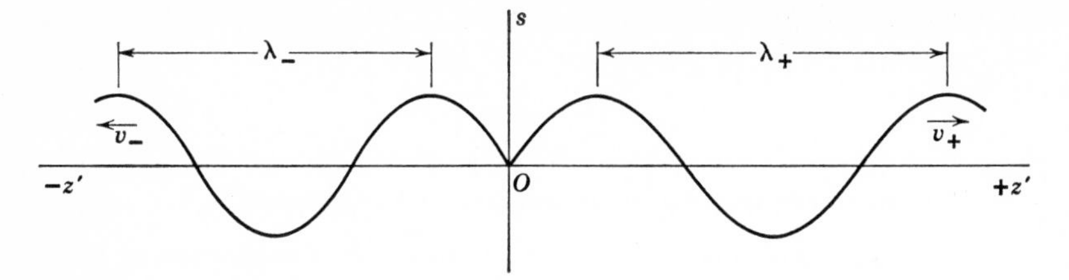

Fig. 15.17. Waves starting from a disturbance at $z' = 0$ in a stationary plasma at one instant of time.

bering that $\beta = k$)

$$v_+ = \frac{\omega_p}{\beta_+} \tag{15.62}$$

When the same wave is viewed in the laboratory system, its wavelength is the same as in the beam system ($\beta_+ = \beta_f$). However, its velocity is now $v_0 + v_+$ since an observer in the laboratory system sees the velocity v_+ plus the beam velocity v_0.

The frequency of the wave is now ω, so that

$$v_0 + v_+ = \frac{\omega}{\beta_f} \tag{15.63}$$

Eliminating v_+ from 15.62 and 15.63, we have

$$v_0 + \frac{\omega_p}{\beta_f} = \frac{\omega}{\beta_f}$$

or (15.64)

$$\omega - \beta_f v_0 = \omega_p$$

which is an alternate form of 15.60. Equation 15.64 gives the Doppler shift for the fast wave from angular frequency ω_p to ω. Equation 15.61 may be obtained in a similar fashion for the slow wave.

15.10 Velocity, space-charge density, and current density variations in a klystron

In this section we extend the space-charge wave concepts of section 15.8 by finding the space-charge density ρ, the velocity v, and the current density J in a velocity-modulated electron beam as a function of position and time. These quantities are then utilized to further our understanding of klystrons.

Equation 15.44 is the basic equation for the displacement waves:

$$s = \frac{v_1}{2j\omega_p} e^{-j[(\omega-\omega_p)/v_0]z+j\omega t} - \frac{v_1}{2j\omega_p} e^{-j[(\omega+\omega_p)/v_0]z+j\omega t} \tag{15.44}$$

The charge density variation $\tilde{\rho}$ can be calculated using 15.26

$$\tilde{\rho} = \rho_0 \frac{\partial s}{\partial z} \tag{15.26}$$

Differentiating 15.44 and substituting into 15.26 we find

$$\tilde{\rho} = -\frac{\rho_0 v_1}{2v_0} \frac{\omega - \omega_p}{\omega_p} e^{-j[(\omega-\omega_p)/v_0]z+j\omega t} + \frac{\rho_0 v_1}{2v_0} \frac{\omega + \omega_p}{\omega_p} e^{-j[(\omega+\omega_p)/v_0]z+j\omega t} \tag{15.65}$$

This equation represents fast and slow waves with slightly different amplitudes. At the modulating cavity ($z = 0$) the charge density variation is given by

$$\tilde{\rho}_{z=0} = \rho_0 \frac{v_1}{v_0} e^{j\omega t} = \frac{\rho_0}{2} \frac{V_1}{V_0} e^{j\omega t} \tag{15.66}$$

where, in the second step, we have used v_1 as defined in equation 15.33. Hence there is charge density modulation at the input cavity. Note that when $\tilde{\rho}$ is positive there is a depletion of electrons; when $\tilde{\rho}$ is negative there is an excess of electrons. Therefore the numerical excess of electrons is proportional to $-\tilde{\rho}$.

We now find an expression for the velocity variation by using

$$\tilde{v} = \frac{ds}{dt} \tag{15.67}$$

But s, the displacement of an election from its equilibrium position z, is a function of both z and t, and z is also a function of t since

$$z = v_0(t - t_0) \tag{15.42}$$

Thus we may express the total time derivative as

$$\tilde{v} = \frac{ds(z,t)}{dt} = \frac{\partial s}{\partial z}\frac{dz}{dt} + \frac{\partial s}{\partial t}\frac{dt}{dt} \tag{15.68}$$

Differentiating 15.42

$$\frac{dz}{dt} = v_0 \tag{15.69}$$

and substituting 15.69 into 15.68 we have

$$\tilde{v} = \frac{\partial s}{\partial z} v_0 + \frac{\partial s}{\partial t} \tag{15.70}$$

Differentiating 15.44 and substituting into 15.70 and simplifying we obtain

$$\tilde{v} = \frac{v_1}{2} e^{-j[(\omega-\omega_p)/v_0]z+j\omega t} + \frac{v_1}{2} e^{-j[(\omega+\omega_p)/v_0]z+j\omega t} \tag{15.71}$$

Note that at the input cavity where $z = 0$ and $t = t_0$.

$$\tilde{v}_{z=0} = v_1 e^{j\omega t_0} \tag{15.72}$$

which agrees with our original initial condition, equation 15.37.

Finally, we compute the current density modulation $\tilde{J}$. Current density was defined in Chapter 8 as

$$J = \rho v \tag{8.8}$$

In our case v is the sum of the d-c velocity v_0 and the velocity modulation term $\tilde{v}$. Thus

$$v = v_0 + \tilde{v} \tag{15.73}$$

Similarly the electronic space-charge density ρ can be written as the sum of the d-c space-charge density of the electrons $-\rho_0$ and the space charge modulation term $\tilde{\rho}$. Thus

$$\rho = -\rho_0 + \tilde{\rho} \tag{15.74}$$

Substituting 15.73 and 15.74 into 8.8, we find

$$J = -\rho_0 v_0 - \rho_0 \tilde{v} + v_0 \tilde{\rho} + \tilde{\rho}\tilde{v} \tag{15.75}$$

If we neglect the product of the two a-c terms $\tilde{\rho}\tilde{v}$ in comparison with the product of an a-c and d-c term,[1] we may write

$$J \approx -\rho_0 v_0 - \rho_0 \tilde{v} + v_0 \tilde{\rho} \tag{15.76}$$

We see that J is the sum of a d-c current density $-\rho_0 v_0$ and an a-c current density modulation $\tilde{J}$ where

$$\tilde{J} = -\rho_0 \tilde{v} + v_0 \tilde{\rho} \tag{15.77}$$

The negative sign in the d-c term implies a flow of conventional current in the negative z-direction (a flow of electrons in the positive z-direction). We obtain the current density waves by substituting 15.65 and 15.71 into 15.77. The result of this substitution after simplification is

$$\tilde{J} = -\frac{\rho_0 v_1 \omega}{2\omega_p} e^{-j[(\omega-\omega_p)/v_0]z+j\omega t} + \frac{\rho_0 v_1 \omega}{2\omega_p} e^{-j[(\omega+\omega_p)/v_0]z+j\omega t} \tag{15.78}$$

The current density wave is the algebraic sum of fast and slow current

[1] This is a small-signal approximation. The product term $\tilde{\rho}\tilde{v}$ would represent harmonics if included. Thus 15.76 describes only the current at the fundamental frequency ω and the d-c current.

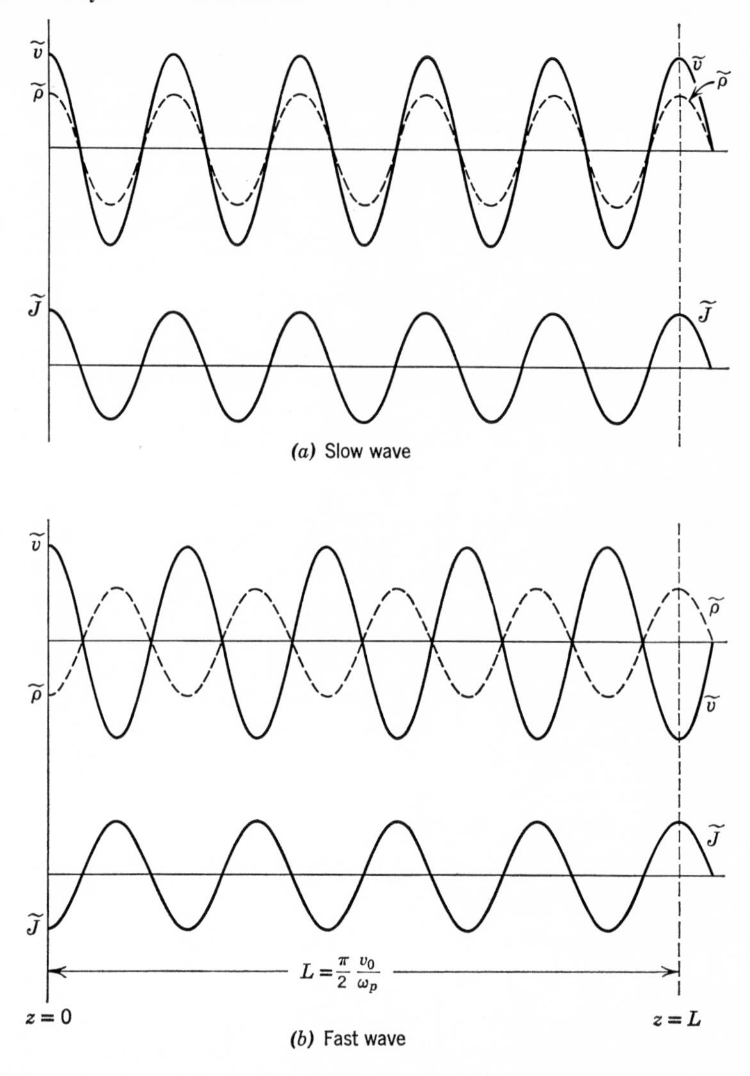

Fig. 15.18. Real parts of a-c space-charge density $\tilde{\rho}$, velocity $\tilde{v}$, and current density $\tilde{J}$ for fast and slow waves. Note that because electrons have negative charges, the electron density variation is 180° out-of-phase with the charge density variation.

density waves which have equal amplitudes. At the input cavity ($z = 0$), these waves are out of phase by 180° and

$$\tilde{J}_{z=0} = 0 \tag{15.79}$$

This zero value of current density modulation at the input cavity is the result of our original initial conditions, equations 15.37 and 15.38. If the electron transit times through the input cavity grids were not negligible, a finite value of $\tilde{J}$ would exist at the input cavity.

In order to understand the physical meaning of the velocity, space-charge density, and current density waves, we plot the real parts of 15.65, 15.71 and 15.78 for one instant of time in Fig. 15.18. The fast and slow waves are plotted separately. We note that at a position $z = L$ where

$$L = \frac{\pi}{2} \frac{v_0}{\omega_p} \tag{15.80}$$

the fast and slow current density waves, which were initially out of phase, have slipped into phase. The fast and slow velocity waves, which were initially in phase, are out of phase at $z = L$. The relative phases of the fast and slow waves change because they travel with different velocities. Note that the velocity waves add destructively at the point where the current density waves reinforce. In a klystron the output cavity should be placed at $z = L$ in order that maximum fundamental a-c current be induced and maximum fundamental a-c power be extracted from the beam.

Considering the fast and slow waves separately, we note from Fig. 15.18 that the a-c current density $\tilde{J}$ and a-c space-charge density $\tilde{\rho}$ are in phase. Thus the total a-c current density $\tilde{J}$ is very nearly proportional to the total a-c space-charge density $\tilde{\rho}$. The a-c current in the beam is primarily due to space-charge density variations (beam bunching) rather than velocity variations.

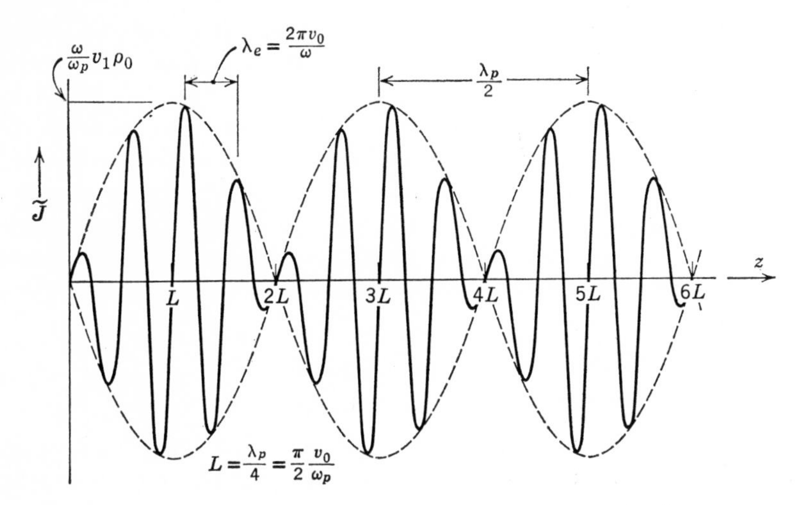

Fig. 15.19. Interference pattern of fast and slow current density waves.

It is instructive to rearrange equations 15.71 and 15.78 to obtain for the total a-c velocity and current density

$$\tilde{v} = v_1 \cos \frac{\omega_p}{v_0} z \, e^{-j(\omega/v_0)z + j\omega t} \tag{15.81}$$

$$\tilde{J} = -j \frac{\omega}{\omega_p} v_1 \rho_0 \sin \frac{\omega_p}{v_0} z \, e^{-j(\omega/v_0)z + j\omega t} \tag{15.82}$$

In Fig. 15.19 we plot the real part of 15.82 for one instant of time. This plot shows the interference pattern of the fast and slow waves. The dotted envelope of this pattern results from the factor $\sin (\omega_p/v_0)z$ in equation 15.82. The wavelength of this factor is called the plasma wavelength λ_p and is given by

$$\lambda_p = \frac{2\pi v_0}{\omega_p} \tag{15.83}$$

The factor $e^{-j(\omega/v_0)z}$ in 15.82 represents the pattern of shorter wavelength λ_e which squeezes through the fixed dotted envelope as time progresses. A graph (not shown) of the total a-c velocity $\tilde{v}$ given by 15.81 would have a cosine function for an envelope, but would otherwise be similar. The velocity would have a null at $z = \lambda_p/4$, where the current has a maximum.

In summary, we have seen that the voltage or velocity modulation at the input cavity of a klystron establishes fast and slow space-charge waves on an electron beam. These waves, moving with different velocities and having different wavelengths, interfere as the beam moves. The fast and slow current-density waves interfere constructively at distances of $\pi v_0/2\omega_p$, $3\pi v_0/2\omega_p$, etc., from the input cavity, and the maximum fundamental current is induced in the output cavity if it is placed at one of these positions. Although we have applied the fast and slow space-charge wave concepts to a klystron, in Chapter 16 we will use these ideas to explain amplification in other types of beam amplifiers. A small-signal approach was used in this development. For larger signal amplitudes the mathematics becomes more cumbersome but the same basic principles apply.

15.11 Cyclotron waves in a magnetically confined electron beam

In section 15.7 we derived the resonant frequency ω_p for longitudinal vibrations in a plasma. When an electron-beam plasma is magnetically

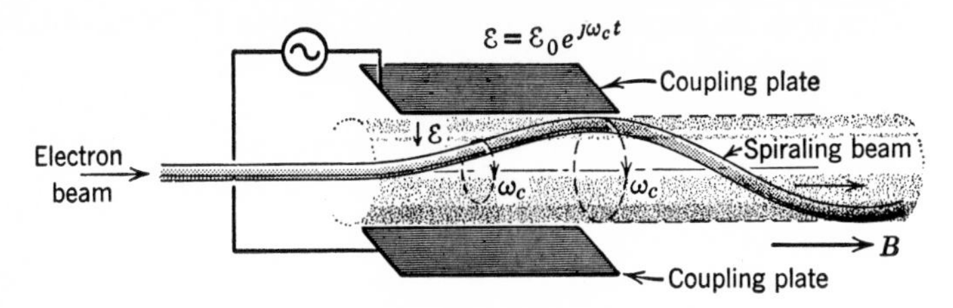

Fig. 15.20. Generation of cyclotron waves.

confined, another basic resonant frequency, the cyclotron frequency, appears.

As we saw in Chapter 5, the cyclotron frequency ω_c is the angular frequency at which free[1] electrons spiral in a magnetic field.

$$\omega_c = \eta B \tag{5.49}$$

In section 15.1 it was shown that in the presence of electric fields, such as those due to space charge, the angular frequency is not necessarily equal to ω_c. Cyclotron waves may be excited by passing a beam through a set of parallel plates as shown in Fig. 15.20. These parallel plates must be a part of a special type of cavity, a Cuccia[2] coupler, at high frequencies. The potential across the plates is varied at a frequency equal to the cyclotron frequency. The oscillating transverse electric field causes the electrons to spiral at the cyclotron frequency. Since the electrons remain in step with the changing field, the radius of the spiral will increase linearly with distance between the plates. Energy taken from the signal generator appears as a rotational kinetic energy of the electrons.

Cyclotron waves can be removed from a beam by a similar technique as shown in Fig. 15.21. The cyclotron spiral motion induces a current in the load resistance. As power is transferred from the cyclotron waves to the load resistance, the radius of the spiral decreases.

If the cyclotron wave is excited at a frequency ω somewhat different from the cyclotron frequency, a set of fast and slow cyclotron waves is generated in a fashion similar to the generation of the fast and slow space-charge waves previously discussed. The phase velocities of

[1] This is equivalent to assuming $\omega_c \gg \omega_p$.

[2] C. L. Cuccia, "The Electron Coupler—A Developmental Tube for Amplitude Modulation and Power Control at Ultrahigh Frequencies," *RCA Rev.*, **10,** 270 (1949).

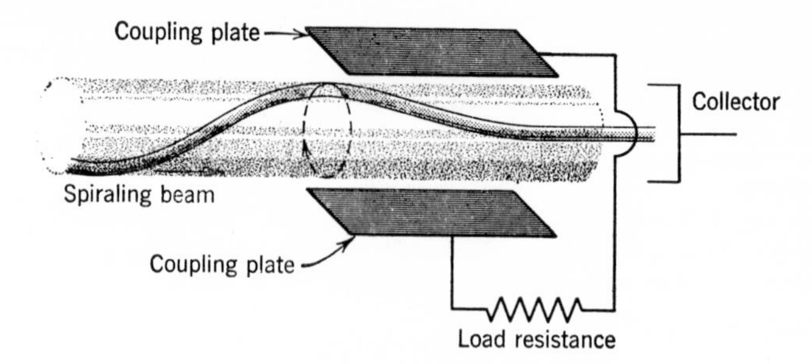

Fig. 15.21. Extraction of energy from a cyclotron wave.

these fast and slow cyclotron waves are given by

$$v_{\substack{f\\s}} = \frac{v_0}{1 \mp \dfrac{\omega_c}{\omega}} \tag{15.84}$$

which is similar to the expressions found in the case of space-charge waves. Note that when $\omega = \omega_c$, $v_f = \infty$. Interactions involving these waves will be described in Chapter 16.

Suggested References

J. R. Pierce, *Theory and Design of Electron Beams*, D. Van Nostrand Co., 1954. Pierce's "Beams" is the standard reference for the material of our section 15.1. His Chapter 9 and particularly section 9.3 to the end of the chapter develop more fully the concepts briefly discussed here at approximately the same level.

W. W. Harman, *Fundamentals of Electron Motion*, McGraw-Hill Book Company, Inc., 1953. Harman has a basic approach to the klystron using space-charge waves in his Chapter 7. After assuming the existence of space-charge waves, he carries his analysis beyond ours and considers large signals.

W. J. Kleen, *Electronics of Microwave Tubes*, Academic Press, 1958. Kleen has an excellent, but somewhat more advanced approach to the klystron in his Chapter 5.

W. H. Louisell, *Coupled Mode and Parametric Electronics*, John Wiley and Sons, 1960. This is an advanced text that will be hard to understand unless the notation of the first chapter is completely mastered. The concepts of fast and slow waves in space-charge and cyclotron modes are described very fully in Chapter 2. His pictures of cyclotron modes are very instructive.

S. Ramo, "Space-Charge and Field Waves in an Electron Beam," *Phys. Rev.*, **56**, 276 (1939) and

W. C. Hahn, "Small Signal Theory of Velocity-Modulated Electron Beams," *General Electric Review*, **42**, 258 (1939). The basic work on space-charge waves was first carried out in 1939 independently by Hahn and Ramo. Their work is recorded in the preceding publications. These papers start from Maxwell's equations and derive the space-charge klystron analysis, which is more basic and more accurate than our one-dimensional mechanistic model. The reduction of plasma frequency for finite beams is developed in their analyses.

L. Tonks and I. Langmuir, "Oscillations in Ionized Gases," *Phys. Rev.*, **33,** 195 (1929). This is the first publication of electron oscillations in plasmas. Our derivation of the plasma frequency follows Tonks and Langmuir.

PROBLEMS

15.1. A single electron passes through the hole in the pole piece of the magnet shown in Fig. 15.1. Before entering the hole, it traveled parallel to the axis of the magnetic circuit at a distance a from the axis. Show that provided there is a finite uniform longitudinal magnetic flux density (and provided the magnet is long enough), the path of the electron crosses the axis of the magnet. Note that the result is independent of velocity, magnetic field intensity, and a.

15.2. (*a*) Calculate the radial force on the outermost electron of a beam of electrons with current 1 amp and diameter 5 mm that has been accelerated to a potential of 100 volts.

(*b*) What is the force if the potential is 1000 volts?

15.3. The Brillouin value B_0 calculated from equation 15.12 is the correct value for a given beam radius a, and beam parameters i and V. Suppose B is equal to twice B_0. Describe the resulting motion and character of the beam.

15.4. According to the approximation of equation 15.17, the average velocity v_0 after modulation is the same as that before. Show that if higher order terms are included in the expansion of equation 15.16, the average velocity after modulation is less than it was before.

15.5. It is proposed to construct a klystron amplifier which will amplify a 1-volt 1000 cps signal. The input voltage is applied between two grids and a 100-volt beam passes through the grids. The load is connected between a second pair of grids which are located further along the tube. Explain why such a tube would be impractical. *Hint:* Draw an Applegate diagram.

15.6. Show that the distance-time diagram for an electron in the resonator-reflector space of a planar reflex klystron is parabolic, and show how bunching occurs.

15.7. Show that the beam current in a klystron (without space-charge) at time t and distance x from the buncher cavity is

$$i = \frac{I_0}{1 - \left(\dfrac{\omega x V_1}{2v_0} V_0\right)} \sin \omega \left(t - \frac{x}{v_0}\right)$$

where $I_0 = dq/dt_0$, the initial beam current at the buncher at time t_0, when the buncher voltage was $V_1 \cos \omega t_0$. Using equation 15.17, find the time t when an electron leaving the buncher at t_0 reaches the catcher x cm away, then use $i = dq/dt = (dq/dt_0)(dt_0/dt)$ for small signals.

15.8. Show that 15.32 can be rewritten for a beam of current density J and voltage V_0 as

$$\omega_p = 1.83 \times 10^8 \frac{J^{1/2}}{V_0^{1/4}}$$

where J and V_0 are in MKS units.

15.9. Compute the electron plasma frequency for an electron beam of 60 ma, cross section 0.1 cm^2, and operated at a beam voltage of 600 volts.

15.10. (*a*) If the beam of Problem 15.9 is used in a klystron, compute the separation of the input and output cavities for maximum power to the second cavity.

(*b*) Compute the average amount of charge present between the two cavities.

15.11. The a-c velocity modulation along a beam can be written as

$$v - v_0 = v_1 \cos 62.8z\, e^{j6.28\cdot 10^9 t - j6.28\cdot 10^2 z}$$

(*a*) What is the excitation frequency in the laboratory system?
(*b*) What is the drift velocity of the beam?
(*c*) What is the plasma frequency?
(*d*) What is the phase velocity of the fast wave?
(*e*) What is the phase velocity of the slow wave?

15.12. Write the equation of continuity in terms of the a-c parts of current density $\tilde{J}$ and a-c space-charge density $\tilde{\rho}$. Then show that 15.65 and 15.78 satisfy the continuity equation (equation 8.9).

15.13. (*a*) In a particular electron beam only the slow wave is present. A cavity is moved along the beam and the measuring device records the time-average a-c convection current squared $|\tilde{\imath}|^2/2 = \tilde{\imath}\tilde{\imath}^*/2$. What type of $|\tilde{\imath}|^2/2$ versus distance curve would be obtained. *Hint:* Consider equation 15.78.

(*b*) Suppose that only the slow wave and its first higher order mode due to a finite beam size are present. Show that in the resulting interference pattern of amplitude $|\tilde{\imath}|^2/2$ the distance λ_H between peaks is given by

$$\lambda_H = \frac{\lambda_p}{1 - \dfrac{\omega_{q1}}{\omega_p}}$$

where ω_{q1} is the plasma frequency for the first higher order mode and ω_p is the fundamental plasma frequency.

(*c*) In a particular case λ_H was measured to be $6\lambda_p$. Compare the value of ω_{q1} with that of ω_p.

15.14. Show that equation 11.3 for the Debye length λ_D may be expressed as

$$\lambda_D = v_T/\omega_p$$

where v_T is the mean thermal velocity. Using this result and the statements following equation 15.29, show that $v_1 > v_T$ for collective oscillations in the plasma. v_1 is defined in equation 15.36.

16. modern amplifiers

In this chapter we first consider amplification from an energy viewpoint. The traveling-wave tube and traveling-wave magnetron are introduced as examples of a continuous interaction between an electron beam and electromagnetic waves guided by an external circuit. A classification of microwave vacuum-tube amplifiers is described in terms of the energy conversion mechanism involved and the d-c electric and magnetic fields associated with the device. The general concepts of kinetic power flow and coupling of wave modes are introduced and utilized to describe the amplification process in some beam-type amplifiers. A discussion of noise is given, followed by descriptions of parametric amplifiers and masers.

16.1 Types of amplification and energy conversion

Amplification is the process by which the energy of an a-c or d-c signal is changed in magnitude. Since energy is conserved in an isolated physical system, amplification may be viewed as a conversion of energy from one form to another and always requires an auxiliary source of energy and a mechanism by which energy is added to a signal in a coherent manner. Let us first consider the source of the energy added to the signal in different types of amplifiers.

Triode, tetrode, and pentode amplifiers convert the d-c energy of a battery to a-c signal power by varying the number of electrons in a beam. In a magnetron the internal source of energy for the amplification of an electromagnetic wave is the change in the d-c potential energy possessed by an electron in an electric field. Klystrons convert the d-c kinetic energy of an electron beam to a-c signal power. In the traveling-wave tube (described in the following section) the internal energy source is again the beam kinetic energy, but the electromagnetic wave to be amplified grows continuously as in a magnetron. In parametric amplifiers and masers (to be described later) the internal source of energy for the device is not a battery, but instead is a separate unmodulated a-c power supply. It is important to keep the energy sources of these devices in mind in order to obtain an understanding of the basic phenomena underlying their operation.

16.2 Traveling-wave tube

The traveling-wave tube (TWT) is a high frequency device which has high gain over a large bandwidth. It makes use of the interaction between a confined electron beam and an electromagnetic field or wave which is traveling slightly slower than the beam. In order that this interaction may occur the electromagnetic-wave velocity must be reduced below its free space value by the use of a slow-wave structure.

The essential elements of a TWT are shown in Fig. 16.1. Here the slow-wave structure is a high conductivity wire wound in the shape of a helix. High frequency electromagnetic waves propagate along the helix with a velocity in the axial direction which is very nearly that which would be obtained if a wavefront traveled in a helical path along the wire with the velocity of light. The axial phase velocity v_p of the wave is therefore approximately the velocity of light c times the ratio of the pitch to the circumference of the helix.

$$v_p \approx c\,\frac{d}{2\pi r} \tag{16.1}$$

The symbols in equation 16.1 are defined in Fig. 16.2. The axial

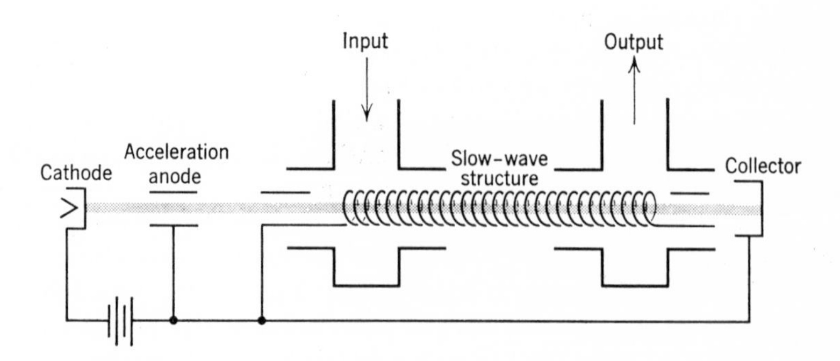

Fig. 16.1. Electrode arrangement in a traveling-wave tube.

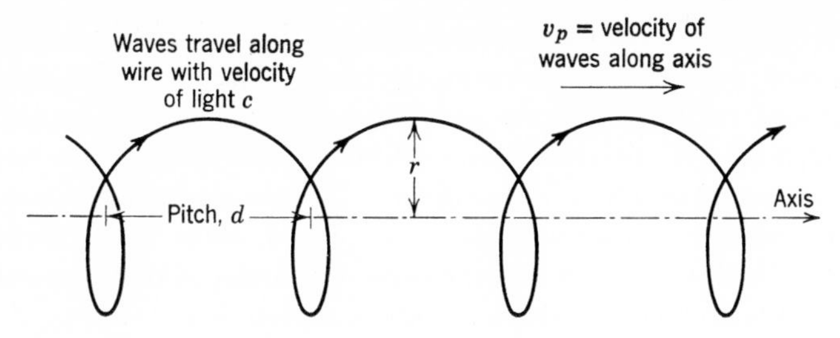

Fig. 16.2. Axial and circumferential velocities along a helix.

phase velocity is relatively constant over a wide range of frequencies' and this characteristic enables traveling-wave tubes using a helix to handle bandwidths that are significantly greater than those handled by any of the tubes discussed in the previous chapters. There are other structures along which electromagnetic waves propagate more slowly than in free space, but the helix provides the least change in phase velocity with frequency and is the structure most frequently used in traveling-wave tubes.

The amplifying action of the traveling-wave tube takes place by a continuous interaction between the axial component of the electric-field wave traveling down the center of the helix and the electron beam also moving along the axis of the helix. The electrons are continually slowed down and their energy is transferred to the wave along the helix. To illustrate how this may come about, we show in Fig. 16.3 the electric field lines associated with an electromagnetic wave propagating along a helix at a particular instant of time. The lines shown are

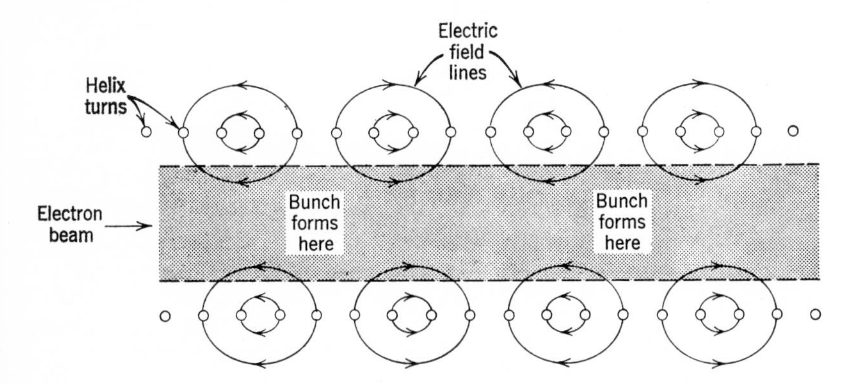

Fig. 16.3. Electric field lines associated with an electromagnetic wave on a helix.

those which lie in a plane containing the axis of the helix. From the figure it is seen that a beam of electrons traveling inside the helix experiences an axial component of the electric field. The electrons initially tend to bunch in regions where the field ahead is decelerating and the field behind is accelerating. *If* the bunches of electrons traveled with the same velocity as the wave, they would experience what is effectively a zero or very weak d-c field. Actually in a TWT the bunches of electrons move slightly faster than the wave on the helix and gain on the wave, thus moving into the decelerating region (see Fig. 16.4). The wave does negative work on these electrons in decelerating them and therefore the wave gains energy at the expense of the kinetic energy of the electrons. If the bunches were to move slower than the wave on the helix, the beam would gain kinetic energy from the wave. This latter case is similar to what occurs in a linear accelerator.

The interaction between a bunched electron beam and a helix may also be viewed in terms of induced currents. In Fig. 16.5 the bunches shown are centered on the helix axis and travel parallel to the axis. The bunches induce positive charges on the helix, and since the bunches are moving, a current flows in the helix in such a way that the induced charge keeps up with the bunches. If the phase is proper this current adds to the current associated with the electromagnetic wave already flowing in the helix and increases the intensity of this electromagnetic

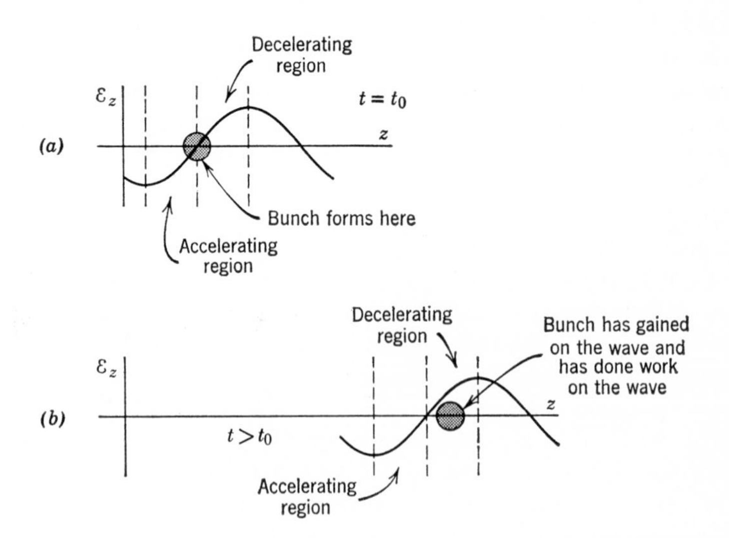

Fig. 16.4. How the bunches of electrons do work on the electromagnetic wave.

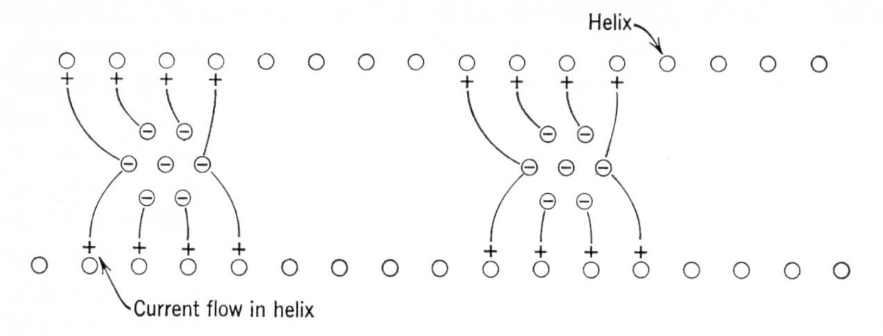

Fig. 16.5. The interaction between a bunched electron beam and induced charges in a helix.

wave. The interaction is a continuous one. The increasing wave amplitude on the helix causes the electrons to become increasingly bunched, and the growing bunches of electrons cause a continuous growth of the wave on the helix. By this mechanism the amplitude of the electromagnetic wave may be increased by a large amount.

As the wave on the helix grows in amplitude the electromagnetic energy increases at the expense of the electrons' kinetic energy, and the electrons slow down. Eventually, after a sufficient distance, the electrons slow down enough to move out of the decelerating phase and a useful interaction no longer takes place. The electron velocities over which useful gain appears are in a small range in the neighborhood of the velocity of wave propagation on the helix. The gain of a traveling-wave tube is limited by the amount of velocity that the beam can lose as the electrons are slowed down through the interacting range of velocities. At high power levels the bunches may become sufficiently dense that electrostatic "debunching" becomes important and limits the power output of the TWT.

A given TWT helix has a high frequency limit above which significant interaction will not occur. This high frequency limit increases as the helix diameter is made smaller. At low frequencies the gain is limited by the length of the helix. Hence, size limitations put upper and lower limits on the frequencies at which a traveling-wave tube employing a helix will operate. Structures other than helices must be used for frequencies greater than 50,000 Mc, and TWT's become too large to be practical for frequencies below 500 Mc.

The traveling-wave tube is an example of a device in which a continuous interaction between a beam and a circuit results in a growing wave. The basic process in a traveling-wave tube involves electrons going slightly faster than electromagnetic waves on a circuit. In section 9.3, we pointed out that charged particles moving faster than the speed of light in a medium lose energy to a type of electromagnetic radiation known as Cerenkov radiation. Thus Cerenkov radiation and the TWT interaction appear to be equivalent.[1] If a high velocity electron beam is directed into a dielectric where the velocity of light is less than the electron velocity, the beam will emit electromagnetic energy via Cerenkov radiation. However, the Cerenkov radiation emitted by an unmodulated electron beam is incoherent radiation, or a form of noise (shot noise, see section 16.8) which is generally not very useful. To achieve useful electromagnetic power it is necessary to modulate and bunch the beam before it is accelerated, so that many electrons may radiate coherently.

16.3 Classification of vacuum tubes

Vacuum tubes fall into two general categories: space-charge-controlled tubes such as the triode, tetrode, and pentode and transit-time tubes such as the klystron, magnetron, and traveling-wave tube. Transit-time tubes may be subclassified as drift-space and growing-wave tubes. We now examine the physical basis for these classifications.

The klystron utilizes a drift region to convert velocity modulation to current modulation. The bunching takes place in this drift region in which there are no external r-f fields interacting with the beam. Any d-c magnetic field present is for beam focusing and is parallel to the beam. The klystron is an example of a drift-space tube.

The traveling-wave tube is an example of a so-called growing-wave tube. In most growing-wave tubes the wave grows exponentially with distance. The d-c magnetic field present in a TWT, as in the klystron, is parallel to the beam for beam-focusing. Such devices as the TWT and the klystron are subclassified as ordinary or "O-type" tubes. This type does not have any d-c fields in a direction transverse to the beam direction.

The magnetron is also a growing-wave device, but is subclassified as a magnetron-type or "M-type" because of the transverse static electric and magnetic fields. An "M-type" tube is also known as a "crossed-field" tube. There are also growing-wave tubes which have only transverse d-c electric fields; these are called transverse E field tubes or "E-type" tubes.

[1] J. R. Pierce, "Interaction of Moving Charges with Wave Circuits," *Jour. App. Phys,* **26** 627 (1955).

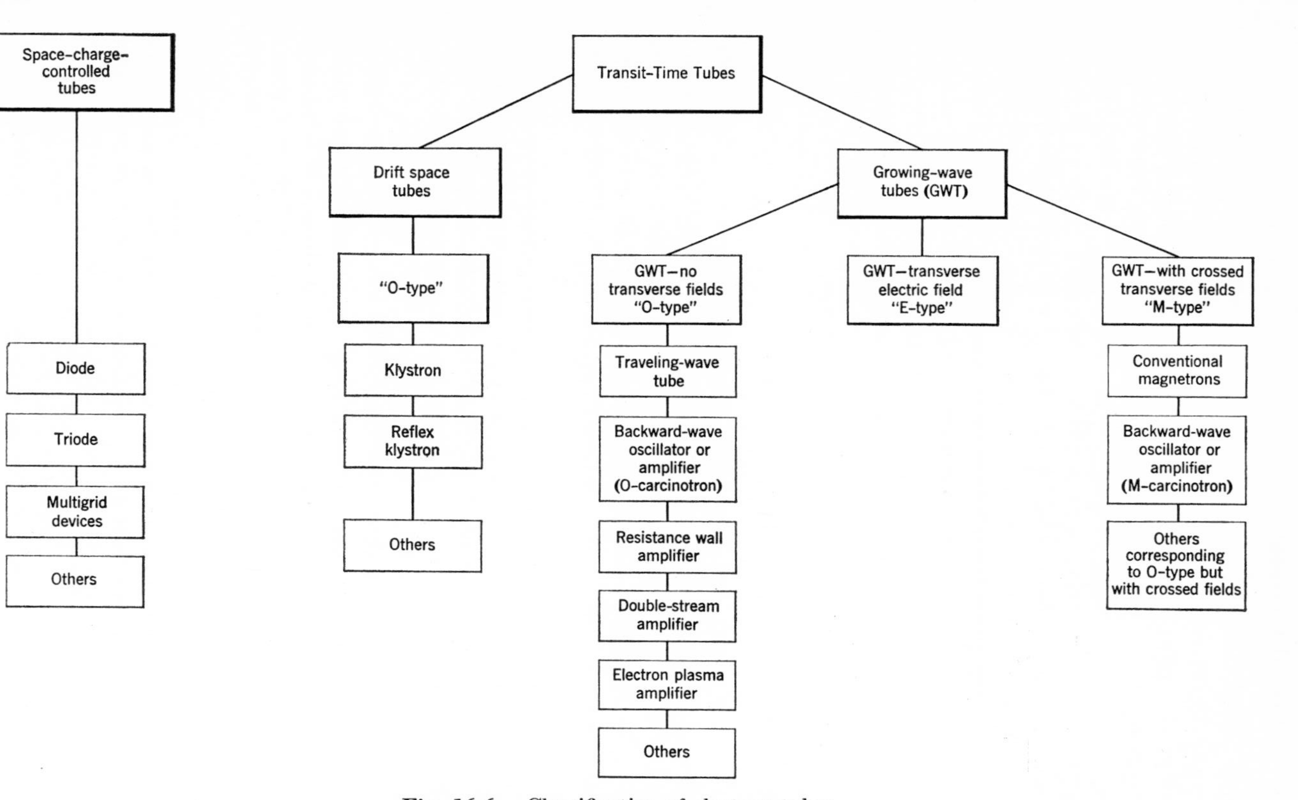

Fig. 16.6. Classification of electron tubes.

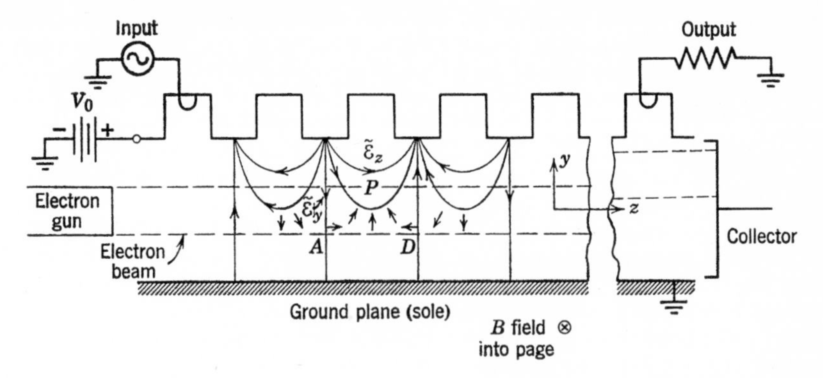

Fig. 16.7. Traveling-wave magnetron schematic representation. Solid lines with arrows show r-f electric field lines at one instant of time. Short arrows represent additional resultant forces on electrons due to r-f electric and d-c magnetic fields.

In space-charge-controlled tubes such as the triode the amplification takes place through direct space-charge-density or current modulation, and negligible cathode-plate transit time is desired. High frequency tubes such as the klystron, magnetron, and TWT require long transit times for their operation. The chart in Fig. 16.6 illustrates a possible classification of vacuum tubes according to the basic features which delineate their operation. Most beam-type devices, some yet to be invented, fall under this classification.[1]

16.4 Traveling-wave magnetron

In section 16.2 we discussed the traveling-wave tube, an O-type device. Here we point out the pertinent features of the "M" analog of a traveling-wave tube, the so-called traveling-wave magnetron.

This device and its r-f field distribution at one instant of time are sketched in Fig. 16.7. We note the same type of serated slow-wave anode structure as in the ordinary magnetron of Fig. 5.15. Here the ground plane is nonemitting and the electrons are injected by an electron gun. The reader may immediately note the similarity to a traveling-wave tube, if the electron beam travels at the drift velocity $\mathcal{E}/B$ determined by the crossed fields and the electromagnetic wave travels from left to right at approximately the same velocity.

It is instructive to study the axial bunching that takes place in crossed-field devices. In Fig. 16.7 we consider the additional forces on electrons due to the application of an r-f field; the d-c forces are balanced for electrons with the drift velocity. Electrons near point A experience an additional upward electric force due to $\tilde{\mathcal{E}}_y$, and the resulting upward velocity brings about a resultant

[1] W. J. Kleen, *op. cit.*, pp. 155, 157, 160.

magnetic force in the $+z$-direction, bunching the electrons toward the region P. Similarly, electrons near point D will be bunched in a backward direction to region P. As the electrons travel with the same velocity as the wave on the structure, they see nearly the same fields. Bunches are built up at regions such as P, where the axial r-f retarding field component $\tilde{\mathcal{E}}_z$ attempts to slow down the electrons in the z-direction, and brings about a resultant force upward. As the electrons are forced upward, they lose potential energy to the $\tilde{\mathcal{E}}_z$ component of the r-f field.

In O-type devices bunching is produced by an axial r-f electric field $\tilde{\mathcal{E}}_z$, and axial space-charge debunching forces take over when the electrons bunch, lose kinetic energy, and finally go out of synchronism with the wave. In crossed-field devices axial bunching is produced by the r-f transverse electric field $\tilde{\mathcal{E}}_y$ which does not go out of synchronism, and the debunching forces are less effective at high power levels. As a result, M-type devices can handle large signal powers.

Figure 16.8 illustrates how an electron may lose potential energy to the wave. The kinetic energy of the electrons is not appreciably changed. (v is determined by $\mathcal{E}/B$.) The energy source in M-type devices is potential energy whereas the energy source for O-type devices such as the traveling-wave tube is kinetic energy. The electronic efficiency or ratio of output r-f power to input d-c power can approach 90% or more in a crossed-field device because an electron with very little kinetic energy can convert a large amount of potential energy into r-f energy while drifting from sole to anode. On the other hand, the efficiency of an O-type traveling wave device must be small, since only the amount of energy corresponding to the small difference between the velocity of the electrons and the wave velocity can be converted to electromagnetic field energy.

Because of the possibilities of high efficiency and also high power output, crossed-field devices are of great importance. Almost all of the O-type devices indicated in Fig. 16.6 have M-type analogues.

16.5 Power flow in space-charge waves

In this section and the next we develop a general viewpoint that will serve to describe the operation of many high frequency amplifiers. We

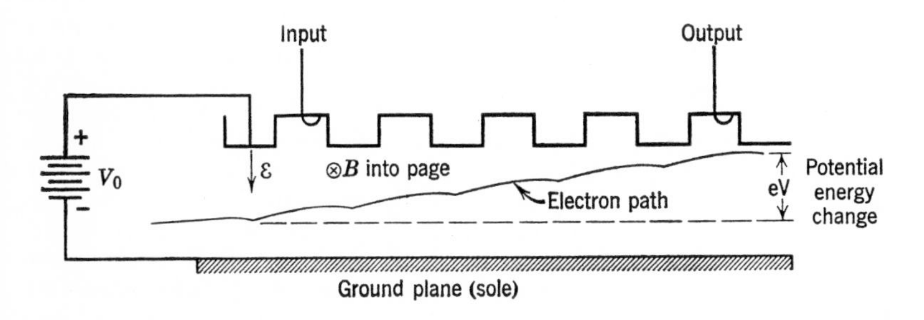

Fig. 16.8. An electron trajectory in a traveling-wave magnetron showing the loss of potential energy.

do this by considering the power flow in waves on a beam and the transfer or coupling of the power between wave modes. Power flow in an electron beam may be defined as the rate of flow of the kinetic energy of electrons across any plane perpendicular to the beam. The kinetic energy dK which crosses an area A in the time interval dt is given by

$$dK = \frac{K}{V} A v_0 \, dt \tag{16.2}$$

where K/V is the total kinetic energy of the electrons per unit volume and $A v_0 \, dt$ is the volume containing those electrons which will cross the area A in the interval dt if they all have a velocity equal to v_0. The power flow is defined by

$$P \equiv \frac{dK}{dt} = \frac{K}{V} A v_0 \tag{16.3}$$

The kinetic energy per unit volume is equal to the number of electrons per unit volume $\rho/-e$ times the kinetic energy $mv^2/2$ of each electron; thus

$$\frac{K}{V} = \frac{1}{2} \frac{\rho}{(-e)} mv^2 = \frac{1}{2} \frac{-\rho}{\eta} v^2 = \frac{1}{2} \frac{(-J)v}{\eta} \tag{16.4}$$

and

$$P = \frac{v_0 A(-J)v}{2\eta} = \frac{v_0(-i)v}{2\eta} \tag{16.5}$$

We are interested in the time average of the power flow $\bar{P}$ in a beam for three situations: (1) for no modulation, $\bar{P}_0$, (2) when modulation due to the fast space-charge wave only is present, $\bar{P}_f$, and (3) when modulation due to the slow space-charge wave only is present, $\bar{P}_s$. The time variations of $(-J)$, v, and $v_0 A(-J)v/2\eta$ are shown in Fig. 16.9. For the case of no modulation, $(-J) = J_0 =$ positive constant and $v = v_0 =$ constant. For the fast space-charge wave, J is equal to the sum of current density in the absence of modulation $(-J_0)$ and the first term of equation 15.78, which for a given fixed z may be written in the form $-J_m e^{j\omega t}$. J_m may be considered a positive constant. Thus

$$-J = J_0 + J_m e^{j\omega t} \tag{16.6}$$

The velocity in the fast-wave case is the sum of v_0 and the first term in 15.71, which for a given fixed z may be written in the form $v_m e^{j\omega t}$, where v_m may be considered a positive constant. Thus

$$v = v_0 + v_m e^{j\omega t} \tag{16.7}$$

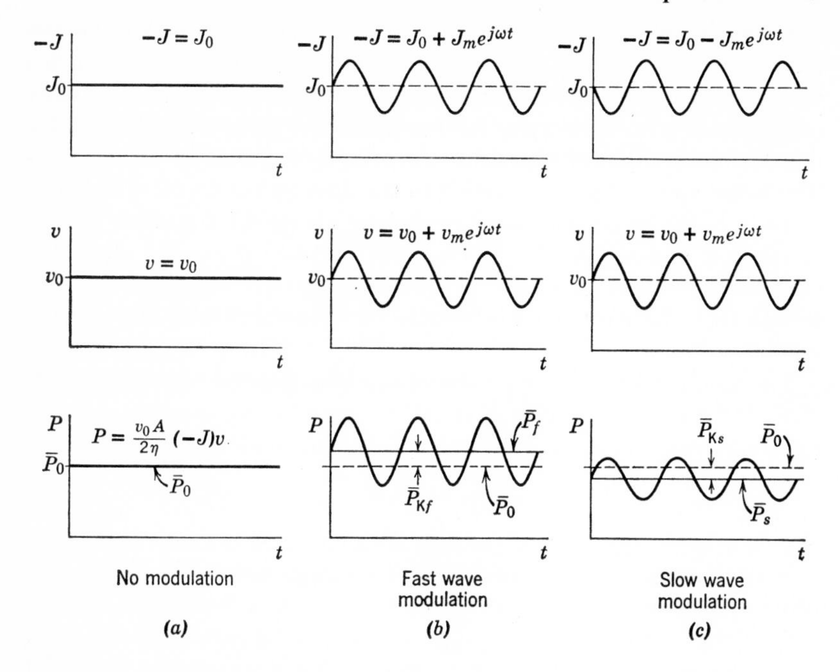

Fig. 16.9. Graphs illustrating the calculation of power flow in an electron beam.

Notice from Fig. 16.9*b* that the sinusoidal variations for the fast wave of $-J$ and v are in phase at all times. A similar argument for slow-wave modulation leads to Fig. 16.9*c* in which the sinusoidal variations of $-J$ and v are out of phase. The average powers $\bar{P}_0$, $\bar{P}_f$, and $\bar{P}_s$ are shown by the solid horizontal lines on the graphs of P versus t. The important result indicated on the figure is that

$$\bar{P}_f > \bar{P}_0 > \bar{P}_s \tag{16.8}$$

In the manner of section 7.3 we may define an a-c power or kinetic power flow as the power flow with modulation minus the power flow without modulation. Thus using Fig. 16.9, the kinetic power flow $\bar{P}_{Kf}$ for fast-wave modulation may be written

$$\bar{P}_{Kf} = \bar{P}_f - \bar{P}_0 > 0 \tag{16.9}$$

and the kinetic power flow $\bar{P}_{Ks}$ for slow waves

$$\bar{P}_{Ks} = \bar{P}_s - \bar{P}_0 < 0 \tag{16.10}$$

The positive kinetic power flow associated with the fast-wave modulation means that there is more kinetic energy in the beam with fast-wave modulation than without. The negative kinetic power flow associated with the slow-wave modulation means that there is less kinetic energy in the beam with slow-wave modulation than without. Note that a negative kinetic power flow does not mean a flow of power in the negative z-direction. Power is carried in the direction of travel of the electrons in both cases. From a mechanistic viewpoint a positive kinetic power flow means that the electrons are bunched in regions where the electron velocity is greatest. Similarly, a negative kinetic power flow means that the electrons are bunched in regions where the electron velocity is least.

The kinetic power flow $\bar{P}_K$ associated with a general current modulation $\tilde{\imath}$ and a general velocity modulation $\tilde{v}$ may be calculated by extending 16.5 and making a small signal approximation. The result is

$$\bar{P}_K = \frac{v_0 \overline{\tilde{\imath}\tilde{v}}}{\eta} \tag{16.11}$$

We will examine the amplification or energy conversion process in terms of the a-c kinetic energy or a-c kinetic power flow of the fast and slow waves. Since the kinetic power flow associated with the slow space-charge wave is negative, it means that it is possible to *remove* energy from an electron beam by *increasing* the amplitude of the slow wave. Similarly, an increase in the amplitude of the fast wave requires an addition of energy to the beam. These concepts, together with an elementary theory of coupling of oscillations, can be used to explain the operation of most microwave tubes.

Let us reconsider the klystron in terms of power flow in space-charge waves. We illustrate the klystron again in Fig. 16.10*a*. The input signal voltage sets up on the electron beam both the slow and the fast space-charge waves in equal magnitudes. The kinetic power flow associated with the fast space-charge wave is equal and opposite to the kinetic power flow associated with the slow space-charge wave. Thus the net kinetic power flow in the beam is zero, and the input resonator under these simplified conditions neither adds nor subtracts power from the beam. As the beam travels in the drift space, the net kinetic power remains zero.

When the beam reaches the output cavity, it induces a voltage across the cavity. This voltage in turn acts on the electron beam to set up new components of the slow and fast waves. The voltage phase is such that the new component of the fast space-charge wave subtracts from the existing component of the fast wave, whereas the new component of the slow wave adds to the existing component of

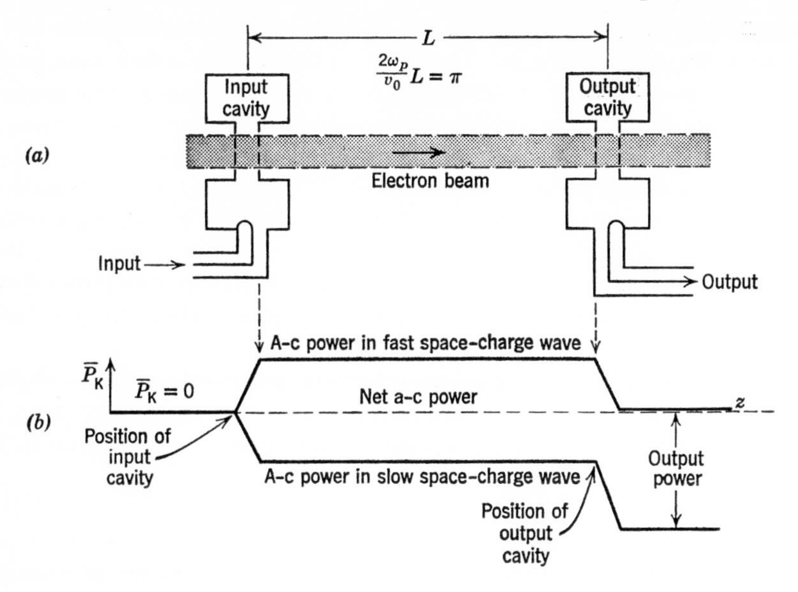

Fig. 16.10. Power flow in a klystron as a function of distance.

the slow wave. Therefore, just to the left of the output resonator the net kinetic power flow is zero, and just to the right of it the net kinetic power flow is negative. Since the beam now has a net negative kinetic power, the total kinetic energy of the beam must be less than that to the left of the resonator as shown in Fig. 16.10*b*. The difference in power appears in the output resonator, and amplification has been achieved.

16.6 The coupling of wave modes

Earlier we presented a physical picture of the interaction between a bunched beam of electrons and an electromagnetic wave on a helix. In this section we take a more general look at the coupling between wave modes and use this concept to describe some other types of growing-wave tubes.

An exchange of energy between modes is a general property of coupled vibrating systems. Perhaps the easiest system to visualize is the pair of coupled pendulums shown in Fig. 16.11. If one of the pendulums is displaced from equilibrium and released, it begins swinging back and forth. The slight resulting motion of the middle (coupling) string produces a periodic force on the other pendulum and it

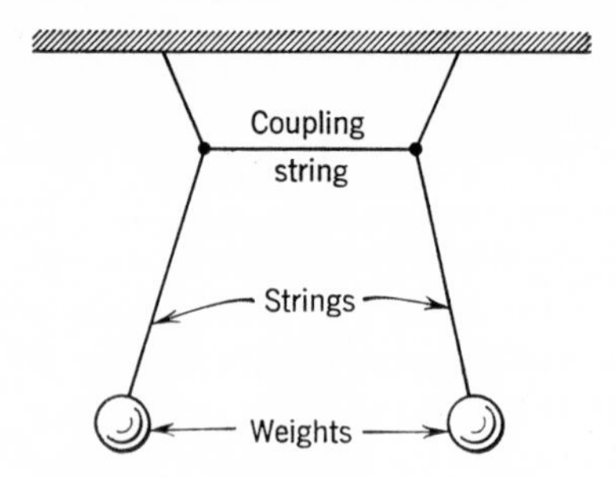

Fig. 16.11. A pair of coupled pendulums.

begins swinging. The amplitude of vibration of the second pendulum slowly increases, its energy coming from the energy of the first pendulum whose amplitude slowly decreases. Eventually the first pendulum will be observed to stop, or nearly stop, while at the same time the second pendulum vibrates with a maximum amplitude. At this point the energy is entirely associated with the second pendulum. As time goes on the energy is transferred back to the first pendulum, after which the entire process repeats. The over-all picture is a slow transfer of energy back and forth between pendulums (or modes) superimposed on the much more rapid vibrations of the pendulums themselves.

Although we are concerned only with couplings between motions in which energy is transferred, we should point out that there are possible motions (called normal modes) in which there is no energy transfer between parts of a system. For the coupled pendulums there are two normal modes: in one, the pendulums vibrate exactly in phase and in the other they vibrate exactly out of phase. In order for an energy transfer to occur there must be a phase difference which is not zero or 180°.

Coupling and energy transfer among space-charge waves, cyclotron waves, and electromagnetic circuit waves differ from the coupling between pendulums in two very important respects. The first is that the coupling associated with wave modes is distributed continuously over a region of space, whereas in the coupled pendulums the coupling is localized in the middle string. The second difference is that in wave systems there may be an additional source of energy which vibrating modes can draw upon to increase their amplitudes. This source of energy can be, for instance, the d-c kinetic energy of the beam.

The principal requirement for "distributed" coupling is that the waves involved must move at nearly the same speeds and have different phases in order to achieve significant coupling. This is suggested by the mechanical model of Fig. 16.12 in which Coulomb coupling exists between identical sets of charged mechanical oscillators. In part (*a*) the upper set of springs and charged masses is moving to the right with a uniform velocity, and in addition each spring and mass is vibrating up and down in a pattern as shown. Each lower mass will experience a periodic force which, in general, has a different frequency than its natural resonant frequency of vibration, and little energy is given to the lower sets of oscillators. In this case the effective coupling is weak. In part (*b*) the two sets of charged oscillators are moving with the same velocity and each of the lower masses feels a *periodic force* due to a continuous out-of-phase interaction with a single upper mass. In this case the effective coupling is strong, and energy is transferred back and forth from one set of oscillators to the other.

The important point is that coupling can take place between different wave systems if the phase velocities of the systems are nearly equal and if, as was suggested in the mechanical analog, the phase difference between the interacting modes is different from zero or 180°. Coupling cannot violate conservation of energy, so that the net power flow of any two isolated wave modes must be constant. For example, a wave with negative kinetic power flow can increase in amplitude and give energy to a wave with positive kinetic power flow only if the amplitude of the latter also increases. It is found that the transfer of energy between two interacting wave modes always takes place in such a direction that the total modulation in the system increases. An increase in modulation corresponds to an increase in "disorder" or in entropy.

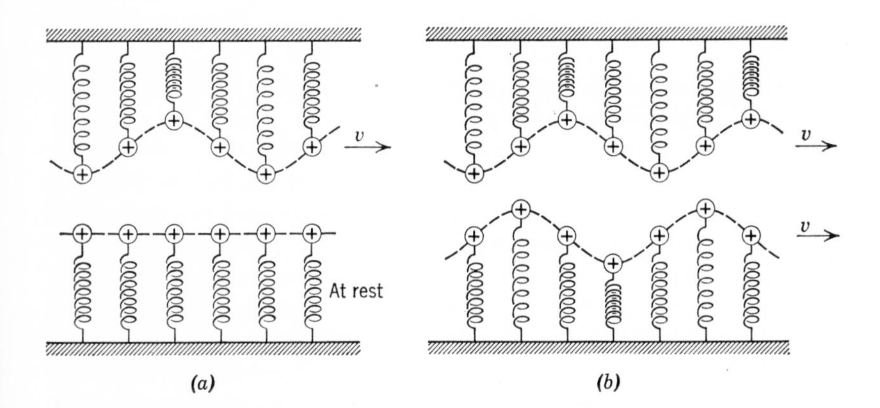

Fig. 16.12. Identical sets of springs and masses coupled by Coulomb forces.

16.7 Growing-wave amplifiers

This section is devoted to a description of several growing-wave tubes in terms of the flow and exchange of energy between modes. Let us first reexamine the traveling-wave tube in the light of these ideas. Figure 16.13 portrays the helix and beam of the TWT and a graph of the kinetic power flow along the system. The TWT interaction represents mainly a coupling between a circuit wave in the $+z$-direction (a forward circuit wave) along the axis of this helix and the slow space-charge wave of the electron beam. In the forward circuit wave the kinetic power flow is positive, and in the slow space-charge wave the kinetic power flow is negative. The net effect of the coupling of these two waves is that the amplitude of both increases exponentially with distance. (We neglect any coupling with the fast wave.) As the disturbances grow exponentially along the device the circuit power or electromagnetic wave power in the helix becomes more positive, and the beam kinetic power becomes more negative. The increasing negative kinetic power flow of the beam means that kinetic energy is being removed from the beam. Although the total a-c power remains constant, amplification of the circuit wave has occurred.

We next utilize the kinetic power flow concept to describe some additional microwave beam devices. Figure 16.14 indicates schematically the basic interactions and graphs the power flow for three such devices.

The resistive-wall amplifier sketched in Fig. 16.14*a* is not a practical device, but is one which illustrates particularly well the energy flow

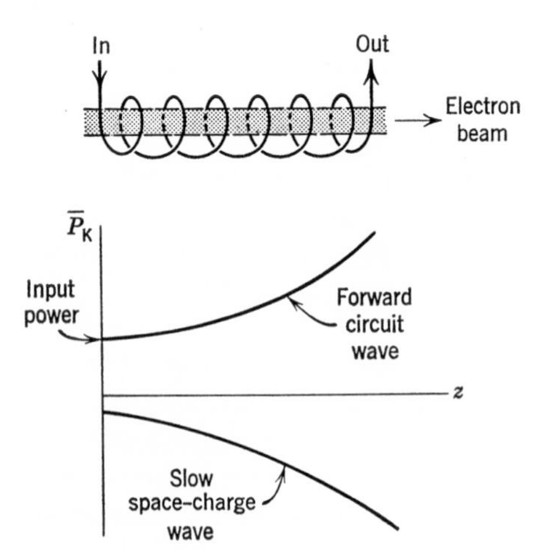

Fig. 16.13. Kinetic power flow in a traveling-wave tube.

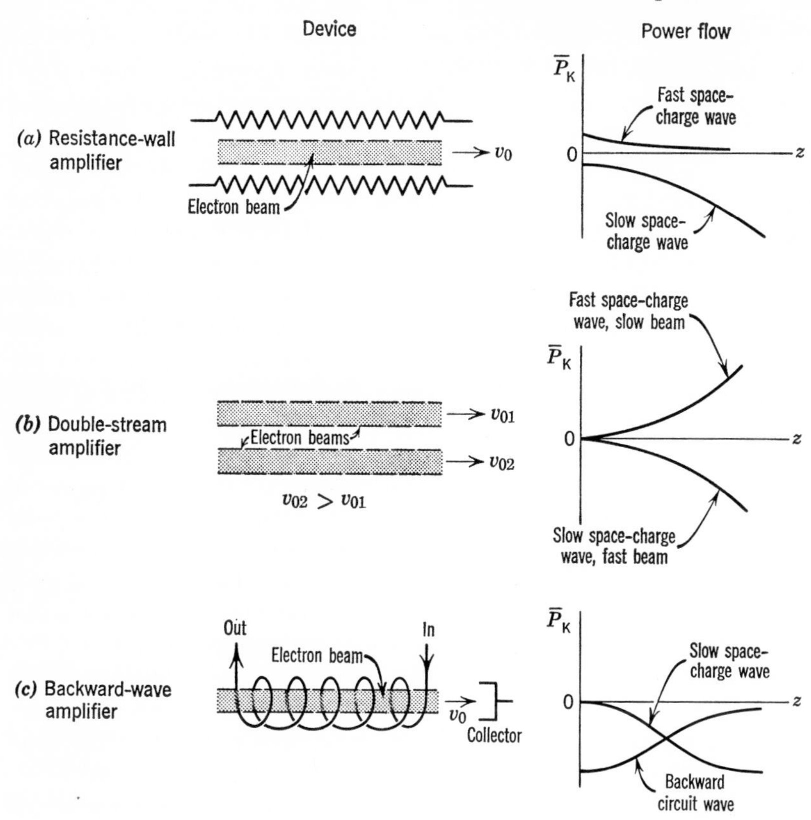

Fig. 16.14. Examples of microwave interactions and power flow.

point of view. In this device an electron beam travels past a resistive material which removes energy continuously from the electron beam. This interaction is an example of the coupling of one propagating mode, the slow space-charge wave, and a dissipative circuit. A disturbance set up by a cavity resonator or a helix produces both slow and fast waves in the beam. As each wave travels it induces currents in the resistive wall surrounding it and dissipates power in the wall. Thus the total kinetic power in the beam decreases continuously. The amplitude of the fast wave decreases exponentially to zero, and its positive kinetic power flow decreases to zero as it loses energy. On the other hand, the amplitude of the slow wave increases exponentially with distance and its negative kinetic power flow becomes more negative as it loses energy. If an output cavity is placed further along the beam, the large current amplitude of the slow space-charge wave may induce a large voltage across the cavity, providing output power. The energy conversion process at the output is similar to that in a klystron.

The space-charge-wave double-stream amplifier shown in Fig. 16.14*b* makes use of the interaction of the electrons of one beam with electrons of another beam moving at a different velocity. Interactions of this type have been found in other branches of physics such as astrophysics. In practical cases the two beams must be in close proximity and there must be two relatively well-defined velocity groups. Coupling occurs between the fast space-charge wave of the slow electron beam and the slow space-charge wave of the fast electron beam provided the phase velocities of these two waves are nearly equal. Both of these waves grow exponentially with distance, and their kinetic power flows exactly balance as the disturbance increases along the beam. Energy is transferred from the slow wave of the fast beam to the fast wave of the slow beam, and modulation and bunching are achieved. The a-c energy due to the bunching may be extracted by an appropriate coupling circuit. It is important to note that in the double-stream amplifier there is no r-f structure or circuit such as a helix. Thus there are no circuit problems, except for input and output couplers. The frequency of operation, gain, and bandwidth are similar to a TWT. The space-charge-wave double-stream amplifier is a practical device, but one which has not yet found wide application.

The backward-wave tube shown in Fig. 16.14*c* is similar to the traveling-wave tube in the sense that a slow space-charge wave increases in amplitude and gives energy to an electromagnetic circuit wave. However, in the backward-wave tube the helix is used in a frequency range in which the expression $d\omega/d\beta$ is negative. This results in a backward group velocity (see equation 1.11). In the backward-wave tube of Fig. 16.14*c* the slow space-charge wave and the phase velocity of the circuit wave are in synchronism and the space-charge wave loses energy to the circuit wave. The energy lost to the circuit wave travels to the left because the group velocity is to the left and the circuit wave interacts with electrons in the beam further to the left. These electrons then travel to the right and in turn give their energy to the leftward moving circuit wave. This "regenerative feedback" mechanism can lead to large amplification and oscillations, the frequency of which can be controlled by varying the beam voltage and thus the velocity of the slow space-charge wave. Voltage-tunable backward-wave oscillators and amplifiers are technologically important.

In section 15.11 we discussed the nature of cyclotron waves. Beam tubes can be designed which utilize the interaction between cyclotron waves and space-charge waves or circuit waves. In one type of double-stream tube the slow space-charge wave of the faster beam couples with the fast cyclotron wave of the slower beam. In such a tube, energy is transferred from the fast beam to the slow beam and amplification of the cyclotron wave is achieved. This tube has the advantage of requiring no slow-wave structure, has a high power capability, and may be operated at very high frequencies.

It is also possible to achieve amplification from the interaction of an electron beam with a stationary plasma. For example, one may utilize the interaction of a slow space-charge wave of a moving beam and a backward cyclotron wave of a stationary plasma. In such tubes the plasma replaces the slow-wave circuit of more conventional amplifiers. Many more beam-type devices can be analyzed through the concept of wave coupling.

16.8 Noise

An important characteristic of the many different amplifiers we have discussed is their relative freedom from "noise." Noise is a random signal that is present all of the time in all electrical devices and in the atmosphere. It is characterized by nonperiodic fluctuations of voltage and current or electromagnetic fields. The ratio of the signal power to the noise power (signal-to-noise ratio) is a useful parameter for describing the "visibility" of a signal in the presence of noise. If the signal-to-noise ratio is small (close to one or less), it generally will be difficult to recognize or even detect the signal.

Noise has many sources. However, in electron devices we are mainly concerned with "thermal noise" and "shot noise." Thermal noise (also known as Johnson noise) is the name for the random voltage pulses (and at high frequencies the incoherent electromagnetic radiation) generated by any lossy warm object such as a resistor or resistive surface. The cause for this noise is the fluctuations (random motions) of electrons in the material. The thermal-noise power P_N within the bandwidth B generated by such an object is given by

$$P_N = kTB \tag{16.12}$$

where k is Boltzmann's constant and T is the absolute temperature.

The electron beam in a tube consists of discrete electrons emitted at random times by the cathode. Hence the current has a random density modulation, that is, a noise-current modulation. The associated noise power is proportional to the average current drawn from the cathode and is known as *shot noise.*

If the current is space-charge limited rather than temperature limited so that a potential minimum exists immediately in front of the cathode, individual electrons depress the potential minimum while passing its position. This space-charge depression of the potential minimum tends to limit the passage of other electrons, and in effect produces negative pulses of current which partially cancel the pulses due to the original electrons. Because there is a slight time delay between the negative and positive pulses, the cancellation is effective only at frequencies below about 300 Mc. At higher frequencies, the cancellation disappears and full shot noise is observed.

Not only is the time at which electrons are emitted random, but so is the velocity with which they are emitted. Thus an electron beam also has a noise-velocity modulation. This is known as Rack noise, after the man who first investigated it. The higher the temperature of a cathode, the greater the velocity spread of the emitted electrons, and hence the greater the noise-velocity modulation.

In all devices employing modulated electron beams to achieve gain, the noise modulation, due to both current (shot noise) and velocity (Rack noise), will be amplified along with the signal and any noise (such as kTB heat noise) introduced with the signal. Thus the amplifier itself tends to degrade the signal, and there is great impetus to achieve low-noise amplifiers which keep the degradation to a minimum.

A useful parameter for measuring the noise an amplifier introduces is the noise figure F, defined by

$$F \equiv \frac{P_{S_i}/P_{N_i}}{P_{S_o}/P_{N_o}} \tag{16.13}$$

Here P_{S_i}/P_{N_i} is the signal-to-noise ratio at the input of the amplifier and P_{S_o}/P_{N_o} is the signal-to-noise ratio at the output of the amplifier. Since the input noise power P_{N_i} depends on the input noise temperature T_r, this noise figure definition is generally with reference to an input source temperature T_r of 290°K (room temperature). Noise figures are often expressed in decibels ($10 \log_{10} F$).

It is also convenient and sometimes more physically meaningful to describe the noise contribution of an amplifier in terms of its equivalent internal noise temperature T_e. T_e is the temperature at which an input source would have to operate to yield as much noise output from a noise-free amplifier as the actual amplifier yields with no noise input. The temperature T_e, representing the noise generated internally by the amplifier, is related to the noise figure F by

$$T_e = (F - 1)T_r \tag{16.14}$$

In an amplifier system which includes external devices (such as an antenna) the noise figure or temperature must include the noise contribution of the external devices as well as that of the amplifier itself. Both noise temperature and noise figure are convenient measures of the "noisiness" of an amplifier or system.

Devices such as the triode, pentode, klystron, traveling-wave tube, magnetron, and many beam-type devices, all derive their energy from the kinetic and potential energy of an electron beam emitted by a hot cathode and generally are noisy devices. However, the traveling-wave tube can be constructed to have noise figures as low as 1.8 (2.5 db) at 3000 mc. Magnetrons and klystrons may have noise figures as high as 1000 (30 db). Parametric amplifiers and masers, which are discussed next, have noise figures approaching one. They are very important as receivers in long-distance communication and radio astronomy where the signals to be amplified are very weak.

In devices which do not have hot cathodes, such as varactor diodes (used in parametric amplifiers,) tunnel diodes, and transistors, the noise due to temperature effects may not contribute as much as in hot cathode devices. However, transistors have shot noise and other disturbing noise sources. The tunnel diode is a low-noise device. The main noise source is the shot noise, which is proportional to the average current flowing and is independent of frequency. The noise may be low because the average operating current is low.

16.9 Parametric amplifiers

Parametric amplifiers and masers differ from the amplifiers previously discussed in that an a-c power source (of a frequency different from the signal frequency) provides the energy required for amplification. The parametric amplifier is attractive in its inherent simplicity. It is an example of the coupling of mode concept described in section 16.6, but here the coupling takes place via a time-varying circuit parameter. Such a parameter can provide frequency mixing, just as a nonlinear circuit parameter causes mixing of two different modes of vibration (for example, the r-f signal and local oscillator modes in superheterodyne receivers). The frequency mixing allows energy supplied to the system at one frequency to be converted to another frequency. The maser, on the other hand, uses a crystal or gas, brought

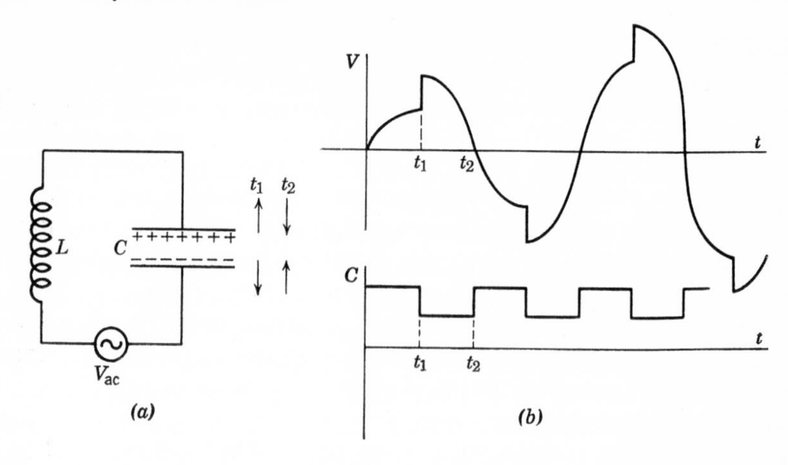

Fig. 16.15. Simple resonant circuit illustrating energy transfer via the variable-parameter principle.

to an unbalanced population of energy states by electromagnetic power at a high frequency, to provide amplification at a lower frequency. One of the fascinating aspects of these devices is their low noise figures.

To understand the mechanism of energy transfer in parametric amplification, it is convenient to think of a capacitor with movable plates which is connected to an inductance and a sinusoidal a-c voltage source as shown in Fig. 16.15*a*. Imagine that at the instant t_1 when the voltage is a maximum the plates are suddenly pulled apart in a very short time. Mechanical work must be done to separate the plates since the opposite charges residing on them give rise to an attractive force. After separation the capacitance C is smaller, but the charge Q is unchanged if the separation time is very short compared with the period of the resonant circuit. Since

$$V = \frac{Q}{C} \tag{16.15}$$

we see that the voltage must increase instantaneously as indicated in part (*b*) of Fig. 16.15. This increased voltage across the capacitor continues its cycle and returns to zero at t_2. At this instant the plates are pushed to their original separation. Now no work needs to be done since the charge on and the force between the plates are zero. If the plates are continually pulled apart at the times of maximum voltage and pushed together at the times of zero voltage, the signal voltage will increase until the energy dissipated per cycle in any circuit resistance equals the mechanical energy supplied per cycle. Thus the addition of mechanical energy by "pumping" the capacitor at twice the signal frequency leads to an increase in the signal energy, producing amplification. In this case the maximum energy transfer requires that the capacitance be varied in the proper phase and at exactly twice the signal frequency. The name "parametric" amplifier refers in this case to the variation of the parameter, capacitance.

A mechanical scheme of capacitance variation is obviously impractical at high frequencies. In practice it is possible to use electronically variable reactances (a reactance is considered here to be an element of a circuit that stores energy). Three types of electronic energy storage elements that may be used in parametric amplifiers are: (1) the junction capacitances of semiconductor diodes, (2) electron beams, and (3) electron spins in ferromagnetic materials. We consider here the first two types, after a brief study of parametric circuits employing variable reactances.

A general parametric amplifier network is represented in Fig. 16.16. The network consists of three circuits. The first is tuned to the signal frequency ω_S by L_S and C_S, and connected to the signal source. The second circuit is tuned to the so-called pump frequency ω_P by L_P and C_P, and is driven by a local oscillator. The third circuit at frequency ω_I is tuned to the sum of or the difference between ω_S and ω_P; it is known as the idler circuit. All three circuits are coupled by a nonlinear reactance C, which represents any one of the storage elements listed in the preceding paragraph.

To understand the operation of this network, suppose that the idler loop is disconnected at X-X. The pump current i_P and the signal

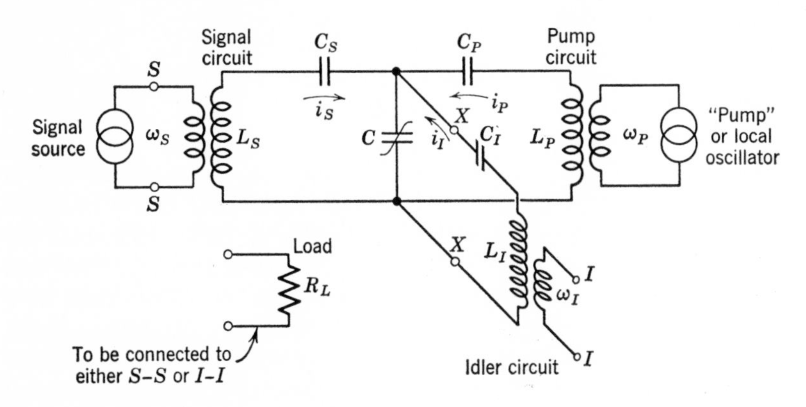

Fig. 16.16. A general parametric amplifier network.

current i_S add in the non-linear capacitance C. Because the voltage V_C across the capacitance C is a non-linear function of the current through C, V_C will consist primarily of components ω_P and ω_S, and the beat frequencies $\omega_P + \omega_S$ and $\omega_P - \omega_S$, as well as harmonics of these and other frequencies with reduced amplitudes. Thus C acts like a generator of many frequencies. We next consider some amplification possibilities when the idler loop is connected at terminals X-X.

Suppose ω_I, tuned by L_I and C_I, is set equal to the difference frequency $\omega_P - \omega_S$, and an output load R_L is connected across the input terminals S-S. The current at frequency $\omega_P - \omega_S$ which flows in the idler circuit beats with the pump current in the non-linear reactance C to produce a voltage at the signal frequency. This voltage excites the signal circuit which produces a current that adds coherently to the original signal current, amplifying it. Power at the signal frequency is delivered to the load resistance at the input signal terminals and has come from the local oscillator or pump. Another way of describing this process is to say that the amplifier presents a negative resistance to the signal, as does a tunnel diode. Note that the input and output terminals are identical in this amplifier, requiring somewhat complicated circuitry in order to separate the input and output power.

If the output load R_L is connected instead across the terminals I-I, the output terminals of the amplifier are now separate from the input terminals. The output frequency is ω_I, different from the signal frequency. If ω_I is higher than ω_S, the amplifier is called an upconverter; if ω_I is lower than ω_S, it is called a downconverter. In the above we have let the idler be tuned to the difference frequency $\omega_P - \omega_S$. It is also possible to tune the idler to the sum frequency $\omega_P + \omega_S$ for certain applications. It should be noted that for both output connections ω_P is no longer required to be equal to $2\omega_S$, as it was for the so-called degenerate parametric amplifier of Fig. 16.15. The phase requirements between the pump and signal frequencies have been satisfied by the introduction of the idler circuit.

The major advantage of parametric amplifiers over other amplifiers discussed is their low noise figures. Because the active element is a reactance, it displays no Johnson or heat noise, and hence provides low-noise amplification. Junction diodes are suitable reactances for use in parametric amplifiers with low-noise characteristics. We saw in Chapter 14 that the "capacitance" of a junction diode varies with the applied voltage. Figure 16.17 shows a possible curve of incremental depletion-layer capacitance C_D versus voltage for a reverse-biased junction diode. The variation exhibited indicates that a biased junction diode may possess the necessary capacitance versus voltage characteristic to be used as the nonlinear capacitance C of Fig. 16.16.

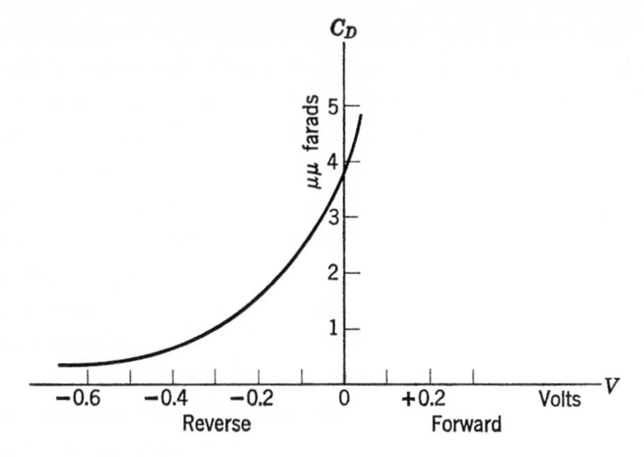

Fig. 16.17. Incremental depletion-layer capacitance versus voltage in a junction diode.

Electron beams have also been used as the nonlinear reactance. Parametric amplifiers using the longitudinal space-charge waves employed in ordinary traveling-wave tubes have been successfully operated, but they have not had low-noise characteristics. The difficulty appears to be that all the idler frequencies produced in the beam cannot be suppressed as with the idler circuit of Fig. 16.16, and these additional frequencies carry noise which is amplified. On the other hand, the cyclotron waves of electron beams have been very successfully employed in parametric amplifiers to yield a low-noise tube. The pertinent components of this device, known as the Adler[1,2] tube, are shown in Fig. 16.18. A beam enters the input coupler and is given a spiraling cyclotron modulation at frequency ω_c by the input signal. When the beam enters the so-called quadrupole-pump region, additional energy is given to the cyclotron waves by a tangential electric field oscillating at twice the cyclotron frequency. This r-f field is zero on the axis and increases with increasing displacement from the axis. In effect it rotates in synchronism with the electrons. As the signal obtains more energy the electrons move to a larger radius. The increased energy of the electrons is extracted at the output coupler and parametric-type amplification has been realized. In the Adler tube the initial noise in the beam associated with transverse motions of electrons is damped out as the beam passes through the input

[1] R. Adler, "Parametric Amplification of the Fast Electron Wave," *Proc. I.R.E.*, **46,** 1300 (1958).

[2] R. Adler, G. Hrbek, and G. Wade, "The Quadrupole Tube Amplifier, a Low-Noise Parametric Device," *Proc. I.R.E.*, **47,** 1713 (1959).

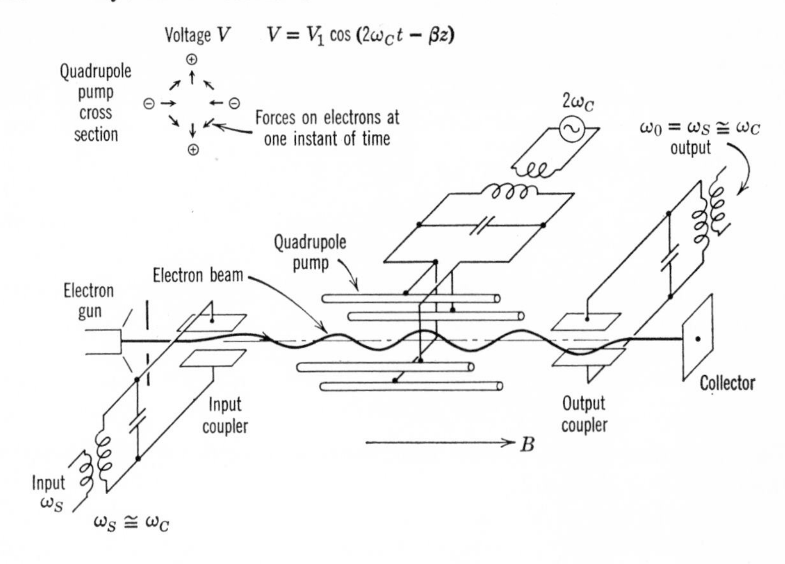

Fig. 16.18. Adler-type parametric amplifier.

coupler and receives its cyclotron-wave modulation. This tube has an inherent low-noise capability and has demonstrated noise figures as low as 1.3.

It should be pointed out that the principles of parametric amplification have been known for a long time. The basic ideas were described by a number of people, among them Faraday in 1831 and Lord Rayleigh in 1883 (mechanical resonant systems). Thus the parametric amplifier principle is a "classical" one, which began to be applied in electronics around 1955 as variable reactance elements operable at high frequencies were made available.

We now consider parametric amplification from the viewpoint of energy conservation. The output powers that can be obtained in parametric amplifiers and masers depend on frequency in a way which we now derive. The three resonant circuits of Fig. 16.16 permit the addition or subtraction of energy to or from the system at three frequencies, one of which is the sum of the other two. This system is then analogous to a quantum mechanical system having three energy levels with electrons partially filling each level. Such a system of energy levels and transitions is shown in Fig. 16.19. As in a quantum mechanical system, the addition of energy to the system at a resonant frequency causes electrons to make upward transitions. Energy is released from the system when downward transitions occur.

Conservation of energy can be assured if the number of electrons in each level remains constant. If we let $\partial N_{21}/\partial t$ represent the net rate of transitions from level 2 to level 1 and $\partial N_{31}/\partial t$ that from level 3 to level 1, the condition that the population of level 1 remains constant may be written as

$$\frac{\partial N_{21}}{\partial t} + \frac{\partial N_{31}}{\partial t} = 0 \tag{16.16}$$

If we multiply and divide each rate by its corresponding angular frequency and multiply through by $\hbar$, we have

$$\frac{\hbar\omega_{21}}{\omega_{21}}\frac{\partial N_{21}}{\partial t} + \frac{\hbar\omega_{31}}{\omega_{31}}\frac{\partial N_{31}}{\partial t} = 0 \tag{16.17}$$

The rate at which the system radiates energy at the frequency ω_{21} is the power P_{21} given by

$$P_{21} = \hbar\omega_{21}\frac{\partial N_{21}}{\partial t} \tag{16.18}$$

For transitions from level 3 to level 1 we write in an analogous fashion

$$P_{31} = \hbar\omega_{31}\frac{\partial N_{31}}{\partial t} \tag{16.19}$$

Using 16.18 and 16.19, 16.17 becomes

$$\frac{P_{21}}{\omega_{21}} + \frac{P_{31}}{\omega_{31}} = 0 \tag{16.20}$$

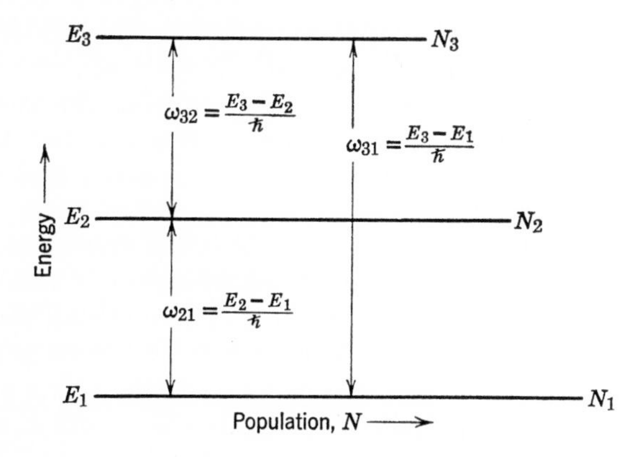

Fig. 16.19. Three energy levels with populations N_1, N_2, N_3.

or

$$P_{31} = -\frac{\omega_{31}}{\omega_{21}} P_{21} \tag{16.21}$$

A similar expression may be derived for levels 3 and 2,

$$P_{31} = -\frac{\omega_{31}}{\omega_{32}} P_{32} \tag{16.22}$$

(In our development a positive power represents power taken from the system; a negative power represents power given to the system. By convention we say that a power P_{12} would refer to energy absorbed at the frequency ω_{21}. Thus

$$P_{12} = -P_{21} \tag{16.23}$$

and a change of order of subscripts requires a change of sign.) Combining 16.21, 16.22, and 16.23 we may write

$$P_{12} = -\frac{\omega_{21}}{\omega_{32}} P_{32} \tag{16.24}$$

Equations 16.21, 16.22, and 16.24 are specific examples of a set of general equations known as the Manley-Rowe[1] relations which were originally derived for energy transformations in non-linear reactances. As derived here[2] they apply to masers equally well. These relations describe the energy and power flowing through the non-linear reactance at a given frequency. For example, if ω_{31} represents the pump frequency ω_P, ω_{21} the signal frequency ω_S, and ω_{32} the output idler frequency ω_I, then equation 16.24 indicates that if $\omega_{32} > \omega_{21}$ (an upconverter), then the output power P_{32} can be much larger than the signal input power P_{12}.

16.10 Masers

In our previous discussions of microwave amplifiers, the electron has been treated as a structureless point-charge that moves under the influence of applied electric and magnetic fields. However, the electron has structure, that is, its spin, and therefore a magnetic moment.

[1] J. M. Manley and H. E. Rowe, "Some General Properties of Non-linear Elements," *Proc. I.R.E.*, **44**, 904 (1956).

[2] M. T. Weiss, "Quantum Derivation of Energy Relations Analogous to Those for Nonlinear reactances," *Proc. I.R.E.*, **45**, 1012 (1957).

The maser is a device which utilizes an a-c energy source of one frequency to store energy in an atomic system, often using the magnetic moment or spin energy states of paramagnetic ions to provide the atomic system. This stored energy, in the form of an excess population of electrons in higher energy levels, can be released in a controlled fashion by stimulating the system with electromagnetic radiation at a lower frequency. The radiation triggers the electrons to fall to a lower energy level, releasing signal energy in the form of electromagnetic quanta at the stimulating frequency.[1] The maser can thus be either a source or an amplifier of electromagnetic radiation. The name "maser" stands for "microwave amplification by stimulated emission of radiation."

A possible energy system for maser amplification may be constructed by placing a crystal containing a paramagnetic impurity in a d-c magnetic field. Ruby (Al_2O_3) doped with chromium ions has been used successfully. The atomic structure of the crystal is such that the spins of some of the electrons of the impurity atoms couple together to form a total spin which is greater than $\frac{1}{2}$. This spin then has at least three quantized orientations with respect to the externally applied magnetic field. The potential energy associated with the orientations of the spin magnetic moment relative to the magnetic field gives rise to a multiplicity of energy levels. Three such energy levels at room temperature are indicated in Fig. 16.20*a*. The spacing of the energy levels depends on the strength of the applied magnetic field. Under equilibrium conditions the relative populations (horizontal length of lines in Fig. 16.20*a*) of the individual energy levels are described by the Boltzmann relation (equation 8.31). If electromagnetic radiation is applied at frequency ω_{13}, transitions will occur between levels 1 and 3, bringing electrons from level 1 to level 3 and vice versa. An individual transition will have equal probability of going from 1 to 3 or from 3 to 1, but the rate of transitions out of a level is proportional to the number of electrons in that level. Thus the level with the larger population loses electrons at a faster rate than the level with the smaller population, and the two populations tend to become equal in the presence of stimulating radiation.

If enough power is applied there will be "pumping" of electrons from level 1 to level 3 until the populations are equal as indicated in

[1] Gas discharges producing visible light provide a familiar example of the emission of light quanta which is caused by electrons dropping from a high energy state to a low energy state. However, in a gas discharge, the atoms emit energy independently of each other, i.e., incoherently. Electromagnetic signal amplification and oscillation is generally only of interest if it is coherent (phase related).

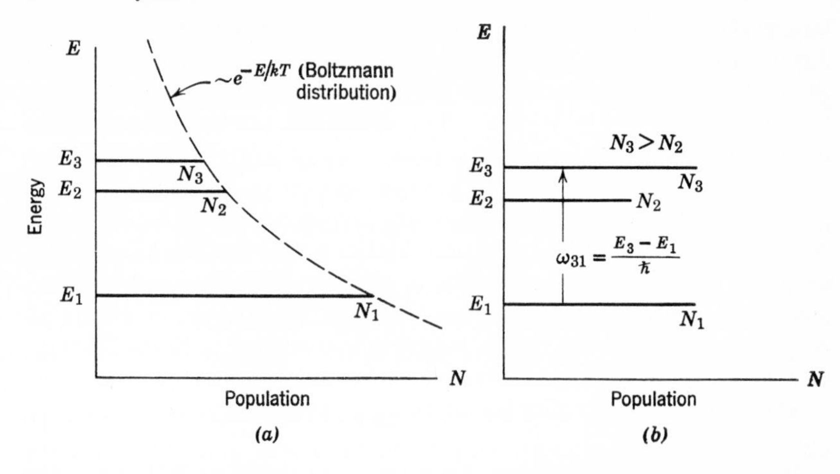

Fig. 16.20. Energy-levels versus population of an atomic system at room temperature (such as paramagnetic ions in a static magnetic field). (*a*) Natural equilibrium distribution. (*b*) Distribution under irradiation with electromagnetic power at frequency ω_{31}.

Fig. 16.20*b*. This condition is called saturation; the source of the radiation which produces the saturation is called the pump as in a parametric amplifier.

Under saturated pumping the population of level 2 can be less than level 3 as indicated in Fig. 16.20*b*. Whether N_2 is less than N_3 is determined by the relaxation times for the naturally occurring transitions tending to bring the system back to equilibrium (see next paragraph). If the average time for a transition from level 3 to level 2 is long compared with the average time for transitions from level 2 to level 1, then N_2 will become less than N_3, and conversely. If signal radiation at frequency ω_{32} is applied, it can trigger transitions from level 3 to level 2 and vice versa, but more downward than upward transitions will occur if $N_3 > N_2$. The transitions yield electromagnetic quanta of energy, adding coherently to the signal, and the signal frequency is amplified. It may be noted that exchange of electrons between levels 2 and 1 also produces radiation at frequency ω_{21}. This frequency would correspond to the idler frequency of the parametric amplifier. As another example, if we had a different system where under pumping $N_2 > N_3$ or N_1, then the signal frequency would be ω_{21} and the idler frequency would be ω_{32}. The Manley-Rowe relations as derived in section 16.9 apply here.

The situation shown in Fig. 16.20 is not an efficient one at room temperature. The pump is competing with the naturally occurring downward transitions due to interactions with lattice vibrations, and the system tends to return to the normal thermal equilibrium distribution represented in Fig. 16.20*a*. This relaxation process removes spins from excited states so rapidly at ordinary temperatures that in practice it is impossible to maintain an overpopulation in the excited states. In masers, therefore, the crystals are cooled to liquid helium temperatures where the de-excitation lifetimes become so long (milliseconds) that saturated pumping is possible with reasonable pump power. Cooling the maser brings about an equilibrium condition as indicated in Fig. 16.21*a*, and a saturation condition indicated in Fig. 16.21*b*. The excess population has been increased at the low temperature, and a larger number of transitions can be induced than at room temperature.

Another way of describing the cooling requirement is to consider that the pump produces an emissive condition by redistributing among the higher energy states the original (thermal equilibrium) excess population $(N_1 - N_3)$ of a low energy state. The excess population is proportional to $1/T$ (Boltzmann distribution) if the difference in energy between levels is small compared to kT. Since the performance of a maser improves as the excess population increases, the performance of the maser improves as the temperature is lowered.

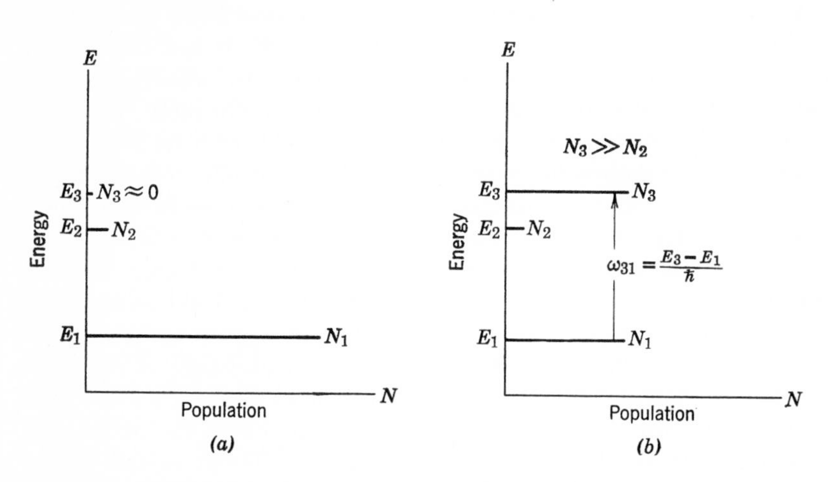

Fig. 16.21. Energy-levels versus population of the atomic system of Fig. 16-20 at liquid helium temperatures ($T = 4°K$). (*a*) Natural equilibrium distribution. (*b*) Saturated distribution under irradiation with electromagnetic power at frequency ω_{31}.

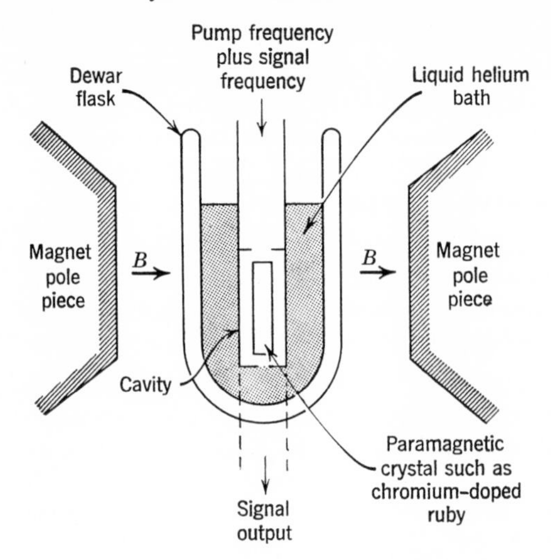

Fig. 16.22. Possible experimental solid-state maser.

Figure 16.22 illustrates a possible experimental scheme for realizing the performance of a solid-state maser. The frequency can be tuned by changing the energy level spacings via the magnetic field. The device also has a small but finite bandwidth due to the width of the energy levels. The almost complete lack of noise in the device ($F =$ 0.06 db) is partly because of the very low temperature (kTB input noise low), but also because spontaneous transitions, giving rise to incoherent radiation at the signal frequency, are infrequent compared with the triggered transitions in the presence of signal irradiation.

The first maser developed used an inhomogeneous magnetic field to separate a beam of ammonia molecules into two beams, one containing molecules in a lower energy level, the other containing molecules in a higher energy level. Only the beam containing molecules in the upper level was allowed to enter a cavity where microwave power of the proper frequency induced downward transitions and thus caused maser amplification.

Masers have also been made to work at visible light frequencies. The performance of the optical maser may not be a function of temperature as it was for the microwave maser, since the energy level separation is generally larger than kT. It should be noted that a maser does not require a coherent pump, as does a parametric amplifier. Therefore an optical maser may be pumped by incoherent light, but may emit coherent optical radiation. Beams of light from optical masers are extremely monochromatic and have extremely narrow angular widths. These characteristics of optical masers suggest that they will play an increasingly important role in communications and in scientific research.

Suggested References

W. J. Kleen, *Electronics of Microwave Tubes,* Academic Press, 1958. This advanced textbook is one of the best treatments of microwave electronics. The classification of tubes discussed in our section 16.3 follows from the author's Chapter 13. The differences between "O" and "M" TWT's are well summarized in Table 13.4.

J. R. Pierce, "The Wave Picture of Microwave Tubes," *Bell System Technical Journal,* **33,** 1343 (1954). This is a basic tutorial paper that first brought together the material underlying power flow and the coupling of wave modes discussed in our sections 16.5 to 16.7. It is not overly specialized, and should be read by students interested in this general approach to microwave devices.

W. W. Harman, *Fundamentals of Electron Motion,* McGraw-Hill Book Company, 1953. Harman carries out a more detailed analysis of magnetrons at about the same level of this textbook. The mathematics of the TWT is carried out at an appropriate level to extend the qualitative discussion given here. The space-charge double-stream amplifier and some other devices are described from a different point of view.

W. H Louisell, *Coupled Mode and Parametric Electronics,* John Wiley and Sons, 1960. Although at an advanced level, this textbook is an appropriate reference for microwave tubes in terms of coupled waves, and parametric amplifiers in general. The notation of the first chapter must be mastered before the details of later chapters can be followed. A detailed bibliography is included.

F. H. Clauser, *Plasma Dynamics,* Addison-Wesley Publishing Company, 1960. This textbook is a collection of articles on plasmas. Chapter 4 by R. W. Gould is a fascinating description of the field of electron beam interactions as a whole.

L. S. Nergaard, "Amplification—Modern Trends, Techniques and Problems," *RCA Rev.,* **21,** 485 (1960). This is an excellent review article summarizing the state of the art through 1960 regarding small-signal amplifiers and power amplifiers. Comparison is made between the characteristics of the amplifiers discussed in Chapter 16.

W. R. Bennett, *Electrical Noise,* McGraw-Hill Book Company, 1960. This text describes and defines all of the noise concepts introduced in this chapter and applies them to an analysis of modern amplifier devices.

PROBLEMS

16.1. In the schematic of the TWT shown on p. 362 the helix does not intercept any of the electron beam.

(*a*) Which power supply provides the power that becomes useful r-f power output?

(*b*) The bunched electron beam induces a-c currents in the helix. If the helix were somewhat lossy, these currents would dissipate energy in the form of heat. Which power supply provides this energy?

(*c*) If the beam current is I_0, what is the net power supplied to the tube by the d-c power supplies?

(*d*) The efficiency of the tube is defined as the ratio of maximum r-f power output to the d-c power input. Can the efficiency of the tube be raised by decreasing the potential V_c? (Neglect secondary emission effects.)

(*e*) If all the electrons are to be collected by the collector, how small can the voltage V_c be made?

(*f*) Does your answer to part (*d*) apply also to a klystron?

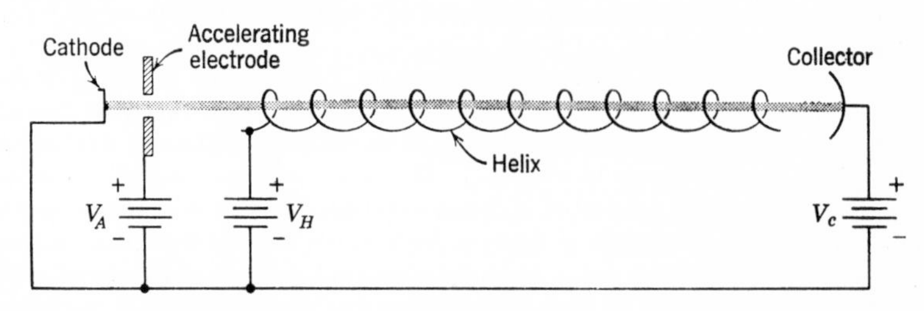

Prob. 16.1

16.2. For a helix that has 100 turns per inch and a diameter of 0.06 in. and assuming the velocity of the wave along the helix is given by equation 16.1, calculate the voltage V_0 at which the helix should be operated above the cathode potential to achieve traveling wave tube gain (synchronism). Assume space charge associated with the beam is zero.

16.3. The helix of Problem 16.2 is to be used in a TWT with a beam of current density 600 ma/cm². Calculate the beam voltage which will give maximum gain at a frequency of 3000 Mc. *Hint:* In the presence of space charge the velocity of the slow space-charge wave and the velocity of the electromagnetic wave on the helix must be approximately equal.

16.4. In a traveling-wave magnetron the beam current is 100 ma, the magnetic field is 0.1 weber/meter², the separation of the sole and anode is considered to be 0.20 cm, and the voltage between sole and anode is 2000 volts. Assuming the beam travels smoothly without cycloidal motion, calculate

(*a*) the expected maximum power output of the device.

(*b*) the theoretical efficiency of the device.

16.5. With reference to klystron and magnetron oscillators, what factors determine (*a*) the upper and lower frequency limits for which these oscillators are used and (*b*) the maximum output power obtainable from them?

16.6. In a traveling-wave injected beam magnetron, what sort of interaction would occur if the sole or ground plane were serrated and the positive anode were smooth? Show that the energy of the electrons would increase.

16.7. (*a*) Show that the net a-c power flow in a beam is zero if there is velocity modulation but no current modulation.

(*b*) If the grid of a triode supplies the beam with a-c kinetic power, then what must be true concerning the induced current in the grid?

16.8. From the definition of noise figure given by equation 16.13, show that the noise power output P_{N0} of an amplifier is given by

$$P_{N0} = FGP_{Ni} = FGkTB$$

where G is the power gain of the amplifier and P_{Ni} is the noise power input.

16.9. Consider a double-stream amplifier, employing coupling between the space-charge waves and designed to operate at 3000 Mc. The plasma frequency of both beams is 300 Mc.

(*a*) If the slower stream has a beam voltage of 500 volts, what must be the voltage of the other beam in order to achieve interaction and coupling?

(*b*) If the faster stream has a beam voltage of 500 volts, what must be the voltage of the other beam for interaction and coupling.

16.10. The figure below is a dispersion curve for a helix employed in a backward-wave amplifier. This graph is analogous to the E versus k diagrams of Chapter 12. Points A and B are possible points of operation for the operation of the backward-wave amplifier because the slope of the curve, which represents the group velocity of the waves on the helix, is negative. Suppose that the backward-wave amplifier operates at 6×10^9 radian/sec. at point A with a beam voltage of 1000 volts. What should the beam voltage be in order to operate at point B with a frequency of 4×10^9 radian/sec. *Hint:* The beam must travel at approximately the *phase* velocity of the waves on the helix.

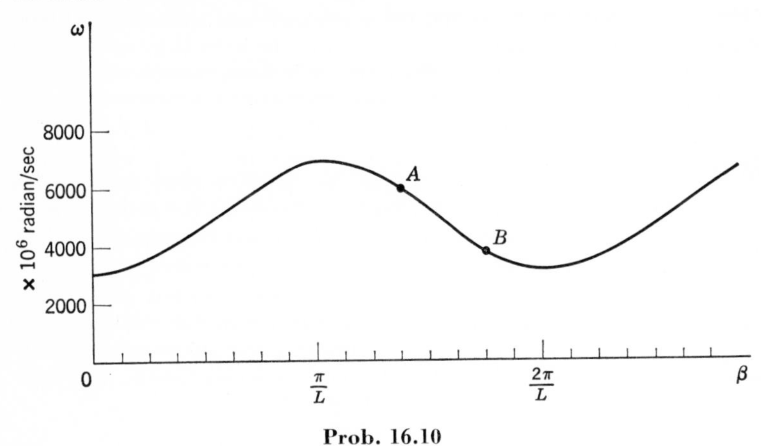

Prob. 16.10

16.11. The voltage V across a certain device is a nonlinear function of the current i through it in the form of a polynomial:

$$V = A_0 + A_1 i + A_2 i^2$$

Suppose that the current is the sum of a-c currents at frequencies ω_P and ω_S where $\omega_P > \omega_S$.

$$i = I_P \sin \omega_P t + I_S \sin \omega_S t$$

Show that the voltage contains terms which vary at frequencies of

$$\omega_P, \ \omega_S, \ 2\omega_P, \ 2\omega_S, \ \omega_P + \omega_S, \quad \text{and} \quad \omega_P - \omega_S$$

16.12. A certain solid-state maser has the following energy-level diagram.

(*a*) What frequency should the a-c power source have?

(*b*) What frequencies could be amplified?

6×10^{-5} ev

4×10^{-5} ev

0 ev

Energy-level diagram

16.13. Derive equation 16.14 relating noise temperature T_e to noise figure F.

16.14. If two amplifiers with noise figures F_1 and F_2 and gains G_1 and G_2, respectively, are connected in series, the noise figure of the system is higher than that of one amplifier only. Show that the system noise figure F is

$$F = F_1 + \frac{F_2 - 1}{G_1}$$

(Do this by considering that the noise powers add, and thus follow the total noise contributed by each amplifier, using the result of Problem 16.8.) Note that if G_1 is large $F = F_1$.

16.15. In the circuit of Fig. 16.16, suppose that a signal of frequency $\nu_s = 50$ Mc is applied, and an output signal of $\nu_i = 1050$ Mc is taken out across a load resistance R_L connected to the idler circuit. (The pump frequency is 1000 Mc.)

(*a*) What is the power gain of the upconverted frequency?

(*b*) Suppose that the idler and signal frequencies are reversed so that $\nu_s = 1050$ Mc and $\nu_i = 50$ Mc. What is the power gain of the down converted frequency?

16.16. Suppose an input cavity supplies a-c power when it modulates an electron beam. If only one space-charge wave is excited, which one is it and why?

APPENDIX A

SYMBOLS USED IN TEXT

Symbols	Meaning
a (subscript)	Referring to anode
A	Area
b (subscript)	Referring to anode
B (subscript)	Referring to base
B	Magnetic field
B	Bandwidth
BE (subscript)	Referring to Bose-Einstein
c (subscript)	Referring to grid
c	Velocity of light in vacuum
C (subscript)	Referring to collector
C	Capacitance
d	Distance
D	Diffusion coefficient
e	Voltage
e	Base of Natural logarithms
e	Absolute value of electronic charge
$\mathcal{E}$	Electric field
E (subscript)	Referring to emitter
E	Total energy
E	Battery voltage
E_F	Fermi energy
F	Force
FD (subscript)	Referring to Fermi-Dirac
g (subscript)	Referring to grid
g_m	Transconductance or mutual conductance
h	Planck's constant
$\hbar$	$h/2\pi$
i	Instantaneous current
$\tilde{\imath}$	Time fluctuating or a-c part of current
I	Current amplitude

Symbols	Meaning
I_0	D-c current
j	$\sqrt{-1}$
J	Instantaneous current density
$\tilde{J}$	A-c part of current density
k	Propagation constant
k	Boltzmann's constant
k (subscript)	Referring to cathode
K	Kinetic energy
l	Quantum number
$\bar{l}$	Mean free path
L	Length
L	Inductance
L	Torque
m	Mass
m	Mass of electron
m^*	Effective mass
m_l, m_s	Quantum numbers
M	Mass of ion
MB (subscript)	Referring to Maxwell-Boltzmann
n	Semiconductor type
n	Numerical density
n	Quantum number
n (subscript)	Referring to electrons
N	Total number
N_0	Avogadro's number
p	Linear momentum
p	Type of semiconductor
p (subscript)	Referring to plate
p (subscript)	Referring to holes
P	Probability or average number of particles per quantum state
P	Power
P_θ	Angular momentum
q, Q	Charge
Q	Sharpness of tuning
r	Radial distance
r (subscript)	Referring to radius
r_p	Plate resistance
R	Resistance
R	Recombination coefficient
R	Radius
s	Electron displacement
s	Secondary emission ratio

Symbols	Meaning
s	Path length
S	Number of states
t	Time (variable)
T	Particular value of time
T	Absolute temperature
U	Potential energy
v	Velocity
$\tilde{v}$	A-c part of velocity
v_g	Group velocity
v_0	Average velocity
V	Volume
V	Potential, voltage
W	Work function
Z	Atomic number
Z	Complex impedance
α	Attenuation coefficient
α	First Townsend coefficient
α	Constant in statistical laws
β	Phase constant or propagation constant
β	Constant in statistical laws
γ	Probability of secondary emission
ϵ_0	Permittivity of free space
κ	Relative dielectric constant
η	Absolute value of charge to mass ratio of electron, e/m
λ	Wavelength
μ	Amplification factor
μ	Mobility
ϕ	Angle
ϕ	Magnetic flux
υ	Frequency (cycles/second)
ρ	Volume charge density
$\tilde{\rho}$	A-c part of volume charge density
ρ_0	Absolute value of average volume charge density
σ	Conductivity
σ	Collision cross section
τ	Volume in momentum space or ordinary space
θ	Angle
ψ	Wavefunction
ω	Angular frequency (radians/second)
ω_c	Cyclotron frequency (radians/second)
ω_p	Plasma frequency (radians/second)

APPENDIX B

SELECTED PHYSICAL CONSTANTS

Constant	Symbol	Value
Speed of light	c	3.00×10^{8} meters/sec
Planck's constant	h	6.63×10^{-34} joule-sec.
$h/2\pi$	$\hbar$	1.05×10^{-34} joule-sec
Boltzmann's constant	k	1.38×10^{-23} joule/°K $= 8.62 \times 10^{-5}$ ev/°K
Electronic charge	e	1.60×10^{-19} coulomb
Atomic mass unit	amu	1.66×10^{-27} kg
Avogadro's number	N_0	$6.02 \times 10^{26} \frac{\text{amu}}{\text{kg}}$ or $\frac{\text{molecules}}{\text{kg-molecular weight}}$
Mass of electron	m	9.11×10^{-31} kg
Charge to mass ratio for electron	η	1.76×10^{11} coulomb/kg
Mass of proton	m_p	$1836m = 1.67 \times 10^{-27}$ kg
Permittivity of free space	ϵ_0	$\frac{1}{36\pi \times 10^{9}} = 8.85 \times 10^{-12} \frac{\text{coulomb}^2}{\text{newton-meter}^2}$
Permeability of free space	μ_0	$4\pi \times 10^{-7} = 1.26 \times 10^{-6} \frac{\text{newton}}{\text{amp}^2}$
Radius of first Bohr orbit in hydrogen	a_0	5.29×10^{-11} meter
Volume of 1 kg-molecular weight of ideal gas at STP	—	22.4 meter^3

APPENDIX C

SOME VECTOR RELATIONSHIPS

1. *Dot product.* The dot product of two vectors **A** and **B**, written as $\mathbf{A} \cdot \mathbf{B}$, is defined to be a *scalar* of magnitude $AB \cos \theta$, where A and B are the magnitudes of the vectors and θ is the angle between them.

The dot product may also be expressed in terms of the components of A and B along rectangular coordinate axes x, y, z. Thus

$$\mathbf{A} \cdot \mathbf{B} = A_x B_x + A_y B_y + A_z B_z \tag{C.1}$$

where (A_x, A_y, A_z), (B_x, B_y, B_z) are the rectangular components of **A** and **B**.

2. *Vector cross product.* The vector cross product of two vectors **A** and **B**, written as $\mathbf{A} \times \mathbf{B}$, is defined to be a *vector* perpendicular to both **A** and **B** in the sense of the advance of a right-handed screw whose head is turned from the direction of **A** to the direction of **B** through the smaller angle. The magnitude of the cross-product vector is $AB \sin \theta$, where A and B are the magnitudes of the vectors and θ is the angle between them.

The vector cross product may also be expressed in terms of the rectangular components of **A** and **B** and unit vectors $\hat{\imath}$, $\hat{\jmath}$, $\hat{k}$ in the coordinate directions.
Thus

$$\mathbf{A} \times \mathbf{B} = \hat{\imath}(A_y B_z - A_z B_y) + \hat{\jmath}(A_z B_x - A_x B_z) + \hat{k}(A_x B_y - A_y B_x) \tag{C.2}$$

This component form of the vector cross product is easily remembered as the expansion of the determinant

$$\begin{vmatrix} \hat{\imath} & \hat{\jmath} & \hat{k} \\ A_x & A_y & A_z \\ B_x & B_y & B_z \end{vmatrix}$$

3. *Gradient of a scalar.*[1] The gradient of a scalar field Q, written as ∇Q, is, by definition, a vector field. The component of this vector field at a point along any direction in space is numerically equal to the directional derivative (rate of change of Q with distance) of the scalar field in that direction. Thus, expressing the gradient vector ∇Q in terms of its components along Cartesian axes, we have

$$\nabla Q = \hat{\imath}\,\frac{\partial Q}{\partial x} + \hat{\jmath}\,\frac{\partial Q}{\partial y} + \hat{k}\,\frac{\partial Q}{\partial z} \tag{C.3}$$

The direction of the gradient vector is the direction in which the directional derivative of Q is a maximum and the magnitude is numerically equal to the magnitude of the maximum directional derivative.

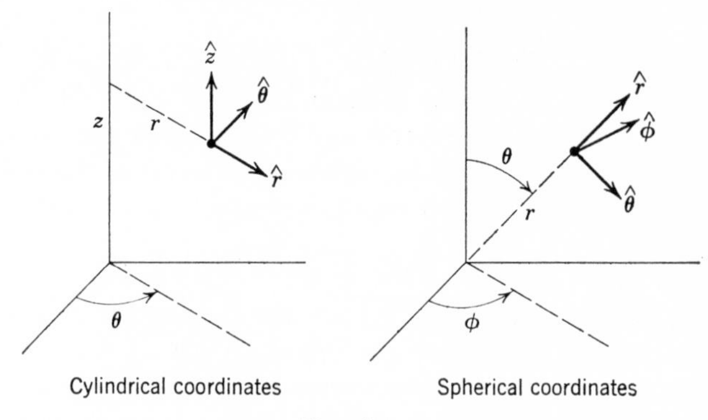

Fig. C.1

In problems involving cylindrical or spherical symmetry it is usually most convenient to express the scalar field Q as a function of cylindrical coordinates (r, θ, z) or spherical coordinates (r, θ, ϕ) (see Fig. C.1), in in which case the gradient may be expressed in terms of unit vectors in the coordinate directions and partial derivatives with respect to the coordinates. Using the definition of ∇Q we have, for cylindrical coordinates,

$$\nabla Q = \hat{r}\,\frac{\partial Q}{\partial r} + \hat{\theta}\,\frac{1}{r}\frac{\partial Q}{\partial \theta} + \hat{z}\,\frac{\partial Q}{\partial z} \tag{C.4}$$

and for spherical coordinates

$$\nabla Q = \hat{r}\,\frac{\partial Q}{\partial r} + \hat{\theta}\,\frac{1}{r}\frac{\partial Q}{\partial \theta} + \hat{\phi}\,\frac{1}{r \sin\theta}\frac{\partial Q}{\partial \phi} \tag{C.5}$$

where $(\hat{r}, \hat{\theta}, \hat{z})$ and $(\hat{r}, \hat{\theta}, \hat{\phi})$ are unit vectors.

[1] In the remainder of this appendix vectors and scalars are field quantities; that is, they are functions of the spatial coordinates.

In this text the gradient concept is utilized in the definition of electric potential and in diffusion problems.

4. *Divergence of a vector.* The divergence of a vector field **V**, written $\nabla \cdot \mathbf{V}$, is a scalar field. The value of the scalar at a point in space is defined with the aid of a closed surface constructed about the point. The divergence is the limiting value (as the volume $\Delta\tau$ enclosed by the surface is allowed to approach zero by shrinking down around the point) of the surface integral of the normal component of the vector field over the closed surface divided by the volume enclosed by the surface. In symbols,

$$\nabla \cdot \mathbf{V} \equiv \lim_{\Delta\tau \to 0} \frac{\int_{\text{closed surface}} \mathbf{V} \cdot d\mathbf{A}}{\Delta\tau} \tag{C.6}$$

The dot product $\mathbf{V} \cdot d\mathbf{A}$ appearing in the surface integral indicates that the integral is the limit of the sum over all elements of surface $d\mathbf{A}$, of

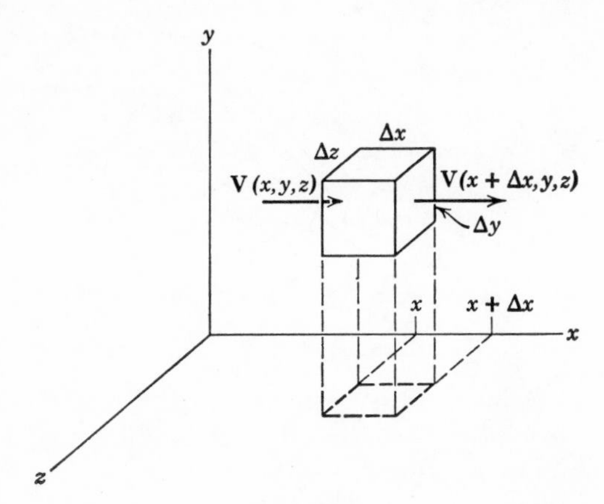

Fig. C.2

the component of **V** along the outward normal to the surface (the direction of $d\mathbf{A}$) times $d\mathbf{A}$. If **V** is expressed as a function of the coordinates of some coordinate system, $\nabla \cdot \mathbf{V}$ may be expressed in terms of partial derivatives with respect to the coordinates. A particularly simple case occurs when **V** lies entirely in one direction, say the x-direction. Then it is convenient to choose as a volume element a rectangular element of sides Δx, Δy, Δz, as shown in Fig. C.2.

The magnitude of **V** at (x, y, z) is written $V(x, y, z)$; the magnitude of **V** at $(x + \Delta x, y, z)$ is written $V(x + \Delta x, y, z)$. Since V is assumed to be parallel to the x-axis, the surface integral becomes

$$V(x + \Delta x,y,z)\, \Delta y\, \Delta z - V(x,y,z)\, \Delta y\, \Delta z$$

The divergence of **V** becomes

$$\nabla \cdot \mathbf{V} = \lim_{\substack{\Delta x \to 0 \\ \Delta y \to 0 \\ \Delta z \to 0}} \frac{[V(x + \Delta x, y, z) - V(x,y,z)]\, \Delta y\, \Delta z}{\Delta x\, \Delta y\, \Delta z}$$

$$= \frac{\partial V}{\partial x} \quad (\mathbf{V} \text{ in } x\text{-direction}) \qquad (C.7)$$

If **V** is in an arbitrary direction, the surface integral must contain contributions due to the top, bottom, front, and back surfaces. The complete result is

$$\nabla \cdot \mathbf{V} = \frac{\partial V_x}{\partial x} + \frac{\partial V_y}{\partial y} + \frac{\partial V_z}{\partial z} \qquad (C.8)$$

where (V_x, V_y, V_z) are the rectangular components of **V**.

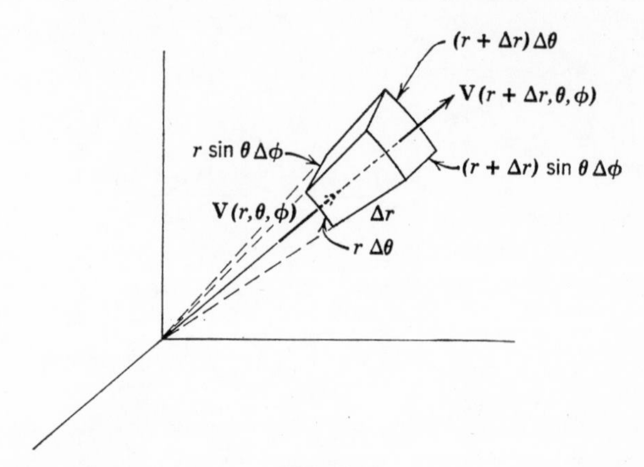

Fig. C.3

In problems involving cylindrical or spherical symmetry it may be more convenient to write **V** as an explicit function of cylindrical or spherical coordinates. Then $\nabla \cdot \mathbf{V}$ may be written in terms of partial derivatives of the various components of **V** with respect to the coordinates. As an indication of how $\nabla \cdot \mathbf{V}$ is obtained for non-rectangular coordinate systems we calculate $\nabla \cdot \mathbf{V}$ for the special case of **V** entirely in the radial direction in spherical coordinates.

The volume element shown in Fig. C.3 is the element in spherical coordinates; the lengths of the sides are shown on the diagram. The magnitude of **V** at (r, θ, ϕ) is written as $V(r, \theta, \phi)$ and magnitude of **V** at $(r + \Delta r, \theta, \phi)$ is written as $V(r + \Delta r, \theta, \phi)$. Since we have assumed the vector **V** to be in the r-direction, the only contributions to the surface integral come from the faces of area $r\,\Delta\theta\, r \sin\theta\,\Delta\phi$ and $(r + \Delta r)\,\Delta\theta\,(r + \Delta r) \sin\theta\,\Delta\phi$. The surface integral of V over the element is

$$V(r + \Delta r,\theta,\phi)(r + \Delta r)^2 \sin\theta\,\Delta\theta\,\Delta\phi - V(r,\theta,\phi)r^2 \sin\theta\,\Delta\theta\,\Delta\phi$$

Since the volume of the element is approximately $\Delta r\, r^2 \sin\theta\,\Delta\theta\,\Delta\phi$, we have

$$\nabla \cdot \mathbf{V} = \lim_{\substack{\Delta r\to 0\\ \Delta\theta\to 0\\ \Delta\phi\to 0}} \frac{[V(r + \Delta r,\theta,\phi)(r + \Delta r)^2 - V(r,\theta,\phi)r^2] \sin\theta\,\Delta\theta\,\Delta\phi}{\Delta r\, r^2 \sin\theta\,\Delta\theta\,\Delta\phi}$$

$$= \frac{1}{r^2}\frac{\partial}{\partial r}(r^2 V) \qquad \text{(C.9)}$$

The second equality follows from the definition of a partial derivative.

The complete expressions for the divergence of a vector field $\mathbf{V}$ written in cylindrical or spherical coordinates are

for cylindrical coordinates

$$\nabla \cdot \mathbf{V} = \frac{1}{r}\frac{\partial}{\partial r}(rV_r) + \frac{1}{r}\frac{\partial V_\theta}{\partial \theta} + \frac{\partial V_z}{\partial z} \qquad \text{(C.10)}$$

for spherical coordinates

$$\nabla \cdot \mathbf{V} = \frac{1}{r^2}\frac{\partial}{\partial r}(r^2 V_r) + \frac{1}{r \sin\theta}\frac{\partial}{\partial \theta}(\sin\theta\, V_\theta) + \frac{1}{r \sin\theta}\frac{\partial V_\phi}{\partial \phi} \qquad \text{(C.11)}$$

where (V_r, V_θ, V_z) and (V_r, V_θ, V_ϕ) are the components of $\mathbf{V}$ in the coordinate directions.

The student can develop a physical interpretation of the concept of divergence by applying it to the flow of an incompressible fluid. If the velocity field of the fluid is $\mathbf{v}$, then $\mathbf{v} \cdot d\mathbf{A}$ represents the volume per unit time that flows through an element of area $d\mathbf{A}$. Since the fluid is incompressible, the net rate of volume flow through a *closed* surface is zero provided there are no sources or sinks of fluid within the volume. Thus at any point where there is no source or sink the divergence of the velocity is zero

$$\nabla \cdot \mathbf{v} = 0$$

in view of the definition of divergence. Zero divergence means that the rate of flow into a volume element equals the rate of flow out of the volume element. If there is a source of fluid at a point in space, then fluid leaves a surrounding volume element faster than it enters and the divergence of $\mathbf{v}$ is positive at the point. If there is a sink of fluid, the divergence of $\mathbf{v}$ is negative.

The concept of divergence appears in this text in the continuity equation and in the production of electric fields by charges.

5. *Laplacian of a scalar.* The Laplacian of a scalar field Q, written as $\nabla^2 Q$, is another scalar field defined as the divergence of the gradient of Q.

$$\nabla^2 Q \equiv \boldsymbol{\nabla} \cdot \boldsymbol{\nabla} Q \qquad \text{(C.12)}$$

Although the definition is independent of a coordinate system, the Laplacian of a scalar is usually expressed in terms of partial derivatives with respect to the coordinates in which Q is expressed. From the rectangular coordinate forms of the gradient and divergence operators, (C.3) and (C.8),

$$\nabla^2 Q = \boldsymbol{\nabla} \cdot \boldsymbol{\nabla} Q = \frac{\partial^2 Q}{\partial x^2} + \frac{\partial^2 Q}{\partial y^2} + \frac{\partial^2 Q}{\partial z^2} \qquad \text{(C.13)}$$

If Q is a function of only one cartesian coordinate, $\nabla^2 Q$ reduces to the ordinary second derivative; thus the Laplacian may be thought of as the three-dimensional analogue of the second derivative. $\nabla^2 Q$ is positive at a point if the average value of Q in the neighborhood of the point is greater than Q at the point. $\nabla^2 Q$ is negative at a point if the average value of Q in the neighborhood of the point is smaller than Q at the point.

A common situation in problems involving cylindrical or spherical symmetry is that a scalar field Q is a function of the radial coordinate only. Then the gradient of Q is a vector field lying always in the r-direction and only the first term in C.10 or C.11 need be considered in evaluating the divergence of the gradient of Q.

For cylindrical coordinates (Q a function of r only)

$$\nabla^2 Q = \frac{1}{r}\frac{\partial}{\partial r}\left(r\frac{\partial Q}{\partial r}\right) \qquad \text{(C.14)}$$

For spherical coordinates (Q a function of r only)

$$\nabla^2 Q = \frac{1}{r^2}\frac{\partial}{\partial r}\left(r^2\frac{\partial Q}{\partial r}\right) \qquad \text{(C.15)}$$

For cylindrical coordinates in the general case the scalar field is a function of r, θ, and z. Then, using the components of the gradient vector as expressed by C.4 in place of V_r, V_θ, and V_z in C.10 we have

$$\nabla^2 Q = \frac{1}{r}\frac{\partial}{\partial r}\left(r\frac{\partial Q}{\partial r}\right) + \frac{1}{r^2}\frac{\partial^2 Q}{\partial \theta^2} + \frac{\partial^2 Q}{\partial z^2}$$

(cylindrical coordinates, general case) (C.16)

For spherical coordinates in the general case the scalar field is a function of r, θ, and ϕ. Using the components of the gradient vector as expressed by C.5 in place of V_r, V_θ, and V_ϕ in C.11 we have,

$$\nabla^2 Q = \frac{1}{r^2}\frac{\partial}{\partial r}\left(r^2 \frac{\partial Q}{\partial r}\right) + \frac{1}{r^2 \sin\theta}\frac{\partial}{\partial \theta}\left(\sin\theta \frac{\partial Q}{\partial \theta}\right) + \frac{1}{r^2 \sin^2\theta}\frac{\partial^2 Q}{\partial \phi^2}$$

(spherical coordinates, general case) (C.17)

In this text the Laplacian occurs in Schroedinger's equation (quantum theory), Poisson's and Laplace's equations (electromagnetic theory), and in the continuity equation when diffusional flow is included.

APPENDIX D

SOME FUNDAMENTAL RELATIONSHIPS OF ELECTROMAGNETISM

1. *Definition of electric field.* If a charged particle, placed at rest at a point, experiences a force in addition to any gravitational (or nuclear) force exerted on it, there is said to be an electric field at that point and the corresponding force $\mathbf{F}_e$ is called the electric force. The electric field is a vector quantity with magnitude equal to the electric force on the charge divided by the magnitude of the charge. The direction of the electric field is the same as that of the electric force if the charge is positive and is opposite to that of the electric force if the charge is negative. In symbols

$$\boldsymbol{\mathcal{E}} \equiv \frac{\mathbf{F}_e}{q} \qquad (q \text{ at rest}) \tag{D.1}$$

Electric fields are established by other charges.[1] If a system is composed of two point charges q and q' which are at rest and isolated from other charges, the electric force F_e exerted on each charge by the other is given by Coulomb's law,

$$F_e = \frac{qq'}{4\pi\epsilon_0 r^2} \tag{D.2}$$

where $\epsilon_0 = \dfrac{1}{36\pi \times 10^9} \dfrac{\text{coulomb}^2}{\text{newton-meter}^2}$, and r is the distance between q and q'. The force is repulsive if the charges have like sign, attractive if they have unlike sign. The force on q may be described by saying

[1] Electric fields are also established by time-varying magnetic fields (Faraday's law).

that q' establishes in the space around it a radially directed electric field of magnitude $q'/4\pi\epsilon_0$, and this electric field exerts the force on q.

The total electric field at a point in space is the vector sum of the electric fields established by all charges (plus any electric field generated by a time-varying magnetic field). It may happen that the electric field established by a charge q placed at a point causes other charges to be rearranged. The rearranged charges in turn produce a different electric field at the position of q than they did when q was not present. It is still correct to say that the electric field is $\mathbf{F}_e/q$ *when q is present.* If the field when q is not present is desired, then one must imagine a vanishingly small charge to be placed at the point and measure the force on it. That is

$$\mathcal{E}_{\text{no charge present}} \equiv \lim_{q \to 0} \frac{\mathbf{F}_e}{q} \tag{D.3}$$

2. *Definition of magnetic field.* If a charged particle at a point experiences a different force when it is moving than when it is at rest, then a magnetic field is said to exist at the point. Experiments in which the magnitude and direction of the velocity are varied indicate that the additional force at a point is always perpendicular to the velocity vector and to a fixed direction in space. The additional force $\mathbf{F}_m$, called the magnetic force, may be described by the vector relation

$$\mathbf{F}_m = q\mathbf{v} \times \mathbf{B} \tag{D.4}$$

This is the defining equation for the vector $\mathbf{B}$, which is called the magnetic induction or flux density. ($\mathbf{B}$ is often loosely referred to as the magnetic field vector but, more correctly, another vector, given the symbol $\mathbf{H}$ and related to $\mathbf{B}$ in free space by a constant factor, is given the name magnetic field.)

Magnetic fields are set up by moving charges (currents), changing electric fields, and by stationary fundamental particles such as the electron, proton, and neutron which all behave like tiny loops of wire which carry current. (Permanent magnets may be described in terms of the fundamental particles comprising the atoms of the magnets.)

The total force $\mathbf{F}$ on a charge q due to both electric and magnetic fields is called the Lorentz force.

$$\mathbf{F} = \mathbf{F}_e + \mathbf{F}_m = q(\mathcal{E} + \mathbf{v} \times \mathbf{B}) \tag{D.5}$$

3. *Definition of potential.* An electric field which is produced only by charged particles (not by time-varying magnetic fields) is called an *electrostatic* field and can always be expressed in terms of the gradient of a scalar field. The scalar field V is called the electric potential and the precise relation between it and an electrostatic field is

$$\mathbf{\mathcal{E}} = -\nabla V \tag{D.6}$$

Equation D.6 is the defining equation for the electric potential, but since the gradient of a constant scalar is zero, V is only defined to within an additive scalar constant. This is not a serious drawback, for it is only differences in potential that have physical significance. Using D.6 and the definition of a gradient the potential difference between two points A and B may be written

$$V_B - V_A = \int_B^A \mathbf{\mathcal{E}} \cdot d\mathbf{l} = -\int_A^B \mathbf{\mathcal{E}} \cdot d\mathbf{l} \tag{D.7}$$

where $\mathbf{\mathcal{E}}$ is the electrostatic field and $d\mathbf{l}$ is the element of length along any path from B to A.

The potential a distance r from an isolated point charge q can be evaluated from the definition D.6 and the expression for the gradient in spherical coordinates in Appendix C. The result is

$$V = \frac{q}{4\pi\epsilon_0 r} + \text{constant} \tag{D.8}$$

Often the constant is chosen to be zero so that $V = 0$ at an infinite distance from the charge. From D.6 and the definition of the gradient in Appendix C the electric field points in the direction in which V is *decreasing* most rapidly.

4. *Gauss' Law.* Gauss' law, a useful theorem relating to electrostatic fields, may be stated as follows. The surface integral, over any closed surface in space, of the normal component of an electrostatic field is equal to the total charge enclosed within the surface divided by ϵ_0.

$$\iint_{\text{closed surface}} \mathbf{\mathcal{E}} \cdot d\mathbf{A} = \frac{q_{\text{enclosed}}}{\epsilon_0} \tag{D.9}$$

The theorem may be proved for an arbitrarily shaped closed surface surrounding a single point charge and extended to any number of point charges. In Fig. D.1, $\mathbf{\mathcal{E}} \cdot d\mathbf{A}$ at the surface element shown is equal to $\dfrac{q\,dA\cos\theta}{4\pi\epsilon_0 r^2}$. But $\dfrac{dA\cos\theta}{r^2}$ is the element of solid angle $d\Omega$ subtended at q by the area dA so that

$$\iint \mathbf{\mathcal{E}} \cdot d\mathbf{A} = \frac{q}{4\pi\epsilon_0}\int d\Omega = \frac{q}{\epsilon_0} \tag{D.10}$$

The last equality follows because the total solid angle surrounding a point is equal to 4π. By similar reasoning, every charge q_i *inside* the surface contributes an amount q_i/ϵ_0 to the surface integral so Gauss' law, equation D.9, follows, provided each charge *outside* the surface contributes nothing to the integral. The proof that the latter condition is true is left as an exercise for the reader.

5. *Maxwell's first equation.* Gauss' law, written for an infinitesimal volume element $d\tau$ leads to another useful formulation of the physics

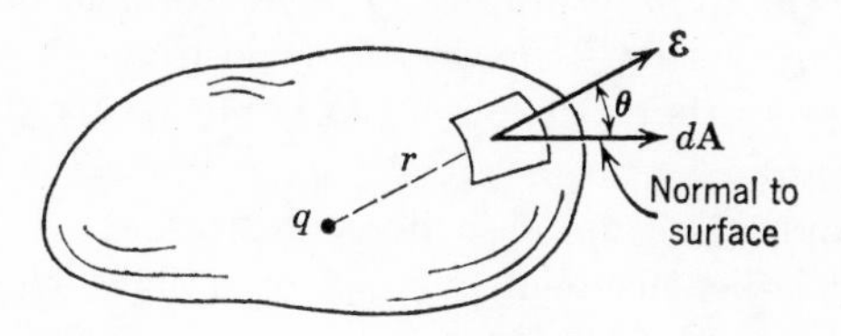

Fig. D.1

contained in Coulomb's law. This new form, known as Maxwell's first equation, is obtained by writing $\bar{\rho}\ \Delta\tau$ for q in Gauss law, where $\bar{\rho}$ is the average charge density inside the volume element $\Delta\tau$. Hence,

$$\frac{\iint \boldsymbol{\mathcal{E}} \cdot d\mathbf{A}}{\Delta\tau} = \frac{\bar{\rho}}{\epsilon_0} \tag{D.11}$$

Passing to the limit as $\Delta\tau \rightarrow 0$, the left side is recognized as the divergence of $\boldsymbol{\mathcal{E}}$ (see Appendix C) and the right side becomes ρ, the charge density in a vanishingly small volume. *Maxwell's first equation* follows:

$$\nabla \cdot \boldsymbol{\mathcal{E}} = \frac{\rho}{\epsilon_0} \tag{D.12}$$

When we speak in terms of fluid flow, the electric field $\boldsymbol{\mathcal{E}}$ is analogous to the velocity field of an incompressible fluid and the charge density ρ acts as a "source" for the electric field. The electric "lines of force" are analogous to stream lines in a fluid; equal numbers of lines of force enter and leave a volume element if $\rho = 0$, more lines leave than enter if ρ is positive and more lines enter than leave if ρ is negative.

6. *Poisson's and Laplace's equations.* If the negative gradient of the electric potential V is substituted for $\boldsymbol{\mathcal{E}}$ into Maxwell's first equation D.12, *Poisson's equation* results.

$$\nabla^2 V = -\frac{\rho}{\epsilon_0} \tag{D.13}$$

Here we have used the definition of the Laplacian ∇^2 (see Appendix C). In the special but very common case of $\rho = 0$ Poisson's equation is called *Laplace's equation.*

$$\nabla^2 V = 0 \tag{D.14}$$

Poisson's or Laplace's equation enables us to calculate the potential as a function of position inside a region, provided the potential at the boundaries of the region and the distribution of charge within the region are known. For example, in a one-dimensional problem in which the charge density is everywhere positive, Poisson's equation tells us immediately that a graph of potential versus distance must be concave downward.

Laplace's equation occurs elsewhere in physics. For example, the equation for the displacement $u(x, y)$ of a light elastic membrane above an x-y plane is

$$\nabla^2 u(x,y) = 0 \tag{D.15}$$

This two-dimensional Laplace's equation expresses the physically reasonable fact that the displacement of a point is equal to the average of the surrounding displacements. If the membrane has weight, then the membrane must have an average upward curvature, and the zero on the right side of D.15 is replaced by a positive term proportional to the density of the membrane.

Answers to selected problems

Chapter 1

1.1. (*a*) 2.9×10^{-14} meter, (*c*) 3.9×10^{-10} meter
1.5. (*b*) $\approx 10^2$ meters/sec
1.6. ≈ 0.04 ev
1.12. 0.026, 1.026, 6.8×10^{-4}, 1.05

Chapter 2

2.2. 2.7×10^{14}, 7.3×10^{14}, 4.5×10^{14} cycles/sec, etc.
2.9. Four
2.10. Fifty
2.12. 8.16×10^{-18}, 10.2×10^{-18}, 12.7×10^{-18}, 13.5×10^{-18} joule
2.15. $\alpha = \dfrac{\sqrt{\beta m}}{2\hbar}$, $E_1 = \dfrac{\hbar}{2}\sqrt{\beta/m}$, $E_2 = 3E_1$, $E_3 = 5E_1$, etc.

Chapter 3

3.2. 8.12 ev
3.5. Zero
3.6. $x = \frac{1}{2}$, $y = -\frac{3}{2}$, $z = 2$
3.7. 4.2×10^9 newtons/meter^2
3.8. 4.6×10^{23} ev
3.9. Na, 3.14 ev; Cu, 11.1 ev; Al, 11.6 ev

Chapter 4

4.1. 10 ev
4.4. 0.024 ev

4.6. J (theoretical) $= 0.63$ amp/cm^2

4.8. (*a*) 10^5 volts/meter, (*b*) 6.0×10^{-8} meter, (*c*) 0.012 ev, (*d*) 8.2%

4.11. $\frac{1}{e}$

4.13. 1.26×10^7 volts/meter

Chapter 5

5.2. 1.06×10^{-7} sec

5.5. (*a*) 5.84×10^{-9} sec, (*b*) 3.23 cm

5.10. (*a*) 1.07 cm, (*b*) helix: radius 0.093 cm, pitch 6.6 cm

5.13. (*a*) 4.8×10^{-3} weber/meter^2, (*b*) 4.2×10^6 meters/sec

5.14. $M = RB^2 \frac{ed}{V}$

5.17. 0.0213 weber/meter^2

5.19. $V_c = \frac{\omega_c{}^2 d^2}{2\eta}$

Chapter 6

6.2. (*a*) $v \sim x^{2/3}$, (*d*) $\rho \sim x^{-2/3}$

6.5. (*a*) (i) 1:1, (ii) 3:2, (*b*) $P \sim V^{5/2}$

6.11. $V_{\text{eff}} = 3.9$ volts, $\mu = 21.8$

6.13. Increased by factor of 2

6.15. (*a*) Increased by $2\sqrt{2}$, (*b*) increased by $\sqrt{2}$

6.20. 110 volts, 2.3 milliamperes

6.24. 95 micromhos

Chapter 7

7.3. (*a*) -13.3

7.5. (*b*) 26.7 volts rms, (*d*) 0.047 watt

7.7. (*a*) 1.01 megacycles/sec

7.9. (*a*) $C_{\text{in}} = 151$ $\mu\mu$f in parallel with ≈ 0.5 megohm

7.12. (*a*) Approximately 0.8 watt

Chapter 8

8.3. $n = n_0 + C_1 e^{-x/\sqrt{D\tau}} + C_2 e^{x/\sqrt{D\tau}}$

8.10. 608 mhos/meter

8.11. 0.326 meter^2/volt-sec

8.12. 184

8.14. 1.02×10^{22}, 8.98×10^{22}

Chapter 9

9.4. (*a*) $\approx 2.6 \times 10^{-3}$ cm, (*b*) ≈ 80 cm

9.7. $\dfrac{\sqrt{q/R}\,(e^{2\sqrt{qR}t} - 1)}{e^{2\sqrt{qR}t} + 1}$

9.9. 1.64 meters

9.12. For electrons: $\sigma = 6.53 \times 10^{-20}$ meter^2, $\bar{l} = 0.0108$ meter; for argon atoms: $\bar{l} = 0.0017$ meter

9.14. (*b*) $\gamma(e^{\alpha d} - 1) = 1$

9.19. (*a*) 99.2%, 98.5%, 95.1%

Chapter 10

10.5. Yes, dead time loss = 2900 counts, rms fluctuation = 200 counts

10.7. 200 milliamperes

10.9. (*a*) ≈ 2000 ohms

10.11. 2800 cycles/sec

Chapter 11

11.2. 4.2° K

11.6. 1.2×10^{-6} meter

Chapter 12

12.4. 6.6×10^{-6} volt

12.7. Assume mean free path is 10× radius (*a*) 54 webers/meter^2, (*b*) 0.98 weber/meter^2

Chapter 13

13.3. 17,200 Å

13.4. 5.63×10^{-6} parts per million

13.8. Below by 0.020 ev

13.12. (*a*) 2.28 ohm-meters, 2.15 ohm-meters, (*b*) $n_p = 2n_i$, $n_n = \dfrac{n_i}{2}$

13.14. $E_F = 2.33$ ev below E_g

Chapter 14

14.2. 9.82 milliamperes, 0.18 volt

14.4. 866° K

14.8. Approximately -4

14.10. $V_{be} = h_{11}i_b + h_{12}V_{ce}$, $i_c = h_{21}i_b + h_{22}V_{ce}$

14.12. $h_{11e} = \dfrac{h_{11b}}{D}$, $h_{12e} = \dfrac{h_{11b}h_{22b} - h_{12b}(1 + h_{21b})}{D}$,

$h_{21e} = \dfrac{-h_{21b}(1 - h_{12b}) - h_{11b}h_{22b}}{D}$, $h_{22e} = \dfrac{h_{22b}}{D}$,

where $D = (1 + h_{21b})(1 - h_{12b}) + h_{11b}h_{22b}$

Chapter 15

15.2. (*a*) 1.94×10^{-13} newton, (*b*) 6.13×10^{-13} newton
15.9. 2.89×10^{9} radians/sec
15.11. (*a*) 10^{9} cycles/sec, (*c*) 10^{8} cycles/sec, (*e*) 0.91×10^{7} meters/sec

Chapter 16

16.3. 930 volts
16.9. (*a*) 749 volts, (*b*) 334 volts
16.10. 275 volts
16.12. (*a*) 14.5×10^{9} cycles/sec, (*b*) 4.8, 9.7×10^{9} cycles/sec

Index